# BREATHING:
# HERING-BREUER CENTENARY SYMPOSIUM

# BREATHING:
# HERING-BREUER
# CENTENARY SYMPOSIUM

A Ciba Foundation Symposium
Edited by
RUTH PORTER

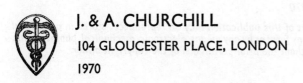
J. & A. CHURCHILL
104 GLOUCESTER PLACE, LONDON
1970

First published 1970

Containing 112 illustrations

International Standard Book Number 0 7000 1456 X

# Contents

* Paper contributed for publication after the meeting.

## Respiratory sensation

## Clinical problems

# Membership

## Breathing: Hering-Breuer Centenary Symposium held 8th–10th July, 1969

| | |
|---|---|
| A. C. Dornhorst (*Chairman*) | Medical Unit, St. George's Hospital Medical School, London, S.W.1 |
| R. C. B. Aitken | University Department of Psychiatry (Royal Edinburgh Hospital), Morningside Park, Edinburgh, EH10 5HF |
| E. J. M. Campbell | Department of Medicine, McMaster University, Hamilton, Ontario, Canada |
| M. I. Cohen | Department of Physiology, Albert Einstein College of Medicine, Yeshiva University, Eastchester Road and Morris Park Avenue, Bronx, N.Y. 10461 |
| J. E. Cotes | Pneumoconiosis Research Unit of the Medical Research Council, Llandough Hospital, Penarth, Glamorgan |
| K. W. Cross | Department of Physiology, The London Hospital Medical College, University of London, Turner Street, London, E.1 |
| P. Dejours | Faculté de Médecine de Paris, Laboratoire de Physiologie, Paris 6 * |
| C. von Euler | Nobel Institute of Neurophysiology, Karolinska Institute, Stockholm |
| Marianne Fillenz | University Laboratory of Physiology, Parks Road, Oxford, OX1 3PT |
| D. C. Flenley | University of Edinburgh Department of Medicine, The Royal Infirmary, Edinburgh, EH3 9YW |
| S. I. Frankstein† | Institute of Normal and Pathological Physiology, Academy of Medical Sciences, Baltyskaya 8, Moscow, USSR |
| S. Godfrey | Institute of Diseases of the Chest, Brompton Hospital, London, S.W.3 |
| A. Guz | Department of Medicine, Charing Cross Hospital Medical School, Fulham Hospital, London, W.6 |
| J. B. L. Howell | Manchester Royal Infirmary, Oxford Road, Manchester, M13 9WL‡ |
| W. Karczewski | Polish Academy of Sciences, Experimental and Clinical Medical Research Centre, Warsaw, 3 Dworkowa Str. |
| E. G. Merrill | Department of Anatomy, University College, Gower Street, London, W.C.1 |
| P. A. Merton | Physiological Laboratory, University of Cambridge, Downing Street, Cambridge |

\* Present address: Laboratoire de Physiologie Respiratoire, Centre National de la Recherche Scientifique, 23, rue Becquerel, 67-Strasbourg 3.
† Author not present at the symposium.
‡ Present address: Department of Medicine, University of Southampton.

# The Ciba Foundation

The Ciba Foundation was opened in 1949 to promote international cooperation in medical and chemical research. It owes its existence to the generosity of CIBA Ltd, Basle, who, recognizing the obstacles to scientific communication created by war, man's natural secretiveness, disciplinary divisions, academic prejudices, distance, and differences of language, decided to set up a philanthropic institution whose aim would be to overcome such barriers. London was chosen as its site for reasons dictated by the special advantages of English charitable trust law (ensuring the independence of its actions), as well as those of language and geography.

The Foundation's house at 41 Portland Place, London, has become well known to workers in many fields of science. Every year the Foundation organizes six to ten three-day symposia and three to four shorter study groups, all of which are published in book form. Many other scientific meetings are held, organized either by the Foundation or by other groups in need of a meeting place. Accommodation is also provided for scientists visiting London, whether or not they are attending a meeting in the house.

The Foundation's many activities are controlled by a small group of distinguished trustees. Within the general framework of biological science, interpreted in its broadest sense, these activities are well summed up by the motto of the Ciba Foundation: *Consocient Gentes*—let the peoples come together.

# Preface

At the beginning of 1967 Dr A. Guz suggested the possibility of a Ciba Foundation symposium at which recent work on the nervous control of breathing, particularly as mediated through afferent pathways and through receptors in the thorax and the lung itself, could be discussed. Miss Diana Trenchard of the Department of Medicine, Charing Cross Hospital Medical School, first drew our attention to the historical appropriateness of holding such a meeting in 1968, or as near to this as possible, because 1968 was the centenary of the publication of Hering and Breuer's work on *Self-steering of Respiration through the Vagus Nerve*. We hoped to provide a forum for a multidisciplinary meeting in which basic research workers in various branches of physiology could discuss the relevance of their findings and techniques to the clinical problem of breathlessness; in which the peripheral and central pathways involved in respiration could be defined; and in which ways of assessing and measuring unpleasant respiratory sensations could be examined and possibilities for future research outlined.

We are pleased to record our gratitude to many people: to Professor A. C. Dornhorst, both for his skilful chairmanship during the symposium and for his help in planning it; to Professor Moran Campbell, Dr (now Professor) Jack Howell and Dr John Widdicombe, as well as Dr Abe Guz, for their help both in the planning of the meeting and in the editing of its proceedings; to Dr Elisabeth Ullmann for her translation of the original papers by Hering and Breuer (p. 357) and for her historical account of these two scientists and some of their colleagues; to Drs B. B. Lloyd and D. J. C. Cunningham, of the University Laboratory of Physiology, Oxford, for help in preparing the additional short paper on p. 41 of this volume; and to Professor S. A. Weinstein, of the Laboratory of Behavioral Physiology, The Johns Hopkins University, for a personal communication contributed after the meeting (see p. 179).

We record our disappointment that Professor S. I. Frankstein, of the Academy of Medical Sciences, Moscow, was unable to come to the symposium, although we have been able to include a contribution from him in this volume. Finally, we would like to thank the many symposiasts (and some others, particularly Professor K. W. Donald of Edinburgh University, who were unable to come to the symposium) who helped us variously before the meeting with their advice and expertise, and afterwards in the preparation of these proceedings for publication.

In general, the conventions for respiratory physiology recommended in *Federation Proceedings, Federation of American Societies for Experimental Biology*, 1950, **9**, 602–605, have been followed in this symposium (cf. Comroe, J. H., Jr., *et al.* [1962]. *The Lung: Clinical Physiology and Pulmonary Function Tests*, 2nd edn., pp. 330–331. Chicago: Year Book Medical Publishers). The following table of symbols is reproduced from Comroe (*loc. cit.*) for the convenience of readers.

### SPECIAL SYMBOLS

— Dash above any symbol indicates a *mean* value.

. Dot above any symbol indicates a *time derivative*.

### FOR GASES

PRIMARY SYMBOLS
(Large Capital Letters)

EXAMPLES

$V$ = gas volume

$\dot{V}$ = gas volume/unit time

$P$ = gas pressure

$\bar{P}$ = mean gas pressure

$F$ = fractional concentration in dry gas phase

$f$ = respiratory frequency (breaths/unit time)

$D$ = diffusing capacity

$R$ = respiratory exchange ratio

$V_A$ = volume of alveolar gas

$\dot{V}_{O_2}$ = $O_2$ consumption/min

$P_{A_{O_2}}$ = alveolar $O_2$ pressure

$\bar{P}_{C_{O_2}}$ = mean capillary $O_2$ pressure

$F_{I_{O_2}}$ = fractional concentration of $O_2$ in inspired gas

$D_{O_2}$ = diffusing capacity for $O_2$ (ml $O_2$/min/mm Hg)

$R$ = $\dot{V}_{C_{O_2}}/\dot{V}_{O_2}$

SECONDARY SYMBOLS
(SMALL CAPITAL LETTERS)

EXAMPLES

I = inspired gas

E = expired gas

A = alveolar gas

T = tidal gas

D = dead space gas

B = barometric

STPD = 0°C, 760 mmHg, dry

BTPS = body temperature and pressure saturated with water vapor

ATPS = ambient temperature and pressure saturated with water vapor

$F_{I_{CO_2}}$ = fractional concentration of $CO_2$ in inspired gas

$V_E$ = volume of expired gas

$\dot{V}_A$ = alveolar ventilation/min

$V_T$ = tidal volume

$V_D$ = volume of dead space gas

$P_B$ = barometric pressure

## For Blood

| PRIMARY SYMBOLS<br>(Large Capital Letters) | | EXAMPLES | |
|---|---|---|---|
| Q | = volume of blood | Qc | = volume of blood in pulmonary capillaries |
| $\dot{Q}$ | = volume flow of blood/unit time | $\dot{Q}c$ | = blood flow through pulmonary capillaries/min |
| C | = concentration of gas in blood phase | $Ca_{O_2}$ | = ml $O_2$ in 100 ml arterial blood |
| S | = % saturation of Hb with $O_2$ or CO | $S\bar{v}_{O_2}$ | = saturation of Hb with $O_2$ in mixed venous blood |

| SECONDARY SYMBOLS<br>(small letters) | | EXAMPLES | |
|---|---|---|---|
| a | = arterial blood | $Pa_{CO_2}$ | = partial pressure of $CO_2$ in arterial blood |
| v | = venous blood | $P\bar{v}_{O_2}$ | = partial pressure of $O_2$ in mixed venous blood |
| c | = capillary blood | $Pc_{CO}$ | = partial pressure of CO in pulmonary capillary blood |

## For Lung Volumes

| | | |
|---|---|---|
| VC | = Vital Capacity | = maximal volume that can be expired after maximal inspiration |
| IC | = Inspiratory Capacity | = maximal volume that can be inspired from resting expiratory level |
| IRV | = Inspiratory Reserve Volume | = maximal volume that can be inspired from end-tidal inspiration |
| ERV | = Expiratory Reserve Volume | = maximal volume that can be expired from resting expiratory level |
| FRC | = Functional Residual Capacity | = volume of gas in lungs at resting expiratory level |
| RV | = Residual Volume | = volume of gas in lungs at end of maximal expiration |
| TLC | = Total Lung Capacity | = volume of gas in lungs at end of maximal inspiration |

# CHAIRMAN'S OPENING REMARKS

## A. C. DORNHORST

THE year 1969 is an appropriate time to reconsider the whole field of the nervous control of respiration, a subject that can be thought about in three sections—respiratory drive, respiratory sensation and the constituents of the sensation of dyspnoea. From my own point of view, that of a clinician who is interested in respiratory physiology, it looks as if we now have good understanding of the mechanical and transfer functions of respiration but are still often quite unable to predict whether any particular patient with disturbances of these functions will underventilate or overventilate or be severely dyspnoeic or not. A good deal is known about the afferent nervous pathways from the chest wall and the airways, and something is also known about reflex effects from the lung in animal preparations. But our animal models—for example anaesthetized and brain-sectioned animals—cannot approach what we are interested in, that is, the situation in conscious man. We need to close the gap between physiological and clinical observations in man on the one hand and detailed work with animal models on the other. During the next three days we shall hope at the least to throw a few ropes across this gap.

Until I became involved in this conference I knew little more about Hering and Breuer than that they were two people and not one! We are fortunate in having Elisabeth Ullmann to present some historical and biographical notes about these two scientists. Dr Ullmann is a Viennese who knows the Viennese academic background personally. Although she cannot have known Joseph Breuer she met his famous collaborator, Sigmund Freud, when she was a child. She has also provided the translation of the original papers by Hering and Breuer, a tremendous task even for a born-and-bred Austrian, because of the particular convoluted style in which scientific papers in German were written a hundred years ago. I will now open these proceedings by asking Dr Ullmann to present her material about Hering and Breuer.

# ABOUT HERING AND BREUER

ELISABETH ULLMANN

*Department of Physiology, The Medical College of St. Bartholomew's Hospital, London*

*Background*

THE discovery of the self-regulation of breathing was the work of young men. In 1868 Ewald Hering was thirty-four years old and Joseph Breuer twenty-six. Although the difference in age was small, that of status was large. Hering was a Professor of Physiology; Breuer a newly qualified doctor in his first clinical job.

Hering was born in Saxony in 1834, studied Medicine at the University of Leipzig and afterwards earned his living there as a general practitioner. In his spare time he investigated the mechanism of binocular vision, having chosen this subject because experimentation was cheap and could be carried out at home. His university provided no support for his research, but made him a *Dozent* in 1862. Hering published his findings and conclusions in a series of *Contributions to Physiology* between 1861 and 1864. They became known as the "Identity" theory of binocular vision in contrast to the "Projection" theory held by Helmholtz and Wundt. Hering thought that learning and experience were *not* needed for the perception of a single image when two disparate images were formed on "identical spots" of the two retinae but that these fused into one in consequence of innate peculiarities of the afferent and efferent innervation of the eyes. Helmholtz held that perception of a single image was the result of an acquired mental activity, entirely dependent on experience and learning. It was this controversy early in Hering's career and not, as is usually thought, his later disagreement with Helmholtz on colour vision which made Hering the odd-man-out among the prominent German physiologists of his generation for the rest of his life. But in 1865 his reputation as an original thinker and physiological experimenter stood high and he was appointed Professor of Physiology at the Joseph's Academy in Vienna.

The Professor of Physiology at the University of Vienna at this time was Ernst von Bruecke. The Joseph's Academy was not part of the University but an independent military institution founded by the Emperor Joseph II in 1785 for the training of army surgeons. It was housed in an imposing

3

building, the work of the fashionable Italian architect Canevale. The Josephinum still stands, and is still remotely connected with the teaching of Medicine.

By the standards of his time Joseph II, an absolute monarch, was a liberal and enlightened man. He took a great interest in what the universities taught, down to the last detail. His aims for medical education, laid down in 1782, were as follows: "The young people must not be taught anything which later on they will need or apply infrequently or not at all for the good of the State; because the essential studies in our Universities must serve the training of the servants of State and not the mere education of scholars" (trans. Lesky, 1965, p. 302). This directive undoubtedly applied with even greater force to the military Joseph's Academy. The administrators of this establishment throughout the period of its existence (till 1873) repeatedly had to remind the professorial staff that it was their job to train army doctors and not to spend time and resources on the furtherance of medical research. This not unfamiliar-sounding theme naturally gave rise to much internal friction. Yet despite its officially hostile attitude towards academic research the Joseph's Academy engaged as professors numerous outstandingly progressive scientific investigators.

Ewald Hering's immediate predecessor at the Joseph's Academy was Carl Ludwig who had held the job for ten years—1855–1865—despite continuous difficulties. An important attraction for him was the presence in Vienna of Bruecke. Almost exact contemporaries, Bruecke, duBois-Reymond and Helmholtz were all renegade former pupils of Johannes Mueller, close friends of Ludwig and the joint leaders and missionaries of the anti-vitalist movement. Exasperated by bad pay, poor facilities and mounting disagreement on policy with the director of the Josephinum, Ludwig left in 1865 for a better-endowed position at the University of Leipzig. Ludwig has described the modest accommodation that was at his disposal at the Josephinum in a letter. It consisted of ". . . a small chemical laboratory, a mechanical workshop containing lathe, carpenter's bench, vice, etc.; a lecture theatre where no one lectures but me; a small room for storing instruments where I myself do all the finer work, . . .; also a dog kennel (heatable), a place to keep rabbits, and an ice cellar in the main k.k. military hospital (*Garnisonshauptspital*) which I have permission to use" (trans. Lesky, 1965, p. 269). These were the premises Ewald Hering took over, and here the experiments on the regulation of breathing were performed.

The young, newly appointed professor, trying to prepare himself rapidly for his lectures on the whole of physiology, did research and published papers on topics remote from his former field, for example, the liver structure in vertebrates and diapedesis of leucocytes. Then, late in 1867 or early in 1868—the exact time is not known—a young man presented himself with the request to carry out an experimental investigation under Hering's guidance.

Joseph Breuer was born in Vienna in 1842. A precocious Jewish boy, he finished his formal schooling at 16 instead of at 18 years of age. He had always wanted to become a doctor but, because he was so young when he entered the university, he first (on his father's advice) attended lectures on history, philosophy and economics. In his *Curriculum Vitae*, written when he was 81 years old, Breuer considered that this "lazy" first year had by no means been a waste of time (Breuer, 1923). In 1859 he began his medical training in earnest, but found little to enjoy in Botany, Zoology, Chemistry and Anatomy, even though Hyrtl, the Professor of Anatomy, was popular because of the theatrical style of his lectures. In 1860 Breuer started to study Physiology under Bruecke and from that moment, as he himself recorded, his "... interests were rooted in Physiology for all time" (Breuer, 1923).

"The highly inadequate previous education of a large section of the students drove Bruecke to preface his lectures with a six-week introductory course on physics—not the least important and useful part of his lectures." (Breuer, 1923). Besides giving all the lectures Bruecke also subjected his students to rigorous laboratory training in histology, using the newest microscopic and staining techniques. But what this passionate anti-vitalist chiefly taught was the application of scientific thinking to problems in medicine.

In 1862, during his clinical course, Breuer reached the Department of Medicine and met the second of his teachers who was to have a permanent influence on him. This was Professor J. R. Oppolzer, a physician of distinction but with no scientific bent of mind whatsoever. He was an astute observer, a brilliant diagnostician and a profoundly humane person. It was he who introduced into the treatment of the indigent poor in the university clinics the attitudes summarized in the latter-day slogan: "patients are people". Oppolzer had an excellent eye for men with ability; he discovered an amazing number of the lights of Viennese Medicine in the latter part of the century. He noticed Breuer's promise as a student and made him his clinical assistant as soon as Breuer qualified in 1867. Breuer (1923) called this appointment: ".... an undeserved stroke of luck". He loved and revered Oppolzer whose example developed in him the "medical libido" (Freud, 1925) for which he himself became renowned later.

*The discovery of the Hering-Breuer reflex*

Soon after the start of his assistantship Breuer was startled by a comment made by L. Tuerck, the laryngologist, on the peculiar breathing of certain patients. Tuerck, originally a neurologist, whose work on the spinal tracts is still known, later became an ear, nose, and throat specialist. Unfortunately, what he said to Breuer is not recorded.

The pharmacologist H. H. Meyer (1928), an intimate friend of Breuer's, stressed in his biography of Breuer that it was this remark of Tuerck's which gave Breuer the idea that breathing was a self-regulatory activity. This hypothesis certainly arose from observations on patients, either first made by Breuer or confirmed by him. (See Breuer, 1868, p. 389 of translation.) At Oppolzer's instigation Breuer went to see Hering.

In his *Curriculum Vitae*, Breuer's own account of the episode is laconic (Breuer, 1923): "Struck by a remark by L. Tuerck I submitted the relevant observation, which was readily confirmed, to Hering who in the kindest manner immediately took me on for joint work. Of course, in this first effort by a pupil, the greater portion of the intellectual content of the work must be credited to the master. It was enjoyable and fruitful work".

Some measure of self-denigration was part of Viennese good manners in Breuer's time. Hering's true share in the discovery of the Hering-Breuer reflex cannot be assessed in retrospect. Breuer (1923) speaks of "... an experimental investigation Professor Hering carried out with me in his laboratory". The papers leave little doubt that Breuer carried out all experiments himself, and Hering gave Breuer full credit for the work (Hering, 1868a). But Hering was an enthusiast and the most helpful of mentors as we know from other men who have worked under him, notably Henry Head (1889b, 1926). Hering was interested in the reflex regulation of breathing, and he and Breuer must have had many talks on the work as it progressed. Hering probably lent a hand in the laboratory more than once. In a letter to Breuer written in his eighties Hering said: "Wasn't it nice when we were winding up the kymographion again and again. No one winds us two up any more nowadays." (Breuer, 1923).

The other instrument besides the kymographion which allowed them to record their observations was the new spring manometer devised by Fick (1864) utilizing a Bourdon gauge. This consisted of a small hollow brass spring with a flat elliptical cross-section. The spring was bent into a circle; one end was open and fixed rigidly to a frame; the closed end was free to move. It was filled with alcohol and the open end connected through tubing to a blood vessel or an air space in which the pressure fluctuated.

A rise of pressure inside the hollow spring made it stretch, and the barely visible movements executed in response to pressure changes by the free end were magnified about thirty times by a lever system made of reed, and recorded with a steel pen on the kymographion. The whole thing weighed only a few grammes and had negligible inertia, but tended to oscillate at its own frequency every time the pressure changed rapidly. According to Fick this disconcerting fault was completely cured when a small piece of paper that dipped into a pot of oil was attached to the lever.

The plates published with Breuer's paper (1868) contain no records of the deflation reflex; for this they relied on visual observation of breathing movements and the movement of the nostrils.

The preferential use of the "natural" mode of excitation of vagal endings was at the time an aspect of their research as new as were the findings and conclusions. Breuer's biographer says: "Breuer conceived the fruitful and fundamentally important idea that, rather than use artificial electrical or mechanical stimuli, he would look at the natural processes of excitation which come into play at the vagal endings that are distributed within the lung itself during its periodic expansion (tension) and retraction (relaxation)" (Meyer, 1928). But S. Garten, a pupil of Hering's who wrote his obituary in *Pflüger's Archiv* (1918) says that although others had previously examined the relationship between vagus and breathing, no one ".... had hit upon the simplest and least objectionable method which Hering's genius led him to employ here, that is, to stimulate the endings of the *Nervus vagus* by inflating and collapsing the lungs".

Whose brain child the idea originally was probably does not matter very much. A hint that it was Hering's may perhaps be discerned in the forceful manner in which he expressed his distrust of electrical excitation of cut nerves in his first announcement of the new discovery. This announcement was made at the meeting of the Vienna Academy of Science of April 30th, 1868. A corresponding member since 1868, Hering was entitled to submit papers for publication in the *Reports of the Meetings*. This brief preliminary account was undoubtedly written by Hering himself, but the title, *Self-steering of Respiration through the Nervus Vagus*, is followed by the sentence: "A communication concerning an investigation carried out by Dr Joseph Breuer ... ". It was not the custom of the Academy that papers handed in for publication be read before the assembled members at the meeting, but an author could summarize in a few sentences the main contents. Hering may have done so on this occasion but there is no record of it. The full account, written by Breuer (1868) was handed over by Hering at the meeting of November 5th, 1868. The fact is not mentioned in the list of items dealt with at this meeting  Either this, or the circumstance that Breuer was not himself a member of the Academy, may have been the reason that this information is printed below the title. Nothing is known of how these publications were received at the time by the authors' scientific colleagues in the Academy and elsewhere.

The two papers contain more than the descriptions of the inflation and deflation reflexes. They record the first satisfactory experimental demonstration of biological feedback in the modern sense. There is also a clear description of the phenomenon later to be called the "paradoxical" reflex, although the authors regarded it as an artefact and did not recognize it as a reflex. Next, there is the description of an attempt—made with the very limited technical resources then available—to demonstrate that the vagi carry afferent impulses which accelerate breathing and do not arise from movements of the lung or from blood-gas changes but have a different origin. Further, Breuer clearly appreciated the problems of threshold and of variation in the sensitivities of all components of the reflex; and he raised the fundamental question as to the specificity of individual afferent fibres in the vagus. Aware of all these problems, and with so many questions left unanswered, why did neither Hering nor Breuer take any subsequent active personal interest in the "self-steering of respiration"?

That Hering and Breuer's collaboration ended with the publication of this discovery, and that the two men moved apart, does not really answer this question. However, their subsequent lives and activities could hardly have been more different.

### Hering's story

For Hering the really important event of 1868 was the publication of his book, *The Theory of Binocular Vision* (1868b), which was a synthesis and extension of the work he had done before being called to Vienna. His next two investigations dealt with *The Influence of Respiration on the Circulation*. In both he used inflation of the lung to stimulate the vagi. In the first (Hering, 1869) the blood pressure fluctuations attributed by Traube to periodic fatigue of the vasomotor centre became the "Traube-Hering" waves; for Hering suggested that excitation spread periodically from the respiratory to the vasomotor centre. In the second paper (Hering, 1871) he showed that sinus arrhythmia is dependent on the integrity of vagal afferents. It was the last time Hering himself worked in the fields of circulation or respiration.

After the death of the 82-year-old Purkinje in Prague in 1869, Hering was invited to take over the vacant chair. He accepted in 1870, probably influenced by a rumour (which later proved to be correct) that the Joseph's Academy would soon cease to exist as a medical school for the military. Hering remained in Prague for 25 years, his most productive.

With a collaborator, Biedermann, he published a large series of electro-physiological studies, mostly concerned with technicalities. Little of lasting influence has survived from this work.

But most of his scientific output was devoted to his principal interest, sensory perception, and to vision in particular. He was strongly influenced by Fechner, and had an ambivalent attitude to psychology as shown, for instance, in his *Contribution to the Theory of the Relationship between Body and Soul* (Hering, 1875).

Hering was a man full of interesting ideas whose misfortune—or mistake—was that hardly any of them could be critically tested in his lifetime. Hering believed all cellular metabolism to be self-steering. He suggested that a given neurone in the central nervous system might react differently if different chemical processes were elicited by impulses reaching it from other neurones. In a fascinating discourse entitled *On Memory as a General Function of Organized Matter*, he elaborated the idea that the memory trace in the brain and elsewhere may consist of a permanent re-arrangement of the molecular structure of the cellular protoplasm (Hering, 1870).

Hering's controversial theory of colour vision is another example of his modern way of thinking. He postulated six colour sensations associated with three visual substances continuously undergoing assimilation ($A$) and dissimilation ($D$). Perception of colour is "self-steering", since the sensitivity of the eye for a particular colour diminishes the further the appropriate ($A$) or ($D$) process has progressed (Hering, 1874). What Hering considered as proofs of his theory—arguments based on the phenomena of simultaneous and successive contrast and on types of colour blindness—were open to different interpretations by the adherents of the Young-Helmholtz theory. To the anti-vitalist physiologists among his colleagues Hering's ideas and supposed proofs were mere speculation. Twice Hering's name was put forward for the second University Chair of Physiology that had been created in Vienna. On both occasions, in 1874 and again in 1890, Bruecke prevented his appointment although the selection committee was in favour (Lesky, 1965, p. 530). Bruecke flew Helmholtz' flag and never trusted Hering.

In Prague, Hering became passionately involved in politics. The Charles University, the oldest German university, founded in 1348, split into two parts in 1883 as the result of rising Czech nationalism: a larger Czech and a much smaller "new" German university. Hering, who had sustained the claims of the German faction in the preceding years of bitter struggle, became the Rector of the new German university; deliberately or not, he seems to have made things awkward for the Czechs when occasion offered. In 1895 he moved finally to Leipzig, to succeed Carl Ludwig for the second time in his life. Hering was then over 60 years of age and his creative period was over, but he still published occasional papers on the fovea and on colour blindness; and, as always, he still trained and inspired pupils. He is said to have become very deaf and grumpy in old age but he did not resign his chair until he was 80 years of age, four years before his death.

## Breuer's story

Breuer's duties as clinical assistant to Oppolzer apparently continued while he worked with Hering; his chief seems to have allowed him time off for his experiments as a special favour. Oppolzer died in 1871. His successor did not re-appoint Breuer who went into private practice as a physician. As Oppolzer had wished, he nevertheless established himself as a *Privatdozent* in medicine, which meant that he had the right to lecture at the university and collect fees from the students, without being employed by the university. But he resigned ten years later because he considered it impossible to teach clinical medicine without access to patients; (such access was reserved for the *Ordinarius*, that is, the official holder of the chair, and his assistants). Billroth, then the dominant personality in the faculty, and in Viennese intellectual life in general, wanted to propose Breuer for the rank of Professor *extra-ordinarius*, an honour intensely coveted by ambitious men in the profession. Breuer's almost unprecedented decision was to ask Billroth not to proceed because he did not wish to return to academic medicine if he could not examine or treat patients in the university hospitals. Meanwhile his private practice flourished. It is a measure of his success and reputation that he was the private and family physician not only of Billroth and Bruecke (which Breuer regarded as a great honour), but also of almost all the other heads of departments in the faculty, as well as of numerous other families who counted for something in Viennese bourgeois and aristocratic society at this period. And unobtrusively he also did much unpaid work among the poor.

This burden of work still left him with enough spare energy and curiosity to conduct, at night in a room of his flat, a physiological investigation into the operation of the semicircular canals.

These were then still regarded as the detectors of the direction of sound, although Flourens had already shown, in about 1830, that they had something to do with balance and that their isolated destruction did not make birds deaf. Goltz confirmed this in 1870, but thought that the different distribution of the hydrostatic pressure of the endolymph in the three planes of the canals was the key to their function. Breuer first inferred from theoretical considerations, and later confirmed by experiments on himself and on pigeons, that the effective stimulus for the semicircular canals was the shear stress created by the inertia of the viscid endolymph at the start and at the end of rotational movement, but that they were not activated at rest or during rotation at constant velocity (Breuer 1874, 1875). No sooner had he sent off his first paper for publication than he discovered that he had been beaten by six days by his friend, the Austrian physicist Ernst Mach, then working in Prague, who quite independently had covered the same ground and reached the same conclusions. The same conclusions, arrived at also independently by Crum Brown in Edinburgh, were published a third time a few weeks later.

By studying as a pastime the comparative anatomy of the otoliths in fishes, amphibia, birds and mammals, and by ingenious experiments, Breuer later showed that this part of the vestibular apparatus was the one sensitive to the vertical component of pressure at rest and during non-rotational movement (Breuer, 1889, 1891). He vigorously defended his work and conclusions on the vestibular apparatus in two papers in 1897 and 1903. But throughout these years his main work was in his practice.

Between 1880 and 1882 Breuer treated a hysterical patient, Miss Anna O. His handling of this famous case started a scientific revolution. He had been the first physician in Vienna to make therapeutic use of hypnosis, and he used it in this case. Proceeding entirely empirically, Breuer and his patient discovered with surprise that a symptom would disappear and never return if he could bring her to relate the exact circumstances in which the symptom had appeared for the first time and to give expression to her feelings on that occasion. The patient's name for the procedure was "talking cure". Breuer later termed it "catharsis".

Breuer first met Freud in Bruecke's laboratory in the late eighteen-seventies. Their long and complex relationship has been extensively described by Ernest Jones (1953) and needs no recounting here. Despite their close friendship at the time Freud did not hear about the case of Miss Anna O. until the treatment had ended in 1882. It took Freud another twelve years to persuade Breuer to publish a detailed report of the case (which was not included in their joint preliminary communication *On the*

*Psychical Mechanism of Hysterical Phenomena*, 1893), and even then it was regrettably ". . . only in a much shortened and censored form, owing to the requirements of medical discretion" (Freud, 1925). To read Breuer's own account of the case (Breuer and Freud, 1895)—rather than summaries of it in books on psychoanalysis—brings this extraordinary man to life as no description of him by others can do. His powers of observation and open-mindedness, combined with great patience and tolerance, make it clear why he was so highly esteemed. He had an enormous circle of friends and a crowded social life. Yet, except as a physician, he appears to have been very conservative, even conventional.

But he was aware of what he had started. Towards the end of his *Curriculum* he says: "This book* was at first rather unfavourably received, but appeared in its fourth edition last year. For Freud it was the seed from which psycho-analysis grew" (Breuer, 1923; see also Cranefield, 1958).

Breuer retired from medical practice when he was 70 years old but returned during World War I to attend to casualties in the Viennese emergency hospitals. He died in 1925, well satisfied with his life.

*The Hering-Breuer reflex, 1868–1933*

Hering and Breuer, then, became absorbed in other interests. Hering, it is true, believed that all metabolism was self-steering, but he took no steps to demonstrate it and probably could not have done so had he tried. Breuer could not perform experiments on mammals in his back-room laboratory at home. But why did *Self-steering of Respiration by the Nervus Vagus* arouse so little interest elsewhere, at least at first? Perhaps to a generation of physiologists mainly out to discover the physical principles at the root of biological processes the whole concept of self-regulation was something to be expected from the laws of nature, and less intriguing than it is to us. The word "self-steering" was not new. In November 1854, E. W. Bruecke (1955) submitted to the Vienna Academy of Science his theory of "self-steering of the heart". The gist of this was that the flaps of the open aortic valve occluded the orifices of the coronary arteries so that the coronary circulation was perfused only during diastole. The diastolic filling of the vessels gave rigidity to the relaxed ventricular muscle (like the expanding spokes of an umbrella to the limp fabric) and this caused the chambers of the heart to open and suck in blood from the great veins (Bruecke, 1928). There followed a notorious feud with Hyrtl on whether or not the coronaries were covered by the open aortic valve, but no one got excited over the self-steering issue. According to Professor E. Neil (personal

---

* *Studies on Hysteria.*

communication), the word *Selbststeuerung* (self-steering) also occurs in Cyon and Ludwig's first description of the depressor nerve in 1866.

The relationship between the vagus and breathing as described by Hering and Breuer also received little attention. Most respiratory physiologists were at that time more interested in the properties of the respiratory centre and the effect of blood-gas changes on its activity.

In sporadic reactions to Hering and Breuer's thesis the argument mainly turned on whether their findings were artefacts, due to poor anaesthesia with opium (the advantages of chloral hydrate being emphasized by most critics); and, second, whether lung inflation activated expiratory muscles. Opinions remained divided (Lockenberg, 1873; Mayer, 1874; Guttmann, 1875). The most perceptive discussions were those by a medical student, J. Wagner (later known as Wagner-Jauregg, and a Nobel Laureate), and by Gad, who invented the method of temporarily blocking a nerve by freezing, and the word "thermode" (Wagner, 1879; Gad, 1880).

As late as 1880 Rosenthal repeated his old experiments by his old method of stimulating the cut vagus electrically "the only precise way of stimulating a nerve", but this time he used an intra-oesophageal catheter to record respiration. He obtained the same results as before—enhancement of inspiration but no expiratory effects. He ignored Hering and Breuer's criticisms (Rosenthal, 1880).

Among the work of his pupils, whom Hering urged to continue the study of respiratory reflexes, the most valuable is that of Kratschmer (1870) on reflexes elicited from the nasal mucosa. Knoll (1876) found that ether and chloroform cause apnoea only as long as the vagi remain intact. From 1882, Knoll published a series of unilluminating papers on the innervation of breathing. He became Professor of Pathology in Prague. When Head began work there under Hering, late in 1884, and news of his early success spread, Knoll sent him a "command" to desist at once from further work on the subject since he, Knoll, had already done all there was to be done (Head, 1926). Head was undeterred and it was he who put the Hering-Breuer reflex on the map. He used two new methods, his own diaphragm-slip preparation and temporary blocking of the vagi by means of Gad's cold thermodes. He discovered that the "paradoxical" series of events previously reported by Rosenthal (1864), Breuer (1868) and Wagner (1879) was a vagal reflex (Head, 1889a,b). At this point the thread of continuity becomes attenuated, but in the year in which Head's papers appeared Lord Adrian was born. It took another 44 years before Adrian showed the correlation between impulse frequency in single vagal afferents and the degree of lung inflation, and the persistence of activity in some fibres during expiration

(Adrian, 1933). Sixty-five years after the discovery of the *Self-steering of Respiration through the Nervus Vagus* the modern study of the reflex control of breathing really got off the ground.

ACKNOWLEDGEMENTS

E. Lesky's book, *The Viennese School of Medicine in the 19th Century*, has been an invaluable source of facts and references used in this account.

I am extremely grateful to Professor Erna Lesky for much additional help that she gave me by supplying copies of articles and documents, photographs, and information on obscure points. Others to whom I am indebted are: Mrs Hester Marsden-Smedley, for permission to use and quote from Henry Head's unpublished autobiographical notes; Professor Kenneth W. Cross; Miss Anna Freud; Dr Wilfried Oberhummer; Dr and Mrs Robert Bermann; Dr P. A. Merton and Professor K. Hierholzer.

I particularly wish to thank the Library staff at the Royal Society of Medicine, London, for their assistance, given with unfailing efficiency and courtesy.

REFERENCES*

ADRIAN, E. D. (1933). *J. Physiol., Lond.*, **79**, 332–357.
BREUER, J. (1868). *Sber. Akad. Wiss. Wien*, **58**, part 2, 909–937.
BREUER, J. (1874). *Medizinisches Jahrbuch*, 72–124.
BREUER, J. (1875). *Medizinisches Jahrbuch*, 87–156.
BREUER, J. (1889). *Pflügers Arch. ges. Physiol.*, **44**, 135–152.
BREUER, J. (1891). *Pflügers Arch. ges. Physiol.*, **48**, 195–306.
BREUER, J. (1897). *Pflügers Arch. ges. Physiol.*, **68**, 596–648.
BREUER, J. (1903). *Sber. Akad. Wiss. Wien*, **112**, part 2, 315–394.
BREUER, J. (1923). *Curriculum Vitae.*†
BREUER, J., and FREUD, S. (1893). *Neurol. Zentbl.*, **12**, 4–10.
BREUER, J., and FREUD, S. (1895). In *Studien über Hysterie*, pp. 15–37, 161–221. Leipzig and Vienna: Deuticke.
BRUECKE, E. Th. (1928). In *Ernest Bruecke*, pp. 67–68. Vienna.
BRUECKE, E. W. (1854). *Sber. Akad. Wiss. Wien*, **14**, 345.
CRANEFIELD, P. F. (1958). *Int. J. Psycho-Analysis*, **39**, 319–322.
CYON, E., de, and LUDWIG, C. (1866). *Ber. sächs. Akad. Wiss.*, **18**, 307–329.
FICK, A. (1864). *Arch. Anat. Physiol.*, 583–589.
FREUD, S. (1925). *Int. Z. Psychoanal.*, **11**, 255–256.
GAD, J. (1880). *Arch. Anat. Physiol.*, 1–30.
GARTEN, S. (1918). *Pflügers Arch. ges. Physiol.*, **170**, 501–522.
GOLTZ, F. (1870). *Pflügers Arch. ges. Physiol.*, **3**, 172–192.
GUTTMANN, P. (1875). *Arch. Anat. Physiol.*, 500–525.
HEAD, H. (1889a). *J. Physiol., Lond.*, **10**, 1–70.
HEAD, H. (1889b). *J. Physiol., Lond.*, **10**, 279–290.
HEAD, H. (1926). *Notes for an Autobiography*. Unpublished.

* This is not a bibliography of the writings of Hering and Breuer. Only items important in the context of this biographical sketch are included.
† When Breuer became a corresponding member in 1894 he was asked by the Vienna Academy of Science to provide a *Curriculum Vitae*, in accordance with custom. Breuer neither wrote nor sent it until 1923. After his death in 1925 a pamphlet containing the text of the *Curriculum* and the text of the address spoken by H. H. Mayer at Breuer's cremation was privately printed for his friends in a limited edition. One of these pamphlets is now in the possession of the Institute for History of Medicine at the University of Vienna. Quotations from the *Curriculum* in this paper were translated from a Xerox-copy of the pamphlet, obtained through the good offices of Prof. Erna Lesky, Director of the Institute.

HERING, E. (1861–1864). *Beiträge zur Physiologie.* Leipzig: Englemann.
HERING, E. (1868a). *Sber. Akad. Wiss. Wien,* **57,** part 2, 672–677.
HERING, E. (1868b). *Die Lehre vom binokularen Sehen.* Leipzig: Engelmann.
HERING, E. (1869). *Sber. Akad. Wiss. Wien,* **60,** part 2, 829–856.
HERING, E. (1870). *Alm. Akad. Wiss. Wien,* **20,** 253–278.
HERING, E. (1871). *Sber. Akad. Wiss. Wien,* **64,** part 2, 333–353.
HERING, E. (1874). *Sber. Akad. Wiss. Wien,* **70,** part 3, 169–204.
HERING, E. (1875). *Sber. Akad. Wiss. Wien,* **72,** part 3, 310–348.
JONES, E. (1953). *Sigmund Freud: Life and Work,* vol. 1, pp. 243–315. London: Hogarth Press.
KNOLL, P. (1876). *Sber. Akad. Wiss. Wien,* **74,** part 3, 233–269.
KRATSCHMER, F. (1870). *Sber. Akad. Wiss. Wien,* **62,** part 2, 147–170.
LESKY, E. (1965). *Die Wiener Medizinische Schule im 19. Jahrhundert.* Gras-Koeln: Hermann Boehlaus Nachf.
LOCKENBERG, W. (1873). In *Arbeiten aus dem Physiologischen Laboratorium der Würzburger Hochschule,* ed. Fick, A. p. 199. Würzburger, unpublished.
MAYER, S. (1874). *Sber. Akad. Wiss. Wien,* **69,** part 3, 111–120.
MEYER, H. H. (1928). In *Neue Österreichische Biographie,* **5,** 30–47.
ROSENTHAL, I. (1864). *Arch. Anat. Physiol.,* 456–477.
ROSENTHAL, I. (1880). *Arch. Anat. Physiol.,* (suppl.) 34–49.
WAGNER, J. (1879). *Sber. Akad. Wiss. Wien,* **80,** part 3, 177–190.

# THE ROLE OF VAGAL INFLATION REFLEXES IN MAN AND OTHER ANIMALS

A. Guz, M. I. M. Noble, J. H. Eisele and Diana Trenchard

*Department of Medicine, Charing Cross Hospital Medical School, Fulham Hospital, London*

This paper will attempt to summarize our work on the Hering-Breuer reflexes, particularly as applied to man. In spite of the title, we shall include the deflation reflex in this account because, first, Hering and Breuer gave it an equal importance to the inflation reflex and, second, there is some evidence to be presented that the former reflex may merely be the inverse of the latter. We shall not deal with any of the non-respiratory effects of these reflexes (Widdicombe, 1964).

## THE RESPONSE TO LUNG INFLATION AND THE RESULT OF VAGOTOMY

Hering (1868) and Breuer (1868) showed in the dog, cat and rabbit that expansion of the lung reflexly inhibited inspiration and promoted expiration; this effect depended on the integrity of the vagus nerves. The reflex effect could be demonstrated by obstructing the trachea at the height of a normal inspiration, implying that it was active during eupnoea. Breathing became slower and deeper with vagal section presumably because of the removal of this reflex. This experiment is very well known, but of equal interest is another of Hering and Breuer's experiments that is less well known. In an open-chest rabbit the lung was kept static and distended, and the blood chemistry constant by blowing air at constant pressure through the trachea and lungs, the latter having been pierced in many places. The rate of breathing was observed at the nostrils and, following vagal section, this rate fell from an average of 20 to 12/min. Since the lungs were static, Hering and Breuer had clearly demonstrated a tonic vagal influence on respiratory frequency.

The inflation reflex has since been demonstrated in amphibia, reptiles, birds and mammals, section of the cervical vagi causing slow deep breathing in all these (Widdicombe, 1964). The stretch receptors believed to be responsible for this reflex lie predominantly in the bronchi and bronchioles

17

rather than in the alveoli or pleura (Widdicombe, 1954). The inhibition by stretch receptors of phrenic motoneurone discharge has been carefully documented by Larrabee and Knowlton (1946), and lung inflation within the tidal-volume range has been shown to decrease breathing frequency. There is, however, no agreement on the question of whether the inflation reflex actively promotes expiration except in the anaesthetized rabbit, a species which normally has conspicuous expiratory muscle contractions during expiration (Troelstra, 1960). Hering and Breuer's studies in dogs and cats were performed under opium narcosis, when breathing was abnormal in that the animals were expiring actively with considerable force.

*Man*

Christiansen and Haldane (1914) distended the lungs of conscious adults (including Professor C. Douglas, the Professor of Physiology at Oxford at that time, and Haldane himself!) and obtained striking apnoeic responses. Neither Widdicombe (1961) nor our group (Guz *et al.*, 1964) have been able to confirm this in subjects ignorant of respiratory physiology. We found that closure of the glottis was a common response to lung inflation. Dejours and co-workers (1962) studied three normal subjects during sleep. Breathing was obstructed at the height of inspiration and the invariable response was some increase in the respiratory rate; there was no evidence of an inhibition of breathing. In the newborn baby a well-marked inhibition of breathing in response to lung inflation occurred in the first few days of life (Cross *et al.*, 1960). The strength of this response diminished greatly over the course of the first three to four days and this weakening of the reflex was not thought to be due to changes in the mechanical properties of the lungs. It appears that the primitive inflation reflex is suppressed by the developing higher centres. It is relevant that when the attention of a conscious cat is attracted by a noise, or flash of light, the apnoeic response to afferent vagal stimulation, using chronically implanted electrodes, is abolished (Frankstein, 1969, 1970).

In adult man, it is only under anaesthesia that a clear-cut inflation reflex can be demonstrated. Widdicombe (1961) compared the results of inflating the lungs in man, monkey, dog, cat, rabbit, guinea-pig, rat and mouse. The reflex was found to be very weak in four subjects studied under sodium thiopentone anaesthesia, but inflation volumes above 800 ml were not tried. Our group (Guz *et al.*, 1964) studied normal subjects under halothane (1–1·5 per cent) anaesthesia. Inflation volumes comparable to tidal volume produced little effect, but with inflation volumes of 1000 ml and more there was a marked inhibition of breathing. A normal range was defined (Fig. 1). Twenty subjects have now been studied, and all have a response within this range. Although halothane causes a 30–40 per cent increase in the amount of stretch-receptor discharge for a given degree of lung inflation (Coleridge

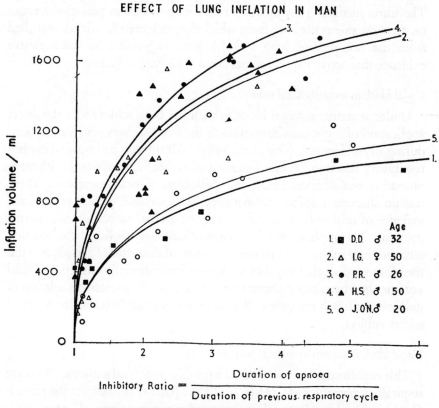

FIG. 1. The Hering-Breuer inflation reflex in five human subjects. J. O'N. was unconscious following a head injury. The other subjects were anaesthetized with 1 per cent halothane in nitrous oxide and oxygen, and the measurements made during minor surgical procedures. The response to an inflation volume (ordinate) was measured as an inhibitory ratio (abscissa) (Guz *et al.*, 1964; reproduced by permission of *Clin. Sci.*).

*et al.*, 1968) the responses were of the same order as those seen under thiopentone anaesthesia and in one subject who was unconscious following a head injury but not anaesthetized (J. O'N, Fig. 1). This response to inflation was abolished in five subjects by the application of 2 per cent lignocaine to exposed cervical vagi during neck surgery. No expiratory responses were seen but electromyography of the appropriate muscles was not done.

One lung was inflated in man so that ventilation of the other lung could be studied without subjecting that lung to a load (Guz et al., 1966b). The magnitude and variability of the apnoeic response to inflation were of the same order as were found with inflation of both lungs. We blocked one vagus nerve at a time in three subjects undergoing partial thyroidectomy. The fibres mediating the inflation reflex were found to pass up the vagus on the same side as the lung from which they originated. Air was expelled from the non-inflated lung and this gave suggestive but inconclusive evidence that active expiration occurred with lung inflation.

## Vagal block in anaesthetized man

Under anaesthesia, vagal block in man has been achieved by the direct application of 2 per cent lignocaine to the exposed nerves in five subjects during thyroidectomy (Guz et al., 1964). All subjects had normal cardio-respiratory function. A block of the parasympathetic efferents with atropine 2 mg was achieved before the application of local anaesthetic. There was no effect on respiratory frequency, tidal volume, pattern of air flow, variance of tidal volume and frequency or arterial carbon dioxide partial pressure. The application of local anaesthetic had abolished the inflation reflex in these subjects. Tidal volumes were of the order of 200 ml, and it is therefore possible that vagal block would have affected ventilation if tidal volumes had been more normal with consequently greater stimulation of pulmonary stretch receptors. We therefore once again turned to the conscious subject.

## Vagal block in conscious normal subjects

This experiment has now been done in three normal subjects. Two are respiratory physiologists—M.N. and J.W. (Guz et al., 1966b); the third is C.W.—a female subject with no knowledge of physiology. The technique used was that of Bertola (1940), also Mushin (1945); the ninth, tenth and eleventh cranial nerves were blocked with 1 per cent lignocaine as they emerge from the base of the skull. Involvement of the glossopharyngeal nerve in the block complicates the interpretation of the study since a baro-receptor denervation, with consequent hypertension to levels of 230/140 mmHg, and a chemoreceptor denervation, with insensibility to hypoxia, result (Guz et al., 1966a and 1966c). Hypertension can be controlled by the use of adrenergic blocking drugs; these were only used in C.W. Para-sympathetic efferents were again blocked with atropine prior to the study. No change in any aspect of eupnoeic breathing followed the ninth and tenth nerve blocks in the three subjects (Fig. 2).

A further, more direct study was done in subject E.J., who had a small carcinoma of the bronchus without respiratory symptoms but with severe joint symptoms due to hypertrophic pulmonary arthropathy. The vagi were exposed low in the neck under local anaesthesia and the nerves were then blocked with 2 per cent lignocaine. The procedure was performed to assess the need for intrathoracic vagotomy for the relief of joint symptoms (Holling, Brodey and Boland, 1961). No change in any aspect of breathing followed this pure tenth nerve block.

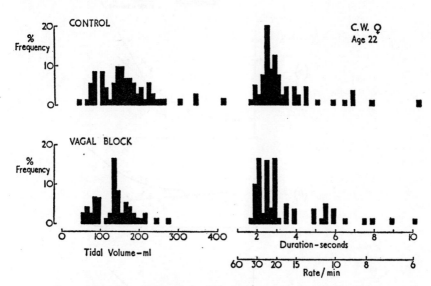

FIG. 2. The effect of bilateral vagal block in man. Percentage frequency (ordinates) of breaths of different tidal volume (abscissae, left) and duration (abscissae, right) before (above) and during (below) bilateral ninth and tenth nerve block at the base of the skull (see text). Corresponding respiratory frequencies are also indicated on the right. The histograms are obtained from 100 consecutive breaths.

*Hyperpnoea and vagal afferents in man and animals*

The absence of a vagal modulation of breathing during eupnoea in man is compatible with the absence of inflation reflex activity within the tidal range. What will happen during hyperpnoea? This problem has been studied during carbon dioxide rebreathing and we have also begun to look at the same problem during exercise. It has been known for some time that the increase of respiratory frequency due to breathing carbon dioxide is prevented by vagotomy in rabbits; this also limits the minute-volume response (Scott, 1908; Sasaki, 1927). More recently this has been confirmed by Richardson and Widdicombe (1969) in the rabbit and by Florez and

Borison (1964) in the decerebrate cat. We have also confirmed this for the
conscious dog (Fig. 3). In man, this experiment has never been done with
vagal block alone, and inclusion of the chemoreceptors, particularly with a
ninth nerve block, would make the interpretation of any experiment with
carbon dioxide difficult. If the study is done during hyperoxia ($Po_2$*
greater than 300 mmHg) then there is some evidence in man that carbon
dioxide will not stimulate ventilation by an action on the chemoreceptors

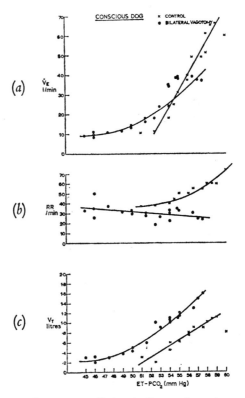

FIG. 3. Response of minute ventilation (ordinate, $a$), respiratory rate
(ordinate, $b$) and tidal volume (ordinate, $c$) to end-tidal $Pco_2$ (abscissa $a$,
$b$ and $c$) before (crosses) and during (circles) bilateral cervical vagal block
in a conscious dog. The animal was rebreathing from a bag containing
7 per cent carbon dioxide and 93 per cent oxygen.

(Bernards, Dejours and Lacaisse, 1966; Wade, 1969). Effectively, one is
only blocking non-chemosensitive fibres under these hyperoxic conditions.
This study has now been done in three subjects: J.W. was the only normal

* $Po_2$ and $Pco_2$ are symbols used to denote the partial pressures of oxygen and carbon dioxide
in blood or tissue; $Pao_2$ and $Paco_2$ denote arterial partial pressures of these gases. (See also
Editor's Note, p. xiii, and Comroe et al., 1965.)

subject (Guz *et al.*, 1966*d*) but a similar effect was seen in H.H., a patient with pulmonary fibrosis (Fig. 4), and to a lesser extent in J.P., a subject with mild chronic asthma. In each case, the carbon dioxide response curve was estimated by rebreathing from a bag initially filled with gas mixtures of

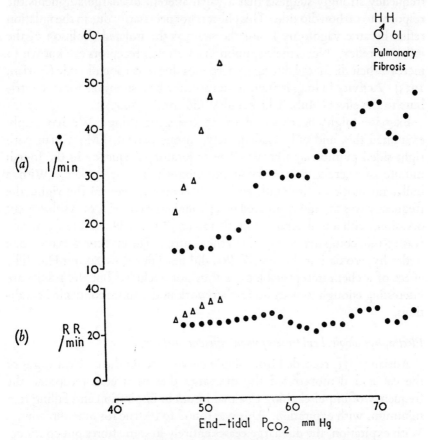

FIG. 4. Response of minute ventilation (ordinate, *a*) and respiratory rate (ordinate, *b*) to end-tidal $P_{CO_2}$ (abscissa *a* and *b*) before (triangles) and during (circles) bilateral vagal block at the base of the skull in a conscious patient (H.H.) with pulmonary fibrosis. The patient was rebreathing from a 5-litre bag containing 7 per cent carbon dioxide and 93 per cent oxygen.

5–7 per cent carbon dioxide and 93–95 per cent oxygen (Read, 1967). The reduction in response to carbon dioxide resulted from a much smaller increase in respiratory rate. The subjects can tolerate higher $P_{CO_2}$ values. The tidal-volume response is of the same order as the control with lower carbon dioxide tensions but is greater at higher carbon dioxide tensions.

The reduction in sensitivity to carbon dioxide with vagal block could arise from an alteration in sensitivity of the medullary respiratory centres. Evidence on this point is contradictory and there are species differences (Widdicombe, 1964). The striking effect of vagal block on respiratory frequency strongly suggests that a vagal afferent discharge augments the response to carbon dioxide. This effect is not necessarily due to the inflation reflex because vagotomy is not the same as the isolated abolition of the inflation reflex. Nevertheless, pulmonary stretch receptors are known to increase their discharge during hyperpnoea due to carbon dioxide (Adrian, 1933). Activity in lung irritant receptors may be responsible for or contribute to the effect (Mills, Sellick and Widdicombe, 1969).

Exercise might be expected to do the same thing. We have only examined this, and only inadequately, in one patient, J.M., a man with right-sided pulmonary fibrosis. The respiratory frequency in the fourth minute of exercise at 300 kilopond metres/min was studied. With a unilateral block of the ninth and tenth cranial nerves on the right, the frequency was 27/min compared to 44/min in the control; on a subsequent occasion, with a unilateral left ninth and tenth nerve block, the frequency was 15/min compared to 25/min in the control. The exercise was not done under hyperoxia but the arterial $Po_2$ did not fall below 80 mmHg. The effect of a chemoreceptor block is thus not excluded but the results are interesting enough to warrant further work under more controlled conditions.

*Electrophysiological evidence of vagal afferent discharge*

Adrian (1933) recorded from single nerve fibres in the cervical vagus of the cat and demonstrated the discharge due to stretch receptors, the frequency of impulses rising to a maximum in inspiration and falling to a minimum with expiration. This was found to be true for quiet breathing. With expiration, the discharge ceases entirely in some fibres but continues in others. According to Paintal (1966) about 60 per cent of stretch receptor fibres continue to discharge during expiration. Adrian showed that the discharge frequency varied linearly with the degree of lung inflation. The receptors were shown to be slowly adapting in response to lung inflation especially when the degree of inflation did not produce a frequency higher than 50/s. The volume threshold for discharge of impulses varied from below the functional residual capacity to many times the tidal volume. Adrian concluded that these stretch receptors and their fibres probably mediate the inflation reflex. This view has been substantially accepted, but it is based on a correlation of properties. Thus the discharge occurs at the time of the inhibition of breathing; in addition, the discharge is blocked by cooling the nerves to 8–10°C, and it is at this temperature that the inflation reflex is blocked (Dawes, Mott and Widdicombe, 1951). In the cat the fibres have conduction velocities ranging from 14–59 m/s. (Paintal, 1953).

*Stretch receptor discharge in man with single fibre recording.* This remarkable feat was accomplished by Langrehr (1964). He isolated single fibres from cut cervical vagi in two patients. The records published are remarkably good. The receptors were slowly adapting, did not discharge in expiration and increased their peak frequency with increasing tidal volume. One of the human fibres was compared with a dog fibre; at all tidal volumes, peak frequency in the dog was approximately double that in man. This is hardly surprising since any given tidal volume will stretch the small lung of a dog more than a large, human lung. Unfortunately, there is no account of the number of fibres studied, the conduction velocity of these fibres or the voltage of the impulses recorded. In spite of these criticisms. Langrehr's study remains unique.

*Stretch receptor discharge in man with the antidromic technique.* We have used the "collision" technique described by Douglas and Ritchie (1957); this method enables recordings to be made from the whole nerve trunk without

TABLE I

CONDUCTION VELOCITY AND STIMULATION CHARACTERISTICS OF "A" WAVE IN MAN

| Patient | Vagus | Conduction distance (cm) | Supramaximal stimulus voltage (V) | Conduction velocity (m/s) | Amplitude (μV) |
|---|---|---|---|---|---|
| 2 | Right | 4 | 4·5 | 45–32 | 140 |
| 3 | Left | 3·5 | 0·6 | 52–36 | 300 |
| 4 | Left | 4 | 0·9 | 45–28 | 400 |
| 5 | Right | 9 | 2·1 | 40–32 | 170 |
| 5 | Left | 4·5 | 1·6 | 30–20 | 600 |

Pulse width 50 μs. Square waves delivered by isolated stimulator (Devices Mark IV—source impedance < 1300 Ω). Recording with Ag-AgCl electrodes and differential preamplifier (Tektronix Type 122).

damaging the nerve in any way. By stimulating a nerve with graded voltages the mass discharge in different groups of fibres can be recorded. A small voltage only stimulates large, rapidly conducting fibres, whereas a large voltage also stimulates small, slowly conducting fibres. The recording, or electroneurogram, permits one to identify groups of fibres of similar conduction velocity (Erlanger and Gasser, 1924). Fortunately, the fibres from the slowly and rapidly adapting stretch receptors form the principal constituent of a well-marked A wave in the electroneurogram of the vagus (Paintal, 1953). We have recorded these waves in the intact vagus in man using a bipolar electrode system and the results are shown in Fig. 5 and Table I. This has been done in the cervical vagi in patients Nos. 3, 4 and 5 during neck surgery, and in the thoracic vagus above the right hilum in patient No. 2 during thoracotomy. The same range of conduction velocity has been found in the neck and the chest. The larger and faster motor fibres of the recurrent laryngeal nerve are absent in the right chest, but we

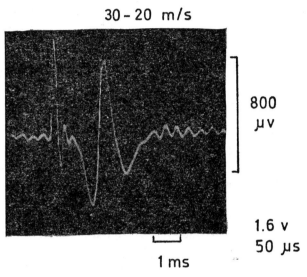

**30 - 20 m/s**

**800 µv**

**1.6 v**
**50 µs**

**1 ms**

FIG. 5. An antidromic electroneurogram ("A" wave) from the cervical vagus nerve in patient No. 5 (Table I) with bipolar recording. Negative: up; positive: down. The initial deflection is the stimulus artefact. Following this a 400-µV, positive, artefactual wave precedes the electroneurogram proper; this results from the recording conditions.
    Stimulus: square wave 1·6 V, 50 µs duration. All stimulations done with isolated stimulator (Devices Mark IV—source impedance < 1300 Ω).

have not seen them as a distinct electroneurographic wave in the cervical vagus.

If stimulating and recording electrodes are placed on the cervical vagus, with the recording electrodes nearer the lung, then an antidromic volley will be picked up when the nerve is stimulated with a voltage that is supramaximal for A fibres. Should any of the fibres also be carrying an orthodromic impulse, then the antidromic impulse will be cancelled out at the point of collision. Thus the total antidromic wave picked up by the recording electrodes will be reduced in proportion to the number of collisions that have occurred between the stimulating and recording electrodes. A decrease in the height of the antidromic wave is therefore an indication of the amount of orthodromic natural activity that is being transmitted in the same fibres. Zeveke (1961) applied this technique successfully to recording pulmonary stretch receptor discharge in the cat.

The discharge from the receptors can be cut off from the recording electrodes by putting 2 per cent lignocaine on the nerve between these

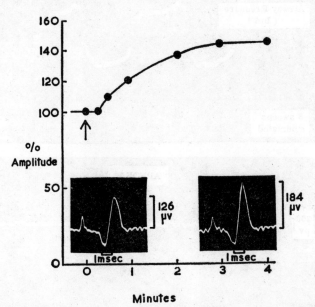

FIG. 6. The amplitude of the A wave of the antidromic electroneurogram plotted as a percentage of the initial value (ordinate) in patient No. 5. At the arrow, 2 per cent lignocaine was applied to the vagus nerve below the recording electrodes. Inserts show the electroneurogram taken immediately before the block (left) and when it was complete (right).

electrodes and the lungs; no collisions can now occur and the antidromic wave will be maximal. This experiment has been done in patients Nos. 4 and 5, apnoeic at their functional residual capacity. In both, the A wave increased in size, clearly demonstrating the existence in man of a tonic orthodromic discharge in these fibres at the end-expiratory level (Fig. 6). We next wished to know if this afferent discharge increased during inspiration; any increase in frequency of discharge and number of fibres involved would increase the number of collisions. Zeveke (1961) has shown that this is so in the cat. We have obtained similar results in dogs and from the

2*

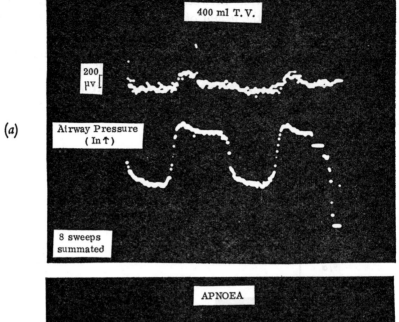

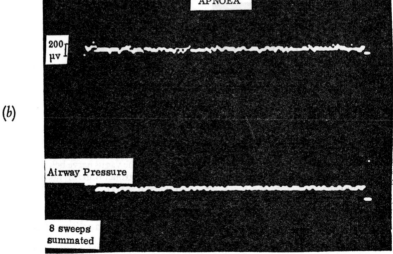

FIG. 7. Patient No. 4. Paralysed with curare and ventilated with a pump. Pattern of inflation constant, thus permitting averaging. Top trace: output of digital averager programmed to *rise* with *decrease* in peak height of antidromic A wave. Lower trace: airway pressure (peak pressure: 25 cmH$_2$O). Air flow ceases during inflation at end of overshoot in airway pressure. (*a*) Tidal volume 400 ml. Note height of antidromic wave decreases more during air flow than when the lung is held static. (*b*) Apnoea. The height of the wave is stable.

cervical vagi in patients Nos. 3, 4 and 5. The height of the antidromic wave has been averaged by digital techniques in one of the human studies. The improvement in signal-to-noise ratio allows a clear-cut discharge to be detected with an inflation volume of 400 ml; this is unequivocally within the tidal range (Fig. 7). A greater degree of discharge is shown as the lung

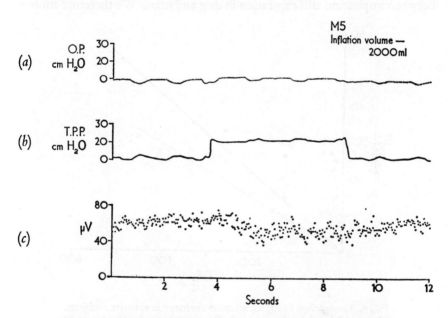

FIG. 8. Inflation reflex; patient No. 5 breathing spontaneously. (*a*) oesophageal pressure (OP); (*b*) transpulmonary pressure (TPP); (*c*) peak amplitude of an antidromic A wave. The lungs are inflated via a small endotracheal tube by turning the airway into a weighted Douglas bag. Plot of volume inaccurate and not shown; plot of oesophageal pressure gives an approximate picture of the time course of changes in lung volume. Note fall in height of antidromic A wave with inflation of 2000 ml. Inflation reflex weak since the other vagus had previously been blocked with 2 per cent lignocaine.

inflates than with the lung held inflated. This may well be due to the additional stimulation of rapidly adapting receptors during the inflow of air. The amplitude of the antidromic wave is reduced in inspiration by 4–28 per cent with inflation volumes ranging between 260 and 800 ml. Inflation volumes of 2000 ml, sufficient to elicit a small inflation reflex, have been associated with a 25 per cent fall in amplitude of the A wave (Fig. 8).

It is possible to deduce the maximum frequency of afferent impulses in these fibres by covering a range of antidromic stimulation frequencies (Zeveke and Khayutin, 1966). From this type of analysis we have concluded that with increasing tidal volume there is an increase in the peak frequency of afferent discharge, and that with tidal volumes of 800 ml this peak frequency is in the range of 100–150 impulses/s. This is in agreement with Langrehr's (1964) records.

We then wished to compare the change in the total number of collisions between inspiration and expiration in dog and man. We therefore studied

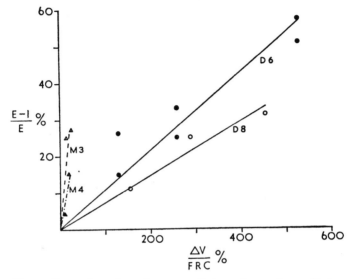

Fig. 9. Comparison of stretch receptor discharge in man (two subjects, M3 and M4) and dog (two animals, D6 and D8). Ordinate: percentage change in height of antidromic wave with inflation; abscissa: degree of lung stretch. ΔV: tidal volume; FRC: functional residual capacity, calculated from the X-rays of the patients using the method of Lloyd, String and DuBois (1966) and taken from the data of Crossfill and Widdicombe (1961) for the dogs. E: peak height of antidromic wave in expiration; I: peak height in inspiration.

the change in amplitude of the antidromic wave with inflation in two dogs and two humans paralysed with curare and artificially ventilated. The change in amplitude was always measured in the latter part of inflation after air flow had ceased to avoid including the discharge of rapidly adapting receptors, and measurements were made over a range of volumes. The antidromic stimulation frequency was 40–60/s. We have related the results to the degree to which the lung tissue is stretched, as measured by the change in volume related to the original volume at the end-expiratory level (Fig. 9).

The receptor discharge is apparently linear with stretch and, on the basis of the comparison used, man appears to be more sensitive than the dog in that a smaller degree of stretch produces a bigger discharge with inspiration. It must be stressed, however, that we are ignorant of the precise physical factors stimulating the stretch receptors and therefore this comparison may be an artefactual result of using an inappropriate reference variable.

We may conclude, therefore, that though there appears to be no vagal modulation of eupnoeic breathing in man, and the inflation reflex is active only outside the tidal range, the sensory information coming up the vagi from stretch receptors is similar to this information in animals.

### THE RESPONSE TO LUNG DEFLATION

Hering and Breuer in 1868 showed clearly in the rabbit that reduction of lung volume arrests any expiratory movement that may be in progress and at once elicits an inspiration. They also noted that the return of a greatly inflated lung to its normal volume was an ineffective stimulus to breathing compared with the stimulus of a diminution in lung size below the resting expiratory position. The response disappeared following vagal section. Subsequently, there has been general agreement that deflation of the lungs in many species increases both the frequency and force of the inspiratory effort (Widdicombe, 1964). Troelstra (1960) has elegantly studied the deflation reflex in the rabbit and concluded that it was active at the resting end-expiratory level.

*Man*

There have been several attempts to demonstrate this in man with conflicting results. Christiansen and Haldane (1914) observed a short apnoea resulting from applying suction to the airway of a conscious subject. Widdicombe (1961) repeated this experiment and noted some stimulation of respiratory rate and inspiratory force in anaesthetized patients, but the response was very weak. McIlroy, Butler and Finley (1962) observed a tachypnoea in conscious subjects as a result of external chest strapping which reduced the functional residual capacity by about one litre. We were unable to obtain a reproducible tachypnoea in conscious or anaesthetized subjects, by either sudden chest compression with an inflatable jacket or by airway suction, but we could not decrease lung volume to less than 870 ml below the end-expiratory level by these methods. But we have studied four patients with spontaneous pneumothorax who were free from pain and had apparently normal lungs. Three of these patients (A.T., male aged 19 years, M.C., female aged 50 years, W.W., female aged 19 years) required removal of air from the pleural space via a chest tube

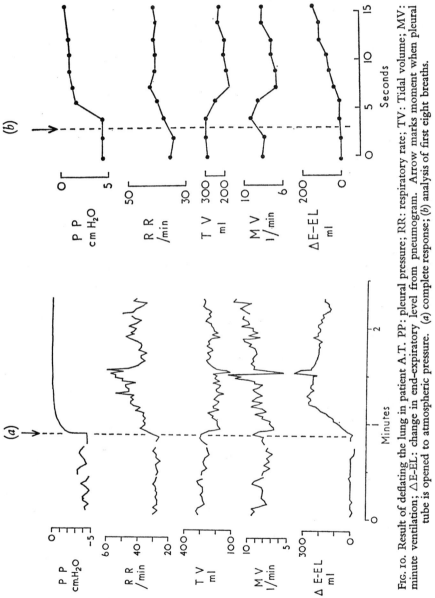

Fig. 10. Result of deflating the lung in patient A.T. PP: pleural pressure; RR: respiratory rate; TV: Tidal volume; MV: minute ventilation; ΔE-EL: change in end-expiratory level from pneumogram. Arrow marks moment when pleural tube is opened to atmospheric pressure. (*a*) complete response; (*b*) analysis of first eight breaths.

with underwater drainage; when the pleural space had been sucked out in this way the tube was opened to atmospheric pressure thus permitting one lung to deflate. Re-expansion of the lung was achieved within three minutes by re-establishing underwater drainage. The fourth patient, (M.F., male aged 33 years) was undergoing thoracoscopy for recurrent pneumothorax. The lung had almost re-expanded at the time of study, and insertion of trochar and cannula established atmospheric pressure within the chest with consequent deflation of the lung. The time course, or the extent of lung collapse, is not known. Respiratory rate increased immediately, within the first breath after the rise in pleural pressure, in all of our patients (Fig. 10). This increase was transient in one patient but in the other three it was sustained. Thus in M.F. the mean respiratory frequency increased from 14–33/min, in A.T. from 23–42/min, and in M.C. from 15–18/min. Tidal volume fell correspondingly. Arterial $Pco_2$ fell from $37 \cdot 5$–$29 \cdot 5$ mmHg in M.F., and from 35–31 mmHg in A.T. and M.C. The arterial $Po_2$ also fell from 88–78 mmHg in M.F., from 70–64 mmHg in A.T., and from 64–61 mmHg in M.C. Blood gas tensions were not measured in S.W. This fall in $Pa_{O_2}$ presumably reflected the inequality of ventilation and perfusion in the collapsed lung; the level reached is unlikely to have been responsible for the degree of alveolar hyperventilation seen and, in any case, could not account for the immediate respiratory stimulation. With deflation of the lung the pneumogram indicated enlargement of the thoracic cage. This would be expected on the basis of the known passive properties of the chest wall, but electroneurograms recorded in M.F. and A.T. from inspiratory intercostal muscles showed an increase in frequency of discharge and a recruitment of new motoneurones which we interpreted as an increase in inspiratory force. These experiments are necessarily accompanied by some mediastinal shift but this is likely to have been small since it was not clinically detectable, there was minimal change in the mean QRS vector, and neither heart rate nor blood pressure altered. These results demonstrate that the effects of acute lung deflation in man are an increased respiratory frequency, an augmented inspiratory force and an increased alveolar ventilation.

The need for a pneumothorax to demonstrate the response implies that the alveoli of at least one lung must deflate to a greater degree with a pneumothorax than after chest compression or airway suction; the last two manoeuvres never reduced lung size below residual volume. The drive to breathe elicited by lung deflation with a pneumothorax is apparent in the impaired ability to breath-hold (Noble et al., 1970) and also in a striking interaction with a chemical stimulus to ventilation. The rebreathing carbon dioxide response curve (Read, 1967) was studied in U.C., a female aged 23 years, with a moderate-sized painless, spontaneous pneumothorax. The curve was then compared with a similar response curve after recovery a week later, with the lung stuck to the chest wall (Fig. 11). The

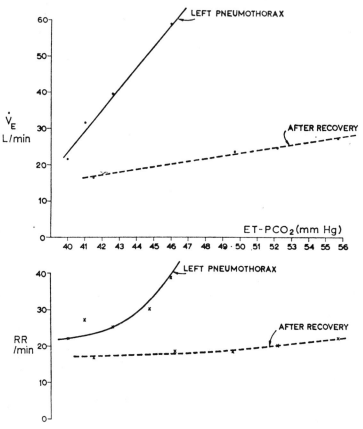

FIG. 11. Response of minute ventilation (above) and respiratory rate (below) to end-tidal $P_{CO_2}$ (common abscissa) in one patient with pneumothorax with the lung deflated (continuous line) and after recovery (dashed line).

response falls within our normal range after recovery but is grossly exaggerated with the lung deflated.*

We cannot legitimately call the response to lung deflation in man the Hering-Breuer deflation reflex until we have shown that this response is abolished by vagal block. We have not yet been able to find the clinical

* Note added in proof: in three similar patients studied since the symposium we have been unable to find this sensitivity to a carbon dioxide stimulus.

circumstances that would permit such a procedure, and all we can therefore say is that the response is analagous to that seen in animals.

*Is the deflation reflex the inverse of the inflation reflex?*

Hering and Breuer ask whether a medium neutral lung volume exists which evokes neither inspiration nor expiration. We can now answer this question for man by saying that there does appear to be a neutral zone, of $\pm 1000$ ml, around the functional residual capacity (FRC). This is to be contrasted with the rabbit where the two influences overlap only at volumes close to FRC (Troelstra, 1960).

Hering and Breuer also ask whether both expiratory and inspiratory stimuli are transmitted in the same or different fibres. There is still no answer to this question a hundred years after it was posed. However, we must examine more closely the basis for the commonly held view that there is a specific vagal deflation reflex with its own pathways. The alternative view is that deflation stimulates breathing by inhibition of the tonic end-expiratory discharge in the inflation reflex pathway which is known to be present in animals and man. The evidence for a specific reflex is twofold. First, when the rabbit lung is deflated, the respiratory rate is higher than it is after bilateral vagotomy (Head, 1889); this is also true for man. This experiment is not quantitative, and vagotomy sections an abundance of afferent pathways. Second, cooling the vagus nerve to 5–8°C abolishes the inflation reflex but deflation still stimulates breathing (Hammouda and Wilson, 1935; Troelstra, 1960). Unfortunately, cooling is not a conclusive method for differentiating between vagal afferent pathways. Paintal (1965) has shown that cooling blocks medullated and non-medullated fibres at about the same temperature. The maximum transmissible frequency through a cold area is reduced, and if the peak frequency of discharge exceeds this maximum then the frequency of discharge emerging from the cooled area is greatly reduced. Thus a reduced tonic discharge in the inflation reflex pathway would pass a cold block while the high frequency discharge associated with the response to inflation would be blocked. There is no evidence that a low frequency discharge or excitation in pulmonary stretch fibres alone stimulates breathing. However, Wyss (1954) stimulated the central end of a cut vagus nerve, so that only the A wave in the electroneurogram was present. Low stimulation frequencies caused rapid shallow breathing whereas breathing was inhibited with high frequencies. On one occasion in man we stimulated a cervical vagus nerve in the same way and obtained a tachypnoea (Fig. 12). Since the stimulus frequency was changed every ten seconds we cannot with certainty correlate the ventilatory response to a particular frequency of stimulation. In previous experiments in man, where the electroneurogram was not monitored, stimulation at a frequency of 100/s with higher voltages produced apnoea (Guz *et al.*, 1964). Unfortunately, in this type of experiment irritant excitatory receptors may also be stimulated (Mills, Sellick

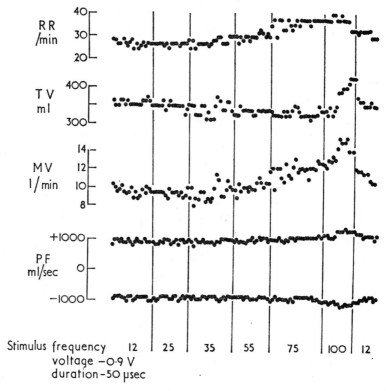

FIG. 12. Response, in patient No. 3, of respiratory rate (RR), tidal volume (TV), minute ventilation (MV) and peak air flow (PF) to electrical stimulation of one cervical vagus nerve using the stimulus frequency indicated at lower left of figure: this was changed every 10 s. The electroneurogram showed an A wave only.

and Widdicombe, 1969). The work raises the possibility that a reduced frequency of discharge in stretch receptor fibres has a different effect from the absence of such a discharge. Paintal (1955) recorded from non-myelinated C fibres from lung receptors in the cat; these fibres respond transiently to vigorous lung deflation especially after sensitization with a chemical excitant—phenyl diguanide. Paintal did not claim that these receptors are responsible for the deflation reflex but we have examined this possibility in rabbits using anodal block (Mendell and Wall, 1964) to differentially block the vagus nerve. One cervical vagus was freed and the other was cut. Bipolar electrodes placed cephalad recorded the electroneurogram in the intact nerve, while stimulating electrodes were a maximum distance away. The direct current used to block the nerve was applied with two further electrodes between the stimulating and recording pair; the current passes preferentially through the larger-diameter fibres with a lower resistance,

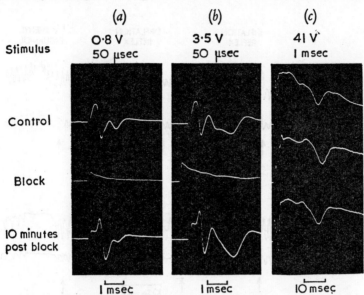

FIG. 13. Differential block of rabbit cervical vagus using direct current and electroneurograms. Stimulus parameters shown at upper part of figure. Control: low voltage elicits response in fast fibres (a); higher voltage stimulates slower fibres (b); high voltage in addition stimulates non-myelinated, slow fibres producing a C wave (c). The upward displacement of the baseline on the right results from a large stimulus artefact. Block: anodal block abolishes conduction in the faster fibres (a and b) but conduction in C fibres (c) is only minimally impaired. 10 min post-block: reversibility of block demonstrated.

and block occurs at the anode. Currents in the range 20–200 μA reversibly blocked conduction in all groups of fibres with conduction velocities above 1·5 m/s (Fig. 13). With this degree of block, the clear-cut C elevation in the electroneurogram, due to fibres with conduction velocities in the range 0·5–1·5 m/s, was only slightly depressed and slowed. No adequate differential block within the faster fibre-groups could be obtained. The block was equally effective for stimulation frequencies in the range 1–100/s. The block outlasts the application of the current by some minutes and is not always reversible. All observations were made with the current switched off to avoid the possibility of any alteration in respiratory pattern due to stimulation of vagal afferents by the currents. This precaution was taken even though the blocking anode had been placed cephalad.

The inflation reflex was studied by turning the airway into a weighted bag, while the deflation reflex was elicited by opening previously inserted pleural tubes to atmospheric pressure, the lung to be deflated being on the same side as the intact nerve. Both the inflation and deflation reflexes were

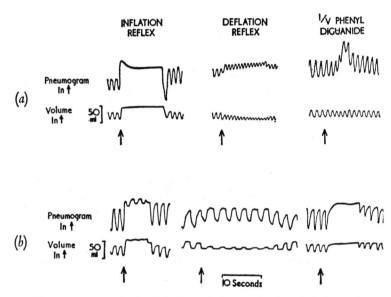

FIG. 14. Anaesthetized rabbit. Record of response to lung inflation (left) lung deflation (middle) and 20 μg/kg phenyl diguanide into the right atrium (right) (*a*) before and (*b*) during anodal block of the myelinated fibres in one cervical vagus. The other vagus has been cut. The block abolishes the inflation and deflation reflexes, but the response to phenyl diguanide is accentuated and converted to an inspiratory apnoea.

reversibly abolished during the block on eleven occasions in five rabbits (Fig. 14). The typical response to phenyl diguanide, an inspiratory gasp followed by tachypnoea, was now accentuated and became an inspiratory apnoea of similar time-course. The evidence from this work is therefore that the deflation reflex is blocked with the inflation reflex, and that the response to deflation has nothing to do with the C fibres that are excited by phenyl diguanide. However, it must be stressed that fibres with a wide range of conduction velocity are included within this block, so no light is shed on the question of whether the response to deflation is mediated by stretch receptor fibres.

## SUMMARY

Inflation of the lungs in animals and man inhibits inspiration and probably promotes expiration; the effect is abolished by vagal block or section. In animals, vagal block or section produces slow deep breathing but in man the effect is only present during hyperpnoea. The lack of effect during eupnoea correlates well with the absence of inflation reflex activity within the tidal range.

Pulmonary stretch receptor activity is present in man (as in animals) at functional residual capacity and increases with inspiration.

Deflation of the lungs in animals increases respiratory frequency and inspiratory force; the effect is abolished by vagotomy. In man, deflation of the lungs by pneumothorax is required to elicit the same response, the reflex nature of which has not been proven.

In rabbits, both the inflation and deflation reflexes are abolished when conduction in myelinated fibres is blocked, leaving conduction in non-myelinated C fibres unimpaired. There is a strong possibility that both reflexes are mediated by the pulmonary stretch receptors.*

## REFERENCES

ADRIAN, E. D. (1933). *J. Physiol., Lond.*, **79**, 332–358.
BERNARDS, J. A., DEJOURS, P., and LACAISSE, A. (1966). *Resp. Physiol.*, **1**, 390–397.
BERTOLA, V. J. (1940). *Prensa méd. argent.*, **27**, 1069–1073.
BREUER, J. (1868). *Sber. Akad. Wiss. Wien*, **58**, part 2, 909–937.
CHRISTIANSEN, J., and HALDANE, J. S. (1914). *J. Physiol., Lond.*, **48**, 272–277.
COLERIDGE, H. M., COLERIDGE, J. C. G., LUCK, J. C., and NORMAN, J. (1968). *Br. med. J.*, **40**, 484–492.
COMROE, J. H., JR., FORSTER, R. E., DUBOIS, A. B., BRISCOE, W. A., and CARLSEN, E. (1965). In *The Lung: Clinical Physiology and Pulmonary Function Tests*, 2nd edn., p. 15 (f.-n.). Chicago: Year Book Medical Publishers.
CROSS, K. W., KLAUS, M., TOOLEY, W. H., and WEISSER, K. (1960). *J. Physiol., Lond.*, **151**, 551–565.
CROSSFILL, M. L., and WIDDICOMBE, J. G. (1961). *J. Physiol., Lond.*, **158**, 1–14.
DAWES, G. S., MOTT, J. C., and WIDDICOMBE, J. G. (1951). *J. Physiol., Lond.*, **115**, 258–291.
DEJOURS, P., RAYNAUD, J., MONSEIN, P., and BECHTEL, Y. (1962). *J. Physiol., Paris*, **54**, 320–321.
DOUGLAS, W. W., and RITCHIE, J. M. (1957). *J. Physiol., Lond.*, **138**, 19–43.
ERLANGER, J., and GASSER, H. S. (1924). *Am. J. Physiol.*, **70**, 624–666.
FLOREZ, J., and BORISON, H. L. (1964). *Am. J. Physiol.*, **212**, 985–991.
FRANKSTEIN, S. I. (1969). Personal communication.
FRANKSTEIN, S. I. (1970). This volume, pp. 53–58.
GUZ, A., NOBLE, M. I. M., TRENCHARD, D., COCHRANE, H. L., and MAKEY, A. R. (1964). *Clin. Sci.*, **27**, 293–304.

* For discussion of this paper, see p. 44.

GUZ, A., NOBLE, M. I. M., TRENCHARD, D., MUSHIN, W. W., and MAKEY, A. R. (1966a). *Clin. Sci.*, **30**, 161–170.

GUZ, A., NOBLE, M. I. M., TRENCHARD, D., SMITH, A. J., and MAKEY, A. R. (1966b). *Resp. Physiol.*, **1**, 382–389.

GUZ, A., NOBLE, M. I. M., TRENCHARD, D., WIDDICOMBE, J. G., and MUSHIN, W. W. (1966c). *Resp. Physiol.*, **1**, 38–40.

GUZ, A., NOBLE, M. I. M., WIDDICOMBE, J. G., TRENCHARD, D., and MUSHIN, W. W. (1966d). *Resp. Physiol.*, **1**, 206–210.

HAMMOUDA, M., and WILSON, W. H. (1935). *J. Physiol., Lond.*, **83**, 292–312.

HEAD, H. (1889). *J. Physiol., Lond.*, **10**, 1–70, 279–290.

HERING, E. (1868). *Sber. Akad. Wiss. Wien*, **57**, part 2, 672–677.

HOLLING, H. E., BRODEY, R. S., and BOLAND, H. C. (1961). *Lancet*, **2**, 1269–1274.

LANGREHR, D. (1964). *Klin. Wschr.*, **42**, 239–244.

LARRABEE, M. G., and KNOWLTON, G. C. (1946). *Am. J. Physiol.*, **147**, 90–99.

LLOYD, H. M., STRING, T., DUBOIS, A. B. (1966). *Radiology*, **86**, 7–14.

McILROY, M. B., BUTLER, J., and FINLEY, T. N. (1962). *J. appl. Physiol.*, **17**, 701–705.

MENDELL, L. M., and WALL, P. D. (1964). *J. Physiol., Lond.*, **172**, 274–294.

MILLS, J. E., SELLICK, H., WIDDICOMBE, J. G. (1969). *J. Physiol., Lond.*, **200**, 78–90 P.

MUSHIN, W. W. (1945). *Proc. R. Soc. Med.*, **38**, 308.

NOBLE, M. I. M., EISELE, J. H., TRENCHARD, D., and GUZ, A. (1970). This volume, pp. 233–246.

PAINTAL, A. S. (1953). *J. Physiol., Lond.*, **121**, 341–359.

PAINTAL, A. S. (1955). *Q. Jl exp. Physiol.*, **40**, 89–111.

PAINTAL, A. S. (1965). *J. Physiol., Lond.*, **180**, 1–20, 21–50.

PAINTAL, A. S. (1966). *Q. Jl exp. Physiol.*, **51**, 151–163.

READ, D. J. C. (1967). *Australas. Ann. Med.*, **16**, 20–30.

RICHARDSON, P. S., and WIDDICOMBE, J. G. (1969). *Resp. Physiol.*, **7**, 122–135.

SASAKI, S. (1927). *J. Biophys., Tokyo*, **2**, 197–213.

SCOTT, F. H. (1908). *J. Physiol., Lond.*, **39**, 308.

TROELSTRA, H. J. (1960). Doctoral thesis, University of Groningen. Hoitsema: Groningen.

WADE, J. G. (1969). Personal communication.

WIDDICOMBE, J. G. (1954). *J. Physiol., Lond.*, **125**, 336–351.

WIDDICOMBE, J. G. (1961). *Clin. Sci.*, **21**, 163–170.

WIDDICOMBE, J. G. (1964). In *Handbook of Physiology*, sect. III, vol. 1, pp. 585–630, ed. Fenn, W. O., and Rahn, H. American Physiological Society, Baltimore: Williams and Wilkins.

WYSS, O. A. M. (1954). *Helv. physiol. pharmac. Acta*, suppl. 10, 26–35.

ZEVEKE, A. V. (1961). *Dokl. Akad. Nauk. SSSR*, **138**, 493–496.

ZEVEKE, A. V., and KHAYUTIN, V. M. (1966). *Fiziol. Zh. SSSR*, **52**, 258–264.

# PATTERN OF BREATHING DURING HYPERCAPNIA BEFORE AND AFTER VAGAL BLOCKADE IN MAN*

A. Guz† AND J. G. Widdicombe‡

†Department of Medicine, Charing Cross Hospital Medical School, London, and
‡University Laboratory of Physiology, Oxford

In 1966, Hey, Lloyd, Cunningham, Jukes and Bolton described a method for displaying the pattern of breathing (tidal volume and respiratory frequency) at different levels of ventilation (minute volume). A graph of minute volume (ordinate) and tidal volume (abscissa) is constructed (Fig. 1). As ventilation changes, a series of points is drawn which represents the changing minute volume and pattern of breathing. If the points trace a vertical line, then tidal volume is constant while frequency changes; if the points trace a straight line extending to the origin, then frequency is constant while tidal volume changes. A fan of straight lines through the origin represents iso-frequency relationships. A series of experimental points will tend to curve to the vertical at large tidal volumes, since eventually maximum tidal volume is reached and only frequency can increase further (Fig. 1, A).

If two series of points for two different conditions in which breathing is altered correspond, then the pattern of breathing for any given minute volume is the same in the two conditions. The method of display gives no information about the size or sensitivity of the ventilatory response (for which a minute volume/stimulus strength curve would be needed [see this volume, p. 23, Fig. 4]) but only about the pattern of the breathing response at different levels of ventilation. Using their method, Hey and co-workers showed similar patterns of breathing for healthy subjects in a variety of conditions such as hypercapnia, hypoxia and exercise, only hyperthermia giving a different result (relatively larger increases in frequency than in tidal volume at any given minute volume).

Fig. 1 shows plots for three conscious subjects responding to hypercapnia before and after the vagus and glossopharyngeal nerves had been

---

* This note was contributed after the symposium to clarify recurrent material about the "Hey plot". The authors and editor wish to thank Drs Hey, Lloyd, Cunningham, Jukes and Bolton for their cooperation and permission to publish this note.

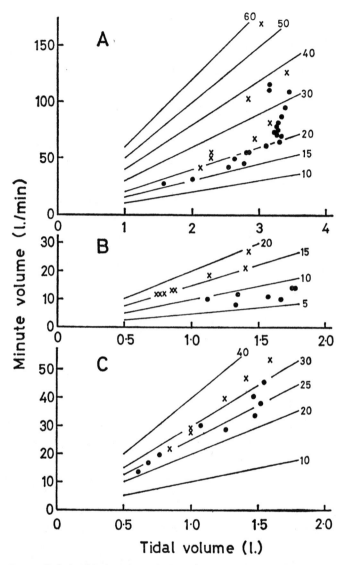

Fig. 1. Relationship between minute volume and tidal volume for the three subjects described in the test. Each point is the mean of three breaths. × ×: before vagal block; ●●: during vagal block. Iso-frequency lines are drawn with numbers representing respiratory frequency (Hey *et al.*, 1966; reproduced by permission of *Resp. Physiol.*).

anaesthetized at the base of the skull. Subjects A and C rebreathed 7 per cent carbon dioxide in oxygen from a spirometer and subject B rebreathed 5 per cent carbon dioxide in oxygen. The results for subject A have been reported previously (Guz et al., 1966) and the results for subject C are shown in this volume (p. 23, Fig. 4). However, none of the results in the figure shown here have previously been reported in this particular way. Subject A (J.W.) (Fig. 1, A) was a healthy male, aged 39 years. The results for him differ from those for subjects B and C because measurements were started after hyperpnoea had begun and because ventilation was increased to a level at which tidal volume was near the maximum. During vagal block the points were displaced to the right; that is, frequency was relatively less and tidal volume more for any given minute volume. The lower part of the series of points for vagal block are close to an iso-frequency line. Subject B (J.P.) (Fig. 1, B) was an asthmatic male, aged 40 years. Both series of points are close to iso-frequency lines, but the series for vagal block is considerably depressed and displaced to the right compared with the control. Subject C (H.H.) (Fig. 1, C), aged 55 years, had diffuse pulmonary fibrosis. The points for vagal block are displaced to the right, but only at the higher parts of the graph; they are close to an iso-frequency line, unlike the control series of points.

Although Fig. 1 shows a clear difference between the two sets of points for each subject, it is difficult to express this difference quantitatively. Hey and co-workers compared the slopes and intercepts of the regression lines, but the physiological meaning of these parameters is unclear, and it does not always seem justifiable to calculate regression equations (for example, for Fig. 1, A). The results of other types of comparison would depend on whether vertical or horizontal displacement was measured, and at which part of the curve, and whether the slope was measured. Possibly the most informative quantitative comparison is the proportionate horizontal displacement for any given minute volume, that is, the proportionate difference in tidal volume (and thus frequency) at any given level of breathing. For subject A, the horizontal displacement is about 20 per cent at a minute volume of 50 l/min, and less at higher minute volumes; for subject B, horizontal displacement is more than 100 per cent at a minute volume of 10 l/min; and for subject C, this displacement is about 15 per cent at minute volumes greater than 25 l/min.

## CONCLUSIONS

Vagal blockade not only decreases the size of the ventilatory response to carbon dioxide, but also changes the pattern of breathing at any given level of ventilation so that respiration frequency is less and tidal volume more. One possible explanation for this is that pulmonary stretch receptors are responsible for adjusting the pattern of breathing in man during hyperpnoea.

REFERENCES

HEY, E. N., LLOYD, B. B., CUNNINGHAM, D. J. C., JUKES, M. G. M., and BOLTON, D. P. G. (1966). *Resp. Physiol.*, **1**, 193–205.
GUZ, A., NOBLE, M. I. M., WIDDICOMBE, J. G., TRENCHARD, D., and MUSHIN W. W. (1966). *Resp. Physiol.*, **1**, 206–210.

## DISCUSSION

*Karczewski:* The absence of the classical response to vagal block in man does not necessarily mean that there is a fundamental species difference in this response between man and other mammals. The differences might be partly artificial, depending to some extent on the experimental conditions. In some unpublished experiments with unanaesthetized rabbits I found that vagotomy did not produce the classical slowing of respiration, in spite of the fact that the Hering–Breuer reflex is very strong in anaesthetized rabbits (Widdicombe, 1961). On the other hand, halothane inhaled at a concentration of 2 per cent (v/v) depresses or even completely blocks electrical discharges from pulmonary stretch fibres in the rabbit (Kamiński, Karczewski and Górzyński, 1968). This would obviously diminish the Hering–Breuer inspiratory-inhibitory effects by increasing the volume threshold. If the same situation is present in man one would hardly expect the classical response to vagal block.

*Guz:* Your findings are at variance with those of Coleridge and co-workers (1968), which I quoted in my paper, but they studied cats and dogs and there may be species differences between these two animals and the rabbit. The first part of the curve of inflation reflex activity in man anaesthetized with halothane (Fig. 1, this volume, p. 19) corresponds closely to the curve obtained by Widdicombe (1961). Two completely different anaesthetics are therefore shown to give similar results. Does any other conscious mammal not sustain a decrease in respiratory frequency after vagotomy?

*Karczewski:* Control of breathing in the guinea-pig certainly depends mainly on the integrity of vagal mechanisms (Oberholzer and Schlegel, 1957). Conscious rabbits, however, show no (or almost no) decrease in respiratory frequency after vagotomy and they can accelerate breathing in response to several stimuli; these observations suggest the more important role of pneumotaxic (that is, central) mechanisms in the guinea-pig.

*Guz:* Under similar conditions of anaesthesia a wide range of mammals show classical slowing and deepening of respiration with vagal block. But in man this does not occur with halothane.

*Cross:* How long after the vagotomy did you record respiratory frequency in the conscious rabbit, Dr Karczewski? Timing is important because the effect of vagotomy in the anaesthetized or decerebrate rabbit diminishes with time.

*Karczewski:* We recorded respiratory rate continuously, before and after vagotomy in conscious and anaesthetized rabbits, for about five hours. When a rabbit is anaesthetized one hour or more after vagotomy, the classical deeper and slower pattern of breathing typical of the anaesthetized, vagotomized animal is immediately elicited. But my own observations (Karczewski, 1965) suggest that the strength of the response to vagotomy *increases* with time; in other words, the activity of some of the respiratory vagal motoneurones reflects a progressive decrease in the central control mechanisms.

*Widdicombe:* Decerebrate cats show slow deep breathing after vagotomy (von Euler, personal communication). Unanaesthetized rabbits in which the vagi have been first blocked by local anaesthetic and then cut show some slowing and deepening of respiration, although these effects are less marked than in the anaesthetized rabbit (Richardson and Widdicombe, 1969).

*Cohen:* The species differences in the Hering–Breuer reflex may be related to the development of cortical function. First, the fact that the reflex is weaker in the anaesthetized than in the unanaesthetized rabbit (Sant'Ambrogio and Widdicombe, 1965) suggests that the cortex may play an inhibitory role; and second, the reflex is stronger in animals which are lower on the phylogenetic scale (that is, in rodents as compared to carnivores and primates) (Widdicombe, 1961).

*von Euler:* In our experience, $Pco_2$ does not have any effect *per se* on the respiratory response to lung inflation or to vagal block; this confirms Adrian's (1933) findings. The effect of increased concentrations of carbon dioxide on respiratory frequency seems to depend almost entirely on the increase in associated tidal volume which, in turn, triggers the Hering–Breuer reflex to terminate inspiration (Euler von, Herrero and Wexler, 1970). The results in man (Guz *et al.*, 1964) indicate that in eupnoeic conditions respiratory frequency is not dependent on vagal afferents. When ventilation is increased by increasing the $Pa_{CO_2}$, on the other hand, the concomitant increase in respiratory frequency appears to be causally dependent on these afferents, in the same way as in the cat or rabbit. This is probably best explained by assuming that in man the volume needed for the Hering–Breuer reflex to terminate inspiration is not quite reached by the eupnoeic tidal volume. In these circumstances man seems to depend largely on his pneumotaxic centres. When tidal volume increases in response to increased concentrations of carbon dioxide, the volume threshold for the Hering–Breuer reflex is reached and the vagal mechanism brought into action; and the larger the tidal volumes the earlier this occurs, so that a progressively higher respiratory frequency is also obtained. Whether or not the volume threshold is actually reached by a single breath (and the duration of the respiratory cycle thus determined by the vagal mechanism) depends not only on the size of the tidal volume in relation to the volume threshold but also on the pneumotaxic mechanism, in other words, on whether or not inspiration is already cut off by the pneumotaxic mechanism before the vagal volume threshold is reached (Euler von, Herrero and Wexler, 1970).

*Guz:* Are any drugs known to block the stretch receptors?

*Paintal:* Many investigators (Paintal, 1964) have shown that intravenous lignocaine or procaine can block pulmonary stretch receptors by acting on the regenerative region of the nerve endings.

*Guz:* Professor Frankstein (this volume, p. 53) draws our attention to the apnoeic response to threshold stimulation of the cervical vagus nerve of the conscious cat: if the attention of the cat is distracted there is no apnoea. This demonstrates the cortical influences that can affect the apparent strength of the Hering–Breuer reflex.

*Campbell:* Stimulation of a nerve has only limited relevance to the nature of a reflex. Stimulation of the vagus and alterations in respiratory function in the cat are not necessarily cause and effect.

*Dornhorst:* The point of Frankstein's observation is that the reflex in the cat was modified by an external event.

*Campbell:* I am just questioning the conclusions we are drawing from these observations. We know that afferent impulses with a respiratory rhythm pass up the vagus, that stimulation of the vagus gives rise to different effects, and that Hering and Breuer described a particular reflex. But jumping about between these three known facts leads to confusion and I am not convinced that it is legitimate to make these leaps.

*Paintal:* The steps that confirm the legitimacy of our assumptions are these: first, the pulmonary stretch receptor fibres are responsible for the inflation reflex; and second, these fibres are known to be the largest in the vagus and therefore to have the lowest threshold to electrical stimulation. It is because of these two facts that we can make the assumption that, if we use threshold stimuli, we shall be stimulating only the pulmonary stretch fibres, in other words, eliciting the inflation reflex (Paintal, 1963).

*Campbell:* Are you saying that the only function of the pulmonary stretch reflexes is to initiate the Hering–Breuer reflex?

*Paintal:* You have misunderstood what I said.

*Dornhorst:* But Professor Paintal, you are at least implying that stimulating the vagus affects no fibres apart from those that are stimulated by inflation; and this assumption goes beyond the known facts.

*Widdicombe:* I also think that this assumption is unjustified. If one takes the example of threshold mechanical stimulation of cough receptors in the larynx, inhalation of a crumb may stimulate only two or three of these receptors, sending impulses up their small myelinated vagal fibres (delta fibres), and yet the entire vigorous act of coughing is initiated. With electrical stimulation of the vagus we cannot be sure that "threshold stimuli" do not excite not only a large number of alpha fibres, but also a few delta fibres which exert a very large final influence on breathing. An additional difficulty is that the fibre diameter spectra (or different modalities of lung afferent nerve) are not very sharply defined (Paintal, 1953).

*Dornhorst:* We should also be aware of another problem: the time course of stimulation. The effects of a simultaneous volley of stimuli may differ from those of a progressive build-up. It is difficult to equate experimental electrical stimulation and natural stimulation of a nerve.

*Paintal:* We know that stretching the muscle is quite different from stimulating its nerve electrically, yet threshold stimulation of group IA fibres, which transmit only a little faster than IB fibres, provides a useful method for studying the stretch reflex.

*Campbell:* I abide by my objections which seem quite clear.

*Merton:* The evidence that Frankstein was stimulating at threshold seems to be that he was getting slowing of breathing, recording not action potentials but periods of apnoea. He did not record that he was stimulating the low threshold fibres; his criterion of threshold was the stoppage of breathing. This is a circular argument. It is not legitimate to say: I am getting a reflex slowing of breathing by stimulating the nerve fibres of lowest threshold; the criterion of threshold should be the strength of stimulus at which I get a slowing of breathing.

*Guz:* I apologize for initiating this discussion. I quoted Frankstein's observations merely to show that apnoea produced by vagal stimulation in the cat could be removed by the cat looking at a light!

*Sears:* In earlier work both with intracellular recording from intercostal motoneurones and with recording alpha and fusimotor discharges to the intercostal muscles (Sears, 1964a, b) I used high frequency (100–300 shocks per second) stimulation of the lowest-threshold afferent fibres in the vagus to modify breathing. The slowing or total inhibition of breathing that this caused was closely similar to the inspiratory-inhibitory or expiratory-excitatory response that could be obtained in the same animal by closing the trachea at the height of inspiration.

*Noble:* The large myelinated fibres in the vagus may be involved in both deflation and inflation reflexes. When they discharge at low frequency they may stimulate breathing whereas at high frequencies they may depress it. If these fibres are not "self-steering" for respiration (as they clearly are not in man) then what is their function? Reynolds and Flom (1968) have studied the occasional spontaneous deep breaths that occur in anaesthetized cats following a decrease in lung compliance. They recorded from single fibres in an intact (unsectioned) vagus nerve. In the breaths before the deep breath the frequency of discharge increased in one group of fibres and decreased in another; this resulted in a bimodal distribution of discharge frequency which was abolished by the deep breath. These occasional deep breaths disappeared after vagal section. Reynolds and Flom deduced from these findings that there is an "inspiratory augmenting reflex" which occurs in response to changes in the stretch receptors during normal quiet breathing. But this may not be a separate reflex because the fibres firing at low frequencies may be merely initiating the classical deflation reflex.

*Dejours:* Dr Guz, when you compared the responses to carbon dioxide in an intact animal and in an animal whose vagi and glossopharyngeal nerves had been blocked, you seemed to attribute the differences you observed exclusively to blocking the afferent fibres from the lung itself. But you may have also blocked some afferent activity from the arterial chemoreceptors. Hyperoxia depresses the chemoreceptors (Bouverot *et al.*, 1965) but in the case you described, in which marked hypercapnia was present, I doubt if the chemoreceptors were completely inactive.

P. Bouverot (unpublished results) has studied dogs in which the connexions of the pulmonary mechanoreceptors to the medullary respiratory centres have been permanently abolished. His fairly simple technique consists in removing the left lung and allowing the dog to recover; it retains normal breathing and a normal Hering–Breuer reflex. Some weeks later the right vagus is cut. In the animal (which then survives for many months), breathing is permanently slowed and deepened;

exercise is difficult; $Pa_{CO_2}$ is higher and $Pa_{O_2}$ lower than normal; responses to hypoxia are less and the reaction to changes in blood carbon dioxide is markedly different from normal, as you also observed, Dr Guz, in acute experiments in man. All these observations should contribute to our attempts during these three days to unravel the full meaning of the Hering–Breuer reflex.

*Merrill:* We may be assuming more precision in our descriptions of the various reflexes than is justified. The general descriptions of inflation as inhibitory for inspiration and excitatory for expiration are too imprecise. Short inflations in excess of a tidal volume and delivered late in inspiration can terminate that inspiration prematurely. This inspiratory termination by inflation is a threshold rather than a graded phenomenon, as might be suggested by the term "inhibition". Curiously, near-threshold-sized inflations produce a prolonged inspiration which must be regarded as a facilitation. Similarly, the effects of inflations on expiration are more complicated than the term "excitation" suggests. Inflations of practically any size or duration "excite" expiration in that they lengthen it. Initially, however, lung inflation causes an inhibition of lateral medullary expiratory units as well as expiratory musculature (to the extent that there is an active expiration). This initial inhibition gradually fades and turns into a facilitation after a couple of seconds or so (Merrill, unpublished observations).

*Cotes:* Dr Guz, you have commented on the slow deep breathing that occurs in conscious man when ventilation has been increased during vagal block. But in your original experiments on one (normal) subject breathing carbon dioxide (Guz et al., 1966), the relation of tidal volume to minute volume, which is an appropriate way of assessing the respiratory frequency, was only altered by vagal block by about 5 per cent. Have the two abnormal subjects whom you mentioned having investigated since 1966 shown more marked changes than this, or on what other evidence do you base your claim that breathing becomes deep as well as slow after vagal block?

*Guz:* These studies were done with the three subjects rebreathing 5–7 per cent carbon dioxide. We found deeper breathing compared to control levels only at end-tidal $Pco_2$ values above 55 mmHg. In the first subject we studied (Guz et al., 1966) we found that tidal volume at a higher $Pco_2$ level was up to 20 per cent greater during the block than in the control state; but in the two subsequent patients the increase in tidal volume with vagal block at raised $Pco_2$ levels varied from 15 to 100 per cent.[*]

[*] See also p. 42.

*Cotes:* So there was an increase in the depth of breathing in your two abnormal patients but not in the normal subject.

*Guz:* Yes. Are you suggesting that because the striking effect of vagal block is a reduction in respiratory frequency rather than an increase in tidal volume during carbon dioxide stimulation of breathing, we must be describing something more than just the effect of blocking the pulmonary stretch receptors?

*Cotes:* We need more data to answer that question.

*Widdicombe:* Dr Cotes may be referring to the "Hey plot". Hey and co-workers (1966) showed that if we make a graphical plot of minute volume (ordinate) against tidal volume (abscissa) then, for most of the factors that stimulate breathing, the points move up the same curve. In other words, the pattern of breathing (tidal volume and respiratory frequency) is similar during stimulations of breathing caused by different conditions. This seems to be always true except under conditions of hyperthermia.*

*von Euler:* Is the increase in tidal volume seen during moderate carbon dioxide stimulation in subjects without vagal block related to the volume threshold of the inflation reflex?

*Guz:* Inflations of four to five litres above the functional residual capacity (FRC) produce inhibitory reflex responses and, if there is spontaneous breathing with this magnitude of tidal volume, vagal block would be expected to result in slower deeper breathing. We do not yet have enough data or subjects to say whether the volume threshold of the inflation reflex correlates with the tidal volume at which slower deeper breathing occurs with vagal block. (See also p. 42, Fig. 1.)

*von Euler:* Is there a break in the ventilation: tidal volume relationship (the "Hey plot") that might be related to such a volume threshold?

*Guz:* No.

*Dornhorst:* A fixed volume threshold is most unlikely. It is bound to vary with such parameters as, for example, bronchoconstriction.

*Plum:* Dr Guz, did I interpret correctly the data on the patient with a pneumothorax (this volume, p. 34, Fig. 11)? Does excitation of the deflation reflex raise the carbon dioxide response curve to levels that are higher than normal?

*Guz:* Yes.

*Plum:* When the lungs of this patient were reinflated the response curve looked very flat. If this finding is confirmed it would fit well with the observation that these very primitive reflexes are barely detectable

---

* These results are analysed in more detail on pp. 41–44.

during eupnoea in the presence of an intact nervous system. But, as higher levels of the nervous system undergo damage or injury primitive reflex activity becomes more and more striking, and this can be observed when, with strong facilitation of peripheral reflexes, one sees an enhancement of the carbon dioxide response. Could you comment on this particular part of your paper?

*Guz:* We have only seen this effect once. When the lung is stuck to the chest wall, the response curve, as you have said, looks flat (Fig. 11); this may be a function of the scale we used but nevertheless the response is in the middle of our normal range. But when the patient's lung was only a few centimetres away from the chest wall the response curve was high and to the left of our normal range.

*Plum:* These interesting findings are similar to our observations in decerebrate man in whom the ventilatory response to carbon dioxide is enhanced (Brown and Plum, 1961). The findings suggest that both excess peripheral stimulation and defects in central inhibition may give rise to facilitation of the respiratory response.

*Guz:* We suggest that excess peripheral input is present when the lung is deflated.

*Dornhorst:* Dr Guz has shown that a mechanism for vagal modulation of breathing exists in conscious man and that this mechanism operates in both directions; whether the same or different peripheral receptors are involved is functionally irrelevant. But because of considerable backlash* this mechanism only becomes important at unusually large or small lung volumes. Dr Guz has also shown that this backlash does not reside mainly in the peripheral part of the mechanism but rather in the way in which afferent vagal traffic is treated at central levels. In some abnormal circumstances, such as inflammation of the lung, peripheral sensitivity can be altered, so it may be that the backlash can be abolished by increased sensitivity at the periphery. The way in which information from lung and chest wall is handled centrally may possibly be altered by disease. Thus, when we consider pathological states in man we must try to distinguish the central and peripheral effects on the Hering–Breuer reflex.

## REFERENCES

ADRIAN, E. D. (1933). *J. Physiol., Lond.,* **79**, 332–358.
BOUVEROT, P., FLANDROIS, R., PUCCINELLI, R., and DEJOURS, P. (1965). *Archs int. Pharmacodyn Thér.,* **157**, 253–271.
BROWN, H. W., and PLUM, F. (1961). *Am. J. Med.,* **30**, 849–860.

*Editorial note.* Backlash is used here to mean that an appreciable increase or decrease in nervous input is needed before any reflex response can be detected.

COLERIDGE, H. M., COLERIDGE, J. C. G., LUCK, J. C., and NORMAN, J. (1968). *Br. J. Anaesth.*, **40**, 484–492.

EULER, C. VON, HERRERO, F., and WEXLER, I. (1970). *Resp. Physiol.*, in press.

GUZ, A., NOBLE, M. I. M., TRENCHARD, D., COCHRANE, H. L., and MAKEY, A. R. (1964). *Clin. Sci.*, **27**, 293–304.

GUZ, A., NOBLE, M. I. M., WIDDICOMBE, J. G., TRENCHARD, D., and MUSHIN, W. W. (1966). *Resp. Physiol.*, **1**, 206–210.

HEY, E. N., LLOYD, B. B., CUNNINGHAM, D. J. C., JUKES, M. G. M., and BOLTON, D. P. G. (1966). *Resp. Physiol.*, **1**, 193–205.

KAMIŃSKI, B., KARCZEWSKI, W., and GÓRZYŃSKI, J. (1968). *Acta physiol. pol.*, **19**, 533–538.

KARCZEWSKI, W. (1965). *Postępy Hig. Med. doświad.*, **19**, 507–569 (in Polish).

OBERHOLZER, R. J. H., and SCHLEGEL, H. (1957). *Helv. physiol. pharmac. Acta*, **15**, 63–82.

PAINTAL, A. S. (1953). *J. Physiol., Lond.*, **121**, 341–359.

PAINTAL, A. S. (1963). *Ergebn. Physiol.*, **52**, 87–89.

PAINTAL, A. S. (1964). *Pharmac. Rev.*, **16**, 341–380.

REYNOLDS, L. B., and FLOM, M. H. (1968). *J. appl. Physiol.*, **25**, 238–243.

RICHARDSON, P. S., and WIDDICOMBE, J. G. (1969). *Resp. Physiol.*, **7**, 122–135.

SANT'AMBROGIO, G., and WIDDICOMBE, J. G. (1965). *J. Physiol., Lond.*, **180**, 766–779.

SEARS, T. A. (1964*a*). *J. Physiol., Lond.*, **175**, 404–424.

SEARS, T. A. (1964*b*). *J. Physiol., Lond.*, **174**, 295–315.

WIDDICOMBE, J. G. (1961). *Clin. Sci.*, **21**, 163–170.

# NEURAL CONTROL OF RESPIRATION*

S. I. FRANKSTEIN

*Institute of Normal and Pathological Physiology, Academy of Medical Sciences, Moscow*

### DEPRESSION OF THE VAGAL INFLATION REFLEX WITH EVOLUTION

ONE of the most astonishing facts about the Hering-Breuer reflexes is that in normal man these reflexes cannot be elicited by the normal tidal volume. Accordingly, vagal blockade in a normal man evokes no change in the pattern of respiration.

Yet Sherrington wrote (1906) that "in the light of Darwin's theory every reflex *must* be purposive", and "the reflex reaction cannot be really intelligible to the physiologist until he knows its aim." Probably it is no less important to understand why in the process of evolution a reflex may disappear, even such a powerful one as the inhibitory Hering-Breuer reflex.

An automatic inhibition that is evoked by each inspiration may be assumed to prevent some special human function. If this inhibition applies to man we might reasonably assume that speech, which is peculiar to man, is the function thus affected.

In this connexion it is interesting that in some conditions the inhibitory respiratory reflex may be eliminated even in the experimental animal. In our experiments on the cat bipolar electrodes were chronically implanted in the central stump of one vagus. The electrical stimuli applied to the nerve were so weak that although the animal paid no attention to the stimulation the latter evoked apnoea. The apnoea resulting from vagal stimulation was consistently greater during sleep than that obtained in the same animal during wakefulness. When the attention of the cat was attracted by something (a click, a flash and so on), the stimulation of the vagus nerve had no effect on respiration. Probably in this state the inhibitory respiratory reflex may also hinder some special activity in the animal.

Although the inhibitory Hering-Breuer reflex has disappeared in man the impulses from the lung stretch receptors evoking this reflex are maintained (Dr A. Guz, personal communication). Similarly, during the

* Paper not read at, but contributed for publication before, the symposium.

53

temporary depression of the inhibitory respiratory reflex in animals (described above), the impulses from the lung are preserved. Thus a question arises: how is the reaction to these impulses eliminated? There are two main general mechanisms by which reflex inhibition occurs; these are postsynaptic and presynaptic. The first is produced by hyperpolarization of the cell membrane and the second by depolarization of the presynaptic terminals. Strychnine has been shown to block postsynaptic but not presynaptic inhibitory mechanisms. In the light of these findings the observation by Creed and Hertz (1933) in Sherrington's laboratory that strychnine does not abolish the inhibitory Hering-Breuer reflex is of great interest. Even after an injection of sub-convulsive doses of strychnine, expansion of the lung evoked an inhibition of breathing and relaxation of the diaphragm, suggesting that the inhibitory Hering-Breuer reflex is not mediated through the postsynaptic mechanism. But the reflex does not seem to be mediated through presynaptic inhibition either.

In our experiments (Frankstein and Sergeeva, 1967) electrotonic potentials evoked by expansion of the lung were recorded on the surface of the medulla oblongata at the site of projection of the tractus solitarius. The $P$ wave of the electrotonic potentials, which reflects primary afferent depolarization, was very small and sometimes absent. We obtained the same result even when we stimulated the central end of the cut vagus nerve with stimuli which involved C fibres. Rudomin (1967) had shown, independently, that stimulation of the vagus did not change the excitability of vagal afferent terminals. And these two sets of experiments suggest that the inhibitory vagal reflex is not affected by presynaptic inhibition. These reflexes are strychnine-resistant and probably depend on the strychnine-resistant postsynaptic inhibition established recently by Granit (1968) and his co-workers. Thus, to explain the absence of the inhibitory Hering-Breuer reflex in man, as well as the temporary depression of the inhibitory respiratory reflex in animals, we must postulate the existence of some special neurones that are inhibitory for strychnine-resistant inhibition. Such inhibitory-inhibitory mechanisms are widely known in neurophysiology. Apparently this mechanism only acts in the animal in special circumstances, whereas in man it is always present.

### TONIC INFLUENCE OF AFFERENT C FIBRES ON THE RESPIRATORY CENTRE

Attention has so far been centred on the Hering-Breuer reflexes when they are evoked by changes in lung volume. But Breuer noticed another influence exerted by lung receptors on the respiratory centre, and this influence does not depend on changes in lung volume; Breuer called this *stetig wirkenden Erregung*, a "continuous excitation" of the respiratory centre. Breuer showed that blocking conduction in the vagi in animals changed the pattern of respiration to slow deep breathing, not only in the normal state but also when movements of the lungs are artificially excluded. "Supposing we succeeded by one means or another in maintaining an animal in a state of steady respiratory chemistry, without at the same time having the volume of the lung affected by breathing movements. In that situation the usual stimuli which arise through volume changes would not be acting on the medulla. If in these circumstances section of the vagi still reduced the rate of breathing, this would indicate that before vagal section some other stimulus must have been transmitted in the vagi, accelerating respiration" (Breuer, 1868, p. 931 [trans. Ullmann, 1970, p. 386]).

Thus, besides the pulmonary stretch receptors and the deflation receptors, there must exist receptors which exert a continuous influence on the respiratory centre. The function of the afferent C fibres of the vagus is of interest in this connexion.

Although most of the vagal afferent fibres from the lung are C fibres, their function is not fully understood. Some of them may be excited by deflation and some by over-inflation of the lung, and at least some may show spontaneous activity which is not synchronized with the respiratory cycles (Paintal, 1955, 1957; Coleridge, Coleridge and Luck, 1965).

To establish the function of the majority of the C afferent fibres we used Douglas and Ritchie's (1957) "collision" technique (Frankstein and Sergeeva, 1966*a,b,c*). With this method we demonstrated the existence of a regular variation in the size of the A wave of the evoked antidromic vagal potential: the potential was at a maximum during deflation, when the natural orthodromic activity was least, and at a minimum during inflation, when the natural orthodromic activity was maximal. This finding is in agreement with Adrian's observation (1933) that most of the large myelinated A fibres of the vagus carry a barrage of impulses with each inspiration.

On the other hand, the size of the C wave of the evoked action potential did not change with changes in lung volume. Most of the C fibres may thus belong to a group of fibres with spontaneous activity which is not synchronized with the respiratory cycles. Probably these fibres take part in maintaining the constant excitation of the respiratory centre. As in other receptors, the spontaneous activity of C fibres may depend on molecular, ionic or thermal agitation.

## THE ACTIVITY OF C AFFERENT FIBRES IN PATHOLOGICAL
## CONDITIONS OF THE LUNG

Further experiments on the cat showed that local pneumonia, elicited by an injection of hot water into the tissues of one lung, evoked impulses spreading along C fibres. On the other hand, the activity of A fibres, which innervate the pulmonary stretch receptors, may even decrease in these circumstances (Frankstein and Sergeeva, 1966b). It is of interest to recall that Zotterman (1939) originally established that any injury of the tissues which increases the activity of C fibres simultaneously decreases the activity of the thick A fibres.

An observation made by H. M. Coleridge and his colleagues (personal communication) in the cat is of interest in this connexion. In one of their experiments in which the activity of C fibres was investigated, one cat had scattered areas of pneumonia throughout the lung fields, and in this animal one of the small fibres belonging to the C-fibre group showed bursts of activity during each normal inflationary phase. Spontaneous pneumonia therefore must increase the activity of C fibres, just as experimental pneumonia does.

Many attempts have been and are still being made—usually without success—to explain the disturbance in the regulation of breathing evoked by lung diseases as being due to changes in the excitability of the stretch receptors. The following experiments make it clear that the influence on the respiratory centre of nociceptive impulses must first of all be taken into consideration to solve this problem. As we have shown in cats with a local, experimentally induced pneumonia, the inhibitory Hering-Breuer reflex is decreased. But the decrease in this reflex does not depend on changes in the activity of the lung stretch receptors: when we evoked the Hering-Breuer reflex by inflating the damaged and undamaged lungs separately, the decreases in the reflex were very similar, regardless of which lung was inflated. So we believe that it is the change in the excitability of the respiratory centre (evoked by the nociceptive impulses from the lungs) rather than changes in the stretch receptors that causes the observed decrease in the inhibitory Hering-Breuer reflex. This conclusion was confirmed by the finding that an injury of lung tissues decreased not only the inflationary Hering-Breuer reflex but also the inhibitory respiratory reflex evoked by electrical stimulation of the central cut end of the vagus—a situation in which stimulation of the lung stretch receptors is completely excluded (Frankstein, 1955).

How do the nociceptive impulses influence the respiratory centre? Do impulses travelling in the C fibres excite the respiratory centre directly or through other nervous structures which, in their turn, excite or disinhibit the respiratory centre? Our knowledge of the central connexions as well as of the central action of C fibres is insufficient to answer this question but the following experiments are relevant and interesting.

SEGMENTAL AND SUPRASEGMENTAL EFFECTS EVOKED BY NOCICEPTIVE<br>IMPULSES FROM THE PLEURA

From clinical observations we know that nociceptive impulses from the lung may facilitate respiratory movements, whereas the same impulses from the pleura lead to restricted expansion of the diseased side of the chest. We have established that a unilateral injury of the pleura (caused by an intrapleural injection of hot water at 80–90°C) decreased the segmental intercostal polysynaptic reflexes on the damaged side. Thus nociceptive impulses from the pleura must inhibit the segmental spinal motoneurones on the damaged side.

The strength of the segmental intercostal polysynaptic reflex increases after transection of the spinal cord (Downman and Hussain, 1958). This was confirmed in our experiments on the animal with unilateral damage to the pleura, but one very important peculiarity was observed. After section of the spinal cord (C7–T1), the segmental intercostal polysynaptic reflexes increased on both sides of the chest, but they increased more on the damaged than on the undamaged side.

So the nociceptive impulses from the pleura, as well as inducing segmental inhibition of the spinal motoneurones, must also activate some suprasegmental inhibitory structures which indirectly take part in restricting the expansion of the diseased side of the chest.

SHIFF–SHERRINGTON PHENOMENON AND THE TONIC ACTIVITY OF<br>THE RESPIRATORY MUSCLES

I began with a quotation from Sherrington. I would like to finish by describing some of Sherrington's experiments, now of great interest in relation to the central regulation of breathing.

In 1960, Massion, Meulders and Colle showed that Sherrington's decerebrate rigidity also involved certain respiratory muscles, namely, the intercostal muscles. Thus it was proved that the respiratory muscles obey not only the respiratory centre but also the brainstem mechanisms which maintain decerebrate rigidity, in other words, tonus.

A post-brachial spinal cord transection in the decerebrate cat, in accordance with the Shiff-Sherrington phenomenon, greatly augments the excitability of the extensor reflexes of the forelimbs in decerebrate cats (Denny-Brown and Liddell, 1926; Ruch and Watts, 1934; and others). In our laboratory we have recently shown that spinal cord transection (at L1–L2) in a decerebrate cat increased the rigidity not only of the forelimb extensor muscles but also of the intercostals. This hypertonia suggests the existence in the animal of ascending tracts which, directly or indirectly, exert a continuous restraining or inhibitory action not only on the extensor motor neurones of the forelimbs but also on the motor neurones of the intercostal respiratory muscles.

Apparently the controls established by the Shiff-Sherrington phenomenon are an important link in the self-regulation of breathing.

REFERENCES

ADRIAN, E. D. (1933). *J. Physiol., Lond.*, **79,** 332.

BREUER, J. (1868). *Sber. Akad. Wiss. Wien,* **58,** part 2, 909.

COLERIDGE, H. M., COLERIDGE, J. C. G., and LUCK, J. C. (1965). *J. Physiol., Lond.,* **179, 248.**

CREED, R. C., and HERTZ, D. H. (1933). *J. Physiol., Lond.,* **78,** 85.

DENNY-BROWN, D. E., and LIDDELL, E. G. F. (1926). *Q. Jl exp. Physiol.,* **16,** 353.

DOUGLAS, W. W., and RITCHIE, J. M. (1957). *J. Physiol., Lond.,* **138,** 19.

DOWNMAN, C. B. B., and HUSSAIN, A. (1958). *J. Physiol., Lond.,* **141,** 489.

FRANKSTEIN, S. I. (1955). *Reflexe Pathologisch Veränderter Organe.* Berlin: VEB Verlag Volk und Gesundheit.

FRANKSTEIN, S. I., and SERGEEVA, Z. N. (1966a). *Selfregulation of Breathing under Normal and Pathological Conditions.* Moscow: Izdatelstvo Meditsina.

FRANKSTEIN, S. I., and SERGEEVA, Z. N. (1966b). *Nature, Lond.,* **210,** 1054.

FRANKSTEIN, S. I., and SERGEEVA, Z. N. (1966c). *Experientia,* **22,** 604.

FRANKSTEIN, S. I., and SERGEEVA, Z. N. (1967). *Expl Neurol.,* **18,** 474.

GRANIT, R. (1968). *Structure and Function of Inhibitory Neuronal Mechansims.* Oxford: Pergamon.

MASSION, J., MEULDERS, M., and COLLE, J. (1960). *Archs int. Physiol. Biochim.,* **68,** 314.

PAINTAL, A. S. (1955). *Q. Jl exp. Physiol.,* **40,** 89.

PAINTAL, A. S. (1957). *Q. Jl exp. Physiol.,* **42,** 56.

RUCH, T. C., and WATTS, J. W. (1934). *Am. J. Physiol.,* **110,** 362.

RUDOMIN, P. (1967). *J. Neurophysiol.,* **30,** 5.

SHERRINGTON, C. S. (1906). *The Integrative Action of the Nervous System.* London: Constable.

ULLMANN, E. (1970). This volume, pp. 357–394.

ZOTTERMAN, Y. (1939). *J. Physiol., Lond.,* **95,** 1.

# THE MECHANISM OF EXCITATION OF TYPE J RECEPTORS, AND THE J REFLEX

A. S. Paintal

*Department of Physiology, Vallabhbhai Patel Chest Institute, Delhi University*

In 1868 Hering and Breuer reported a major reflex (arising from the lungs) that regulates the rhythm of respiration particularly at *rest*. Just over a hundred years later, it gives me great pleasure to report the existence of another important reflex (from the lungs) that must operate principally during muscular *exercise*—the J reflex. The existence of this reflex has become known mainly as a result of two new facts about deflation receptors that have emerged in a recent investigation (Paintal, 1955). First, the afferent nerve endings* are located neither downstream nor upstream from the pulmonary capillaries but near the capillaries themselves. Second, although rapid deflation can infrequently stimulate some of these endings without prior sensitization by a drug (Paintal, 1957), deflation is a far weaker stimulus than pulmonary congestion which, in certain circumstances, produces intense activity in these endings and which can now be justifiably regarded as the natural stimulus. For these reasons we have called the deflation receptors "juxtapulmonary capillary receptors", and refer to them as type J receptors or J receptors for convenience (Paintal, 1969).

The conclusion regarding the juxtapulmonary capillary location of these receptors rests on the following evidence: (*a*) the endings are stimulated within 2·5 seconds (s) of injection of phenyl diguanide into the right atrium (mean latency 1·8 s) or right ventricle (mean latency 1·5 s), indicating that they are accessible through the pulmonary capillaries; (*b*) none of these endings is stimulated by injection of phenyl diguanide into the ascending aorta, which indicates that type J receptors are not accessible through the bronchial circulation; and (*c*) the endings are stimulated within 0·3 s of insufflation of volatile anaesthetics (such as halothane) into the lungs. These three properties also form the criteria on the basis of which the fibres were selected for study (Paintal, 1969). However, the conclusive evidence for the juxtacapillary location of these endings is based on the results obtained following insufflation of halothane or ether into the lungs

---

* In this paper sensory nerve endings are referred to as "endings".

before and after circulatory arrest. These results have shown that there is no difference between the latency for excitation before and after circulatory arrest, thus showing that the flow of blood does not affect the latency period between the insufflation of halothane and the excitation of the endings. Thus the endings can be neither upstream nor downstream, but must be near to the pulmonary capillaries themselves.

In five endings, the latency between the start of insufflation and excitation after allowing for the conduction time from the endings to the recording electrodes (determined in each case) was 78–96 ms. The time taken for the anaesthetic vapour to be transported from the tracheal cannula to the alveoli (taking into consideration the rate of insufflation, the respiratory dead space and the volume of insufflation) is estimated to be about 20 ms. Thus the time taken for halothane to diffuse to the endings and excite them must be between 60 and 76 ms. It should be noted that the major part of the interval between insufflation and the appearance of impulses at the recording electrodes is made up of the conduction time from the ending to the recording electrodes because, although there are some fibres with conduction velocities of the order of 7 m/s, most of the fibres of type J receptors are non-medullated, with conduction velocities of less than 3 m/s (Paintal, 1969).

Interestingly, afferent fibres in the right vagus carry impulses from type J receptors in the right lung only, that is, there is no crossing over; most of the type J receptors (about 66 per cent) are located in the lower lobes, which are, of course, the largest.

## Effect of pulmonary congestion

The most important recent observations relate to the excitation of the endings during pulmonary congestion. Excitation occurs whatever the method of producing congestion, for example, increasing pulmonary capillary pressure by occluding the left atrioventricular junction or the aorta, injecting alloxan (which produces pulmonary oedema [Peralta, 1945]) or the inhalation of chlorine. Even congestion for short periods increases the activity of the endings (Fig. 1). The presence of a significant interval between the increase in pulmonary artery pressure and the increase in the activity of type J endings is important. Similarly, after reducing the raised pressure, there is a time-lag before the discharge starts to fall.

The time-lag between the rise in pressure and excitation of the endings is particularly marked when pulmonary congestion (leading to pulmonary oedema) is produced by injecting alloxan 150 mg/kg into the right atrium or right ventricle. In some fibres this lag was as long as 50–120 s (for

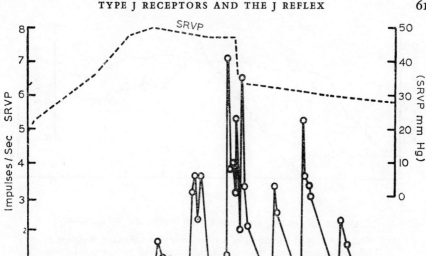

FIG. 1. Response of a type J receptor to occlusion of the aorta at zero time. Note time-lag between the rise in systolic right ventricular pressure (SRVP) and the excitation of the ending and a similar lag at the end of the occlusion (arrow). The ordinate (impulses/s) represents the reciprocal of the interval between individual impulses. Note: for practical purposes SRVP is equivalent to systolic pulmonary artery pressure (Paintal, 1969; reproduced by permission of *J. Physiol., Lond.*).

example, Fig. 2). Fig. 2 also shows that the excitation following injection of alloxan is not due to a direct action of alloxan on the ending. This finding is supported by the observation that alloxan had no excitatory effect on three gastric endings (for over 10 min); these endings also have non-medullated fibres and their responses to drugs are similar to those of type J receptors (Paintal, 1964). The lag between the occurrence of peak pressure and of maximum activity in the endings was even longer (seven minutes for the ending shown in Fig. 3). These results therefore indicate that the endings do not signal pulmonary capillary pressure *per se*, which is consistent with the observation that these endings do not usually have a cardiac rhythm, although infrequently, in very excitable type J endings, a cardiac rhythm may appear. In general, increased activity in the endings seems to be related to the reduction in pulmonary compliance as indicated by the increase in intratracheal pressure (Figs. 2 and 3).

The increased activity produced by congestion can continue for long

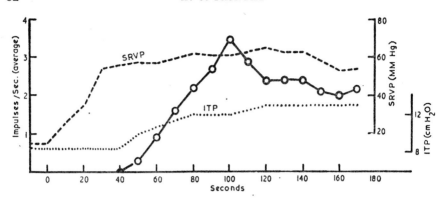

EFFECT OF PULMONARY CONGESTION PRODUCED BY ALLOXAN

FIG. 2. Delayed excitation of a type J receptor following injection of
alloxan at zero time. The first impulse appeared 50 s after injection.
Note time-lag between rise in pressure and the activity of the ending, and
the development of activity with the progressive reduction in pulmonary compliance as indicated by the gradual rise in intratracheal
pressure. Ordinate (left): frequency of discharge averaged over 10-s
periods; ordinate (right): systolic right ventricular pressure (SRVP)
and intratracheal pressure (ITP). The cat was ventilated with a respiratory pump; stroke volume: 60 ml. The excitation of the ending is less
than the average excitation that follows the injection of alloxan.

periods—certainly for about 20–30 min, which was as long as the observations were continued. Thus there is no reason to doubt that such increased
activity can continue for days if the pulmonary congestion persists.

Typically, the pattern of activity during congestion is irregular, somewhat as in chemoreceptors, but the discharge waxes and wanes. In some
fibres cyclical activity, not related to the respiratory cycle, occurs during
acute congestion, interspersed by periods of relative silence; in others,
activity is clearly related to the respiratory cycle. For example in some
endings the activity was set off by deflation of the lungs, as expected from
earlier observations (Paintal, 1955).

The peak frequency of discharge attained is of the order of 20–50
impulses/s in most fibres, which is typical of the endings of non-medullated
fibres (see Paintal, 1964). However, as with the chemoreceptors, it is more
meaningful to consider the average frequency of discharge, that is, the
average number of impulses appearing during 10–20 s. This is especially
important when the discharge is irregular and when there are silent intervals
between periods of activity. When assessed in this way the average
frequency of discharge during acute pulmonary congestion produced by
alloxan or chlorine was 7·5 impulses/s in ten fibres (range: 0·6–19

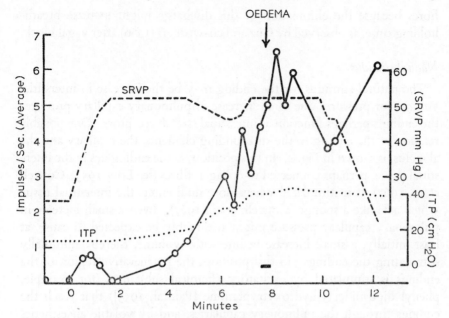

FIG. 3. Graph showing response of average intensity in a type J receptor following injection of alloxan at zero time. The ordinate on the left represents impulses/s averaged over 20-s periods. Oedema fluid appeared in the tracheal cannula after the 7th minute (arrow). Cat on artificial respiration. Note the considerable time-lag between rise in pulmonary artery pressure (SRVP) and the occurrence of peak activity. Development of excitation corresponds to the fall in pulmonary compliance. ITP: intratracheal pressure (Paintal, 1969; reproduced by permission of *J. Physiol., Lond.*)

impulses/s; SD: 6·3). This level of activity does not seem much at first sight but it is in fact intense when compared with the activity in the chemoreceptors (which also have non-medullated fibres). Thus, the mean discharge in aortic chemoreceptors during severe hypoxia was 7·5 impulses/s (Paintal, 1967). It can therefore be concluded that acute pulmonary congestion produced by alloxan and chlorine constitutes a strong stimulus which can presumably also occur in certain pathological conditions. Lesser degrees of stimulation of type J endings would occur during less marked congestion, for example under physiological conditions such as muscular exercise (see below).

Now that it has been shown that an average discharge frequency of 7·5 impulses/s is intense activity in type J receptors, activity of, say, 1 impulse/s seen in occasional fibres under apparently normal resting conditions (Paintal, 1969) acquires considerable significance. Indeed, note must also be taken of activity of the order of 0·2 impulses/s in some fibres because the elimination of this discharge might increase breath-holding time, as observed by Guz and co-workers (1966) after vagal block.

### Natural stimulus

The natural stimulus for the ending may be the increase in interstitial volume (or pressure) due to an increase in pulmonary capillary pressure; the endings perhaps function as interstitial stretch receptors. One possible relation of the ending to the surrounding elements, the capillary and the alveolus, is shown in Fig. 4. In this position, as the ending lies in the interstitial tissue, perhaps connected to collagen fibres (see Low 1953; Cottrell *et al.*, 1967), it is stimulated when more fluid enters the interstitial tissue which acts like a sponge (Cottrell, *et al.*, 1967). Even a small increase in pulmonary capillary pressure might reasonably be expected to cause, at least initially, a small increase in interstitial volume, thereby minimally stimulating the endings. In this position, the regenerative region of the endings is stimulated by excitatory chemical substances (for example, phenyl diguanide, 5-hydroxytryptamine [Paintal, 1955]) that reach the endings through the pulmonary capillaries, and by volatile anaesthetics that reach them through the alveolar epithelium. This scheme fits in with

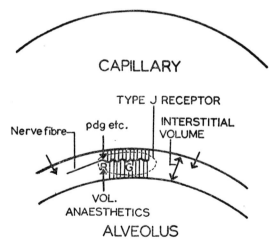

FIG. 4. Schematic representation of the likely location of the type J receptor lying in the interstitial tissue, perhaps connected to collagen fibrils. The ending is stimulated by an increase in interstitial volume (or pressure) produced when the inflow of fluid into the interstitial tissue (which acts like a sponge) exceeds removal of the fluid. Volatile anaesthetics and other chemical substances (for example phenyl diguanide —pdg) act on the regenerative region, R, of the ending, while the rise in interstitial volume acts on the generator region, G, of the ending (see Paintal, 1964).

the observations of Mellins and co-workers (1969). On the other hand, the observations of Staub, Nagano and Pearce (1967) indicate that the earliest accumulation of oedema fluid occurs in the peribronchial and perivascular interstitial tissue, so the endings might conceivably be located in this region. But in this position the endings might not be able to sense the immediate increase in interstitial volume that must occur in the interstitial tissue adjacent to the capillary endothelium (Fig. 4) when pulmonary capillary pressure rises. The peribronchial and perivascular regions, therefore, seem less favourable for the location of the endings. Histologists might profitably look for these endings in the interstitial tissue between the basement membranes of the endothelium and the alveolar epithelium in the position shown in Fig. 4, preferably after supranodose vagotomy (unilateral vagotomy only is needed) and sympathectomy. Judging from the size of the terminal fibres of chemoreceptors (see, for example, De Kock and Dunn, 1968) one would expect to find sensory fibres with a diameter of the order of $0 \cdot 1$–$0 \cdot 3\,\mu m$.

Whatever the actual location of the endings, they are almost certainly not functionally linked to the smooth muscle of the alveolar ducts and respiratory bronchioles, because the endings are not stimulated by histamine which, when injected intravenously, causes this muscle to contract (Alcock et al., 1937; Colebatch, Olsen and Nadel, 1966).

*Physiological role*

The endings would be expected to be stimulated during muscular exercise because this causes the pulmonary capillary pressure to rise, although this fact is not generally recognized. Observations on residents at high altitudes have shown that pulmonary capillary pressure must rise considerably in at least some section of the pulmonary vascular bed during exercise. Thus, in 28 normal residents (aged 13–17 years) at Leadville (ht: 3096 m), Vogel and co-workers (1963) found that the average mean pulmonary artery pressure rose from about 25 mmHg at rest to about 54 mmHg during exercise; cardiac output increased by 80 per cent. In one subject (school skiing champion) the pressures recorded during exercise were 165/96 mmHg. Had the exercise been severe enough to increase the cardiac output fivefold, say, as occurs during severe exercise in athletes, the rise in pulmonary artery pressure would have been even higher.

Again at Morochocha (ht: 4540 m) Penaloza and co-workers (1963) found that whereas the mean pulmonary artery pressure averaged 29 mmHg in 35 subjects at rest, it rose to 60 mmHg during exercise; the cardiac output increased to only twice its resting value on exercise. Although the subjects of these two studies did not develop pulmonary oedema during exercise, they must nevertheless have had some congestion of their lungs. On the other hand, several of the 332 soldiers studied by Singh and co-workers (1965) developed frank pulmonary oedema on exertion at an altitude of 3300–4600 m. Some of these soldiers developed pulmonary oedema during exercise and died within one hour of its onset (Singh, I., personal communication, 1969). During such exercise pulmonary congestion must cause considerable stimulation of type J receptors thereby leading to the sensations of breathlessness which are likely to be caused by these endings (cf. Paintal, 1955; 1968). These sensations, and the reflex inhibition of muscles caused by the endings (see below), lead to the termination of exercise and therefore to a fall in pulmonary pressure.

As far as residents at high altitude are concerned, the physiological role of the endings is clear. The role of the endings must be similarly applicable to man at slightly lower heights and, by extension of this logic, to man at sea level. And at sea level also, an increase in mean pulmonary artery pressures has been recorded during moderate or severe exercise (Donald et al., 1955; Freedman et al., 1955; Bevegård, Holmgren and Jonsson, 1963; Granath, Jonsson and Strandell, 1964). Unfortunately these significant observations seem to have been overshadowed by the prevailing view that pulmonary artery pressure rises very little, if at all, during muscular exercise (see Bell, Davidson and Scarborough, 1959; Keele and Neil, 1965). However, it may be argued that this rise in pulmonary artery pressure may not be transmitted to the pulmonary capillaries. This is unlikely because Bevegård, Holmgren and Jonsson (1963) found that the pulmonary capillary pressures were two or three times the resting values during heavy exercise in some athletes. A similar rise has been recorded in healthy old men (Granath, Jonsson and Strandell, 1964). Other investigators may have recorded an increase in pulmonary capillary pressure during exercise but have ignored this observation, either because it did not interest them at that time or because such an idea conflicted with the prevailing view that pulmonary capillary pressure does not rise during exercise. For example Sapru, Taylor and Donald (1968), in a paper demonstrating that wedge pressures correspond to the left ventricular end-diastolic pressure, provide convincing data that pulmonary capillary pressure more than doubled in three normal subjects during moderate exercise, but these authors do not comment on this important finding.

This information makes it certain that under the physiological conditions described the activity of type J receptors will increase, and this should produce some of the sensations of breathlessness that occur during exercise. Paintal (1968) has presented arguments to show that type J endings must constitute an important source of dyspnoeic sensations arising from the lungs. In view of the marked excitation of these endings during acute congestion, they are likely to be concerned with the production of the dyspnoeic sensations that arise from the lung in certain pathological conditions in which the pulmonary capillary pressure is raised and a marked rise in pulmonary artery pressure occurs during mild exercise, enough to produce frank dyspnoea (Hickam and Cargill, 1948; Blount, 1959; Ferrer and Harvey, 1959). Perhaps it is the elimination of this discharge by vagotomy that provides the notable relief of dyspnoea by vagotomy in some patients (Guz, 1966).

*Reflex effects*

It would be expected that if type J receptors are stimulated by a rise in pulmonary capillary pressure, some reflex mechanism should exist which would reflexly lower pulmonary artery pressure by some means, for example by reducing either pulmonary vascular resistance or cardiac input into the right ventricle. There is no such reflex mechanism (apart from the occasional marginal effects of bradycardia itself) because stimulation of these endings by phenyl diguanide or 2α-naphthylisothiourea does not produce a reflex fall in pulmonary artery pressure or an obvious reduction in pulmonary vascular resistance (see Dawes, Mott and Widdicombe, 1951; Barer and Nüsser, 1958). In view of the absence of such mechanisms for providing reflex cardiovascular adjustments, it was postulated that since type J receptors must be stimulated during exercise only under normal conditions, they should therefore reflexly terminate exercise by producing reflex inhibition of limb muscles (Paintal, 1969).

Accordingly, Deshpande and Devanandan (1970) studied the reflex effect of stimulating type J receptors on the monosynaptic reflexes of hind-limb muscles and, as expected, they found that stimulating the endings produced inhibition of monosynaptic reflexes of both flexor and extensor muscles of the hind limb. This reflex can be conveniently called the J reflex. The inhibition is apparently postsynaptic since it is abolished by strychnine. Moreover, these workers have found that the inhibitory impulses to the motoneurones are carried by a tract of fibres that travels ipsilaterally in the ventromedial part of the spinal cord. Finally they showed that, unlike the respiratory and cardiovascular reflexes of type J receptors, the J reflex is abolished by decerebration thereby indicating that some higher centres are involved (Deshpande and Devanandan, 1970). Kalia (1969) studied this aspect further using the knee jerk as an index of the quadriceps mono-synaptic reflex. Kalia has found that the cerebral cortex of the cat is not needed for the operation of the basic reflex mechanism although it is possible that parts of the cortex may modify the reflex. On the other hand, reflex pathways in the basal ganglia, for example the caudate nucleus, seem to be essential for the reflex because it is abolished by lesions in this region (Fig. 5).

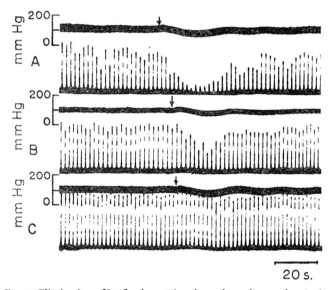

FIG. 5. Elimination of J reflex by cutting through caudate nucleus in the cat. A shows control knee jerks (quadriceps monosynaptic reflex) at start of experiment. At arrow, phenyl diguanide 150 μg was injected into the right atrium (as also in B and C) to stimulate type J receptors. This produced the J reflex (that is, inhibition of the jerk). B. After cutting through the suprasylvian gyrus and the underlying white matter to a depth of 9 mm from the surface of the cortex, the reflex is still present. C. The reflex is abolished (no inhibition of quadriceps monosynaptic reflex) after cutting through the rostral part of the caudate nucleus. The cat was atropinized to eliminate the reflex bradycardia and hypo-tension produced by phenyl diguanide. The upper tracing in each record is of aortic blood pressure; calibration on right lower (Kalia and Paintal, 1969).

The sequence of events leading to the J reflex are summarized in Fig. 6. Exercise causes an increase in cardiac input and this leads to a rise in pulmon-ary artery pressure which causes the pulmonary capillary pressure to rise. As a consequence the outflow of fluid into the interstitial tissue increases, thereby increasing interstitial volume, as a result of which type J receptors are stimulated. This is turn leads to reflex inhibition of limb muscles

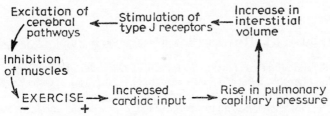

FIG. 6. Suggested sequence of events in the J reflex.

through cerebral pathways and, with the sensations of breathlessness, causes the exercise to end thereby reducing cardiac input.

Unfortunately there are no observations on pulmonary artery pressure during exercise in the cat or dog. In the fish the pressure in the ventral aorta (equivalent to the pulmonary artery) rises significantly during moderate exercise (Stevens and Randall, 1967). There is therefore a possibility that an inhibitory reflex for the tail muscles arising from endings (equivalent to type J receptors) in the gills may be present in the fish; in other words, a reflex originating in the gills may cause the fish to stop swimming.

## SUMMARY

Fresh evidence has shown that the type J receptors (originally called deflation receptors) are not downstream or upstream from the pulmonary capillaries but close to the capillaries themselves. Their natural stimulus is generally pulmonary congestion which, owing to a rise in pulmonary capillary pressure, causes an increase in interstitial volume due to the outpouring of fluid into the interstitial tissue. This stimulates the endings which behave as interstitial stretch receptors. Results obtained with three types of congestion—haemodynamic or induced by alloxan or chlorine—were basically similar.

The physiological stimulus for the endings is the rise in pulmonary capillary pressure that occurs during muscular exercise—the greater the rise, the greater the increase in interstitial volume and the greater the excitation of the endings. Stimulation of type J receptors produces reflex inhibition of limb muscles (in addition to the already known respiratory and cardiovascular reflex effects). This effect is called the J reflex and involves the participation of certain indispensable cerebral pathways located centrally, and especially in the basal ganglia.

### ACKNOWLEDGEMENTS

This investigation was aided by equipment from the Wellcome Trust, London and by a grant from the Atomic Energy Commission, India.

## REFERENCES

Alcock, P., Berry, J. L., Daly, I. de B., and Narayana, B. (1937). Q. Jl exp. Physiol., 26, 13–27.
Barer, G. R., and Nüsser, E. (1958). Br. J. Pharmac. Chemother., 13, 372–377.
Bell, G. H., Davidson, J. N., and Scarborough, H. (eds). (1959). Textbook of Physiology and Biochemistry, 4th edn., p. 515. Edinburgh: Livingstone.
Bevegård, S., Holmgren, A., and Jonsson, B. (1963). Acta physiol. scand., 57, 26–50.
Blount, S. G. (1959). In Pulmonary Circulation, pp. 160–166, ed. Adams, W. R., and Veith, I. New York: Grune and Stratton.
Breuer, J. (1868). Sber. Akad. Wiss. Wien, 58, part 2 909–937.
Colebatch, H. J. H., Olsen, C. R., and Nadel, J. A. (1966). J. appl. Physiol., 21, 217–226.
Cottrell, T. S., Levine, O. R., Senior, R. M., Weiner, J., Spiro, D., and Fishman, A. P. (1967). Circulation Res., 21, 783–797.
Dawes, G. S., Mott, J. C., and Widdicombe, J. G. (1951). J. Physiol., Lond., 115, 258–291.
De Kock, L., and Dunn, A. E. G. (1968). In Arterial Chemoreceptors, pp. 179–187, ed. Torrance, R. W. Oxford: Blackwell.
Deshpande, S. S., and Devanandan, M. (1970). J. Physiol., Lond., 206, 345–357.
Donald, K. W., Bishop, J. M., Cumming, G., and Wade, O. L. (1955). Clin. Sci., 14, 37–73.
Ferrer, M. I., and Harvey, R. M. (1959). In Pulmonary Circulation, pp. 171–186, ed. Adams, W. R., and Veith, I. New York: Grune and Stratton.
Freedman, M. E., Snider, G. L., Brostoff, P., Kimelblot, S., and Katz, L. N. (1955). J. appl. Physiol., 8, 37–47.
Granath, A., Jonsson, B., and Strandell, T. (1964). Acta med. scand., 176, 425–446.
Guz, A. (1966). Doctoral thesis, London University, Faculty of Medicine.
Guz, A., Noble, M. I. M., Widdicombe, J. G., Trenchard, D., Mushin, W. W., and Makey, A. R. (1966). Clin. Sci., 30, 161–170.
Hering, E. (1868). Sber. Akad. Wiss. Wein, 57, part 2, 672–677.
Hickam, J. B., and Cargill, W. H. (1948). J. clin. Invest., 27, 10–23.
Kalia, M. (1969). J. Physiol., Lond., 204, 92P.
Kalia, M., and Paintal, A. S. (1969). Unpublished observations.
Keele, C. A., and Neil, E. (eds). (1965). Samson Wright's Applied Physiology, 11th edn., p. 139. London: Oxford University Press.
Low, F. W. (1953). Anat. Rec., 117, 241–263.
Mellins, R. B., Levine, O. R., Skalak, R., and Fishman, A. P. (1969). Circulation Res., 24, 197–212.
Paintal, A. S. (1955). Q. Jl exp. Physiol. 40, 89–111.
Paintal, A. S. (1957). Q. Jl exp. Physiol., 42, 56–71.
Paintal, A. S. (1964). Pharmac. Rev., 16, 341–380.
Paintal, A. S. (1967). J. Physiol., Lond., 189, 63–84.
Paintal, A. S. (1968). Indian J. med. Res., 56, 1–11.
Paintal, A. S. (1969). J. Physiol., Lond., 203, 511–532.
Penaloza, D., Sime, F., Banchero, N., and Camboa, R. (1963). In Progress in Research in Emphysema and Chronic Bronchitis, vol. 1, pp. 257–268, ed. Grover, R. F., and Herzog, H. New York: Karger.
Peralta, R. B. (1945). Rev. Inst. Salubr. Enferm. trop., Méx., 6, 117–122.
Sapru, R. P., Taylor, S. H., and Donald, K. W. (1968). Clin. Sci., 34, 125–140.
Singh, I., Kapila, C. C., Khanna, P. K., Nanda, R. B., and Rao, B. D. P. (1965). Lancet, 1, 229–234.
Staub, N. C., Nagano, H., and Pearce, M. L. (1967). J. appl. Physiol., 22, 227–240.
Stevens, E. D., and Randall, D. J. (1967). J. exp. Biol., 46, 307–415.

VOGEL, J. H. K., WEAVER, W. F., ROSE, R. L., BLOUNT, S. G., and GROVER, R. F. (1963). In *Progress in Research in Emphysema and Chronic Bronchitis*, vol. 1, pp. 269, 285, ed. Grover, R. F., and Herzog, H. New York: Karger.

## DISCUSSION

*Dornhorst:* Did you stimulate the knee jerk electrically or mechanically in these experiments?

*Paintal:* Both. Deshpande and Devanandan (1970) used the conventional neurophysiological method of stimulating group IA fibres electrically, and Kalia (1969) elicited the knee jerk in the usual clinical way by tapping the quadriceps tendon. It was found that the J reflex was inhibited by both these manoeuvres.

*Dornhorst:* So this reflex cannot be acting only via gamma fibres?

*Paintal:* That's right.

*Dornhorst:* You talked about pulmonary congestion. This is a confusing and ambiguous term. Did you mean incipient pulmonary oedema, with increased transudation in the interstitial space? Pulmonary oedema presumably has a threshold that is dependent on pressure.

*Paintal:* According to Starling's hypothesis, increasing pulmonary capillary pressure by a small amount—say 2 mmHg—should slightly increase the volume of interstitial fluid. We are simply increasing the volume of interstitial fluid from its existing level, whatever this may be, to a slightly higher one.

*Dornhorst:* This line of reasoning is spurious because the normal wedge pressure is so much lower than plasma osmotic pressure, presumably implying a high negative pressure in the interstitial space.

*Paintal:* Nonetheless, if we start with a pressure of (say) $-5$ mmHg, and this becomes $-4$ mmHg, the conditions in the interstitial space have changed.

*Dornhorst:* But we do not know how the interstitial space responds to this change. If a patient is exercised during cardiac catheterization, subjective discontinuity (that is, dyspnoea) occurs somewhere near the point at which capillary and colloid osmotic pressures have the same value. And this coincidence of pressures is probably connected with a large increase in lymph flow. But the change in the interstitial space that you have described may not be "congestion" which, if it means anything, suggests the presence of an increased vascular volume; such an increase in volume is not necessarily accompanied by a change in pulmonary capillary pressure.

*Paintal:* We have used the word congestion in a limited sense to indicate an increase in pulmonary capillary pressure.

*Dornhorst:* This does not necessarily follow either. Endothelial damage may increase the volume of the interstitial space without any change in capillary pressure. For instance, did the chlorine in your experiments increase the capillary pressure?

*Paintal:* It increased pulmonary artery pressure, which is what we measured.

*Dornhorst:* The two are not necessarily related.

*Paintal:* But if a rise in pulmonary artery pressure is followed by pulmonary oedema, then surely the pulmonary capillary pressure must be raised.

*Dornhorst:* I would not accept that without direct measurement. The chlorine may directly damage the endothelium in which case the rise in pulmonary artery pressure may be secondary to, say, anoxia.

*Prys-Roberts:* Could there be two mechanisms operating here? First, an irritant effect from agents like chlorine (halothane and ether, incidentally, are also known to act as irritants on endothelium and on sensory nerve endings in the lung) and second, reflux back pressure causing pulmonary congestion through an increase in pulmonary capillary volume. We (Greenbaum *et al.*, 1967) studied the effects of the higher oxides of nitrogen on the dog and found that although these gases increased pulmonary artery pressure, left ventricular end-diastolic pressures were unaltered. These findings suggest that these higher oxides of nitrogen were producing an irritant lesion with an exudation of interstitial fluid. In other words, they gave rise to chemical pneumonitis. The gases were administered at a fixed concentration in the inspired gas mixture during both spontaneous and artificial ventilation.

*Paintal:* I used alloxan rather than chlorine because there is no initial excitation of nerve endings with alloxan. The initial excitation by chlorine could be caused by a direct effect on the endings whereas subsequent excitation may be due to accumulation of fluid caused by a rise in pulmonary capillary pressure and damage to the endothelium.

*Dornhorst:* Did you measure the pulmonary capillary pressure after chlorine?

*Paintal:* No.

*Dornhorst:* I do not know of any records of pulmonary capillary pressures after chlorine, but nitrous fumes have been studied in this context (Becklake *et al.*, 1957), and I had assumed that these caused capillary damage without increase in capillary pressure but with a secondary rise in precapillary resistance. These distinctions may not matter as far as they affect the respiratory reflexes, but it is very important to avoid confusion in our thinking about the various causes of changes in the interstitial space.

*Paintal:* Both chlorine and alloxan may increase capillary permeability; we do not claim that the effects of these substances on the J receptors are due solely to an increase in pulmonary capillary pressure.

*Dornhorst:* The J receptors are closely associated with collagen, and in normal circumstances water and collagen in the pulmonary capillaries form a gel. Even if the pressure in the interstitial space were negative, changes in the degree of hydration of this gel would occur with changes in pressure. If it is justifiable to extrapolate from the work on interstitial tissue in other areas, one would expect a non-linear relationship between pressure and volume in pulmonary interstitial tissue at about atmospheric pressure (Guyton, Sheel and Murphree, 1966). Thus the onset of increased lymph flow and clinical pulmonary oedema might be associated with a very large increase in the volume of the interstitial space. This might result in a graded linear increase in firing of the J receptors with physiological changes in intrapulmonary capillary pressure, and then a very large increase in firing at the onset of pulmonary oedema. Do your results confirm this hypothesis? For example, does a change in the slope of the rate of stimulation of J receptors occur at the pressure at which pulmonary oedema is first manifest?

*Paintal:* I cannot answer this question. It would certainly be possible to do an experiment fairly easily in the cat, measuring left atrial pressure, which would give us the answer.

*Dejours:* Could one call the type J receptors "pulmonary capillary baroreceptors"?

*Paintal:* No. Although these receptors are stimulated by a rise in pulmonary capillary pressure they differ from the baroreceptors in several ways. For example, I have seen pulsatile impulse activity only once during the time I have studied the J receptors.

*Dornhorst:* Another difference between these two types of receptor is the time-lag after the change in pressure before activity in the J receptors builds up. Is there a pressure threshold below which these receptors will not fire?

*Paintal:* Yes. The pressure threshold is probably a little higher than the pressure in the resting cat.

*Widdicombe:* You have suggested that in man on exercise pulmonary wedge pressure increases by only a few millimetres of mercury when the pulmonary artery pressure has increased a great deal more. I had always assumed from Holmgren's work (Holmgren, Jonsson and Sjöstrand, 1960; Bevegård, Holmgren and Jonsson, 1963) that, in exercise, pulmonary arteriolar constriction may occur and although this would increase the pulmonary artery pressure it might even decrease capillary pressure. In fact these workers showed that pulmonary capillary pressure increased by a mean of 3 mmHg in untrained subjects and 8 mmHg in athletes. Could you comment on this, Professor Paintal?

*Paintal:* The work you describe was done on Swedish athletes. Pulmonary artery pressure and wedge pressure were measured and Bevegård, Holmgren and Jonsson (1963) showed a twofold to threefold rise in wedge pressure during exercise in some of the subjects. Granath, Jonsson and Strandell (1964) observed a similar increase in pressures in healthy old men. This was also recorded by Sapru, Taylor and Donald (1968). These three publications, and maybe other old records, clearly demonstrate a rise in pulmonary capillary pressure with exercise.

*Campbell:* If one deflates the lung in animals by sucking air out, are there widespread reflex effects throughout the body?

*Paintal:* I cannot answer that question because I only used deflation for my early work on the stimulation of nerve endings in the lung (Paintal, 1955); I was recording from vagal single fibres, not studying reflex effects.

*Dornhorst:* Professor Paintal, are you assuming that when you deflate the lung you are causing changes in the interstitial space?

*Paintal:* This is not really my field; Howell and co-workers (1961) studied the relationship between lung inflation and interstitial pressures.

*Cotes:* Howell and co-workers (1961) and also Hamer (1963) showed that as the lung expands the volume of the capillaries decreases, probably because of an alteration in their shape. Do you think that this change in the shape of the capillaries—the walls are presumably both stretched and flattened—could stimulate the J fibres?

*Paintal:* This is unlikely because inflation and deflation stimulate the J receptors only weakly, if at all.

*Cotes:* Is the J reflex associated with tachypnoea? And, if so, is this caused by inhibition of the respiratory muscles or is there some separate mechanism to account for it?

*Paintal:* At least two sets of reflexes are produced by the J receptors. One set operates at the bulbar level causing cardiovascular and respiratory responses (including tachypnoea); these reflexes survive decerebration. The other set is abolished by decerebration and operates through the cerebrum to produce reflex muscular inhibition. It is only the latter type of reflex that we call the J reflex.

*Fillenz:* Is the sensory innervation of the capillaries widespread or scanty? Would you expect these sensory fibres to be extensively and evenly, or only patchily, distributed near the alveolar capillaries?

*Paintal:* Agostoni and co-workers (1957) reported that there were about 4000 non-myelinated fibres in the bronchial branches of the vagus.

*Campbell:* There are 65,000 terminal bronchioles in the human lung (Weibel, 1964).

*Paintal:* So even with the highest magnification one is looking for a needle in a haystack.

*Widdicombe:* The fibres, counted in the vagus or bronchial nerves, may branch distally and have many terminals.

*Guz:* What is the conduction velocity of these fibres?

*Paintal:* This is usually less than three metres per second; a very few fibres *may* have a conduction velocity of up to seven metres per second.

*Guz:* Are these nearly all non-myelinated fibres?

*Paintal:* Yes.

*Prys-Roberts:* What are the effects of an excess of carbon dioxide on firing the J reflex? If one injected a bolus of carbon dioxide intravenously, as one can with halothane or ether, what would this do to the J reflex?

*Paintal:* Dickinson and I (Dickinson and Paintal, 1968) have described the effects of an injection of carbon dioxide gas into the right ventricle. We found that carbon dioxide stimulated the deflation receptors, as phenyl diguanide does, except that the action of carbon dioxide is much weaker than that of phenyl diguanide: about 4 ml carbon dioxide correspond to about 40 μg phenyl diguanide in this situation. The excitation of the sensory nerve endings in the lung by the bolus of carbon dioxide does not occur consistently but about once in every three or four injections. This may be because the gas does not reach the same endings on each occasion.

*Guz:* Could this be just an embolic effect or is there something special about carbon dioxide?

*Paintal:* It cannot be a simple embolic effect because neither nitrogen nor air, when injected as intravenous boli, stimulate the deflation receptors.

*Widdicombe:* Your early work (Paintal, 1955) showed that the deflation endings are stimulated by solid emboli, such as starch grains. Some mechanical characteristic of carbon dioxide, perhaps its solubility, its bubble size or its site of lodgement, might give it embolic properties that these other gases do not have.

*Paintal:* This work was done by Dickinson, Green and Howell (1961). Dr Howell, would you like to comment?

*Howell:* It is unlikely that carbon dioxide acts as an embolus since its effect on the sensory endings is abolished by acetazolamide; it is also unlikely because carbon dioxide is more soluble than nitrogen and air, and neither of these last two gases produced any respiratory response when given as an intravenous embolus.

*Guz:* We have studied the respiratory effects of spherical plastic pulmonary emboli of various sizes injected intravenously in the rabbit anaesthetized with chloralose 40 mg/k. It is not easy to induce tachypnoea unless the particle diameter is about 50 μm. Interestingly, these particles become impacted in vessels within the alveolar wall and the result of this is a considerable distortion of the alveolar surface (Fig. 1). The area where J receptors are located is thus deformed. We have not yet proved that the tachypnoea depends on the stimulation of non-myelinated fibre endings, but the response has nothing to do with stretch receptors; these do not discharge with this type of stimulus, nor is there any sensitization of the inflation reflex after the embolus. It would be very interesting to record from J receptors while injecting emboli into the lung in this way.

REFERENCES

AGOSTONI, E., CHINNOCK, J. E., DALY, M. DE B., and MURRAY, J. G. (1957). *J. Physiol., Lond.*, **135**, 182–205.
BECKLAKE, M. R., GOLDMAN, H. I., BOSMAN, A. R., and FREED, C. C. (1957). *Am. Rev. Tuberc. pulm. Dis.*, **76**, 398–409.
BEVEGÅRD, S., HOLMGREN, A., and JONSSON, B. (1963). *Acta physiol. scand.*, **57**, 26–50.
DESHPANDE, S. S., and DEVANANDAN, M. (1970). *J. Physiol., Lond.*, **206**, 345–357.
DICKINSON, C. J., GREEN, J. H., and HOWELL, J. B. L. (1961). *J. Physiol., Lond.*, **155**, 38P.
DICKINSON, C. J., and PAINTAL, A. S. (1968). *J. Physiol., Lond.*, **196**, 70P.
GRANATH, A., JONSSON, B., and STRANDELL, T. (1964). *Acta med. scand.*, **176**, 425–446.
GREENBAUM, R., BAY, J., HARGREAVES, M. D., KAIN, M. L., KELMAN, G. R., NUNN, J. F., PRYS-ROBERTS, C., and SIEBOLD, K. (1967). *Br. J. Anaesth.*, **39**, 393–404.
GUYTON, A. C., SHEEL, K., and MURPHREE, D. (1966), *Circulation Res.*, **19**, 412–419.
HAMER, N. A. J. (1963). *Clin. Sci.*, **24**, 275–285.
HOLMGREN, A., JONSSON, B., and SJÖSTRAND, T. (1960). *Acta physiol. scand.*, **49**, 343–363.
HOWELL, J. B. L., PERMUTT, S., PROCTOR, D. F., and RILEY, R. L. (1961). *J. appl. Physiol.*, **16**, 71–76.
KALIA, M. (1969). *J. Physiol., Lond.*, **204**, 92P.
PAINTAL, A. S. (1955). *Q. Jl exp. Physiol.*, **40**, 89–111.
SAPRU, R. P., TAYLOR, S. H., and DONALD, K. W. (1968). *Clin. Sci.*, **34**, 125–140.
WEIBEL, E. R. (1964). In *Handbook of Physiology*, sect. III, vol. 1, p. 285, ed. Fenn, W. O. and Rahn, H. American Physiological Society. Baltimore: Williams and Wilkins.

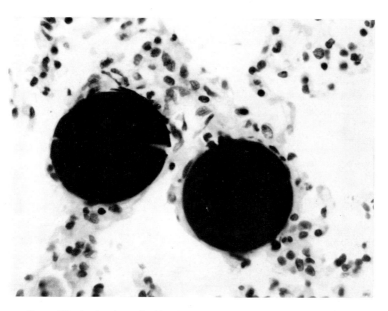

FIG. 1 (*Guz*). Section of rabbit lung after embolization with 50-μm-diameter particles. Tachypnoea resulted and was abolished by cervical vagotomy. Note distortion of alveolar walls (× 416).

[*To face page 76*

# EPITHELIAL IRRITANT RECEPTORS IN THE LUNGS

Janet E. Mills, Hilary Sellick and J. G. Widdicombe

*University Laboratory of Physiology, Oxford*

Many reflexes affecting breathing and autonomic nervous motor systems arise in the lungs (see Paintal, 1963 and Widdicombe, 1964, for references). Two vagal afferent pathways subserving some of these reflexes have been studied previously, mainly by recording action potentials in single vagal nerve fibres. Adrian (1933) recorded from large-diameter myelinated fibres coming from slowly adapting pulmonary stretch receptors. The receptors probably lie in the smooth muscle of the airways, from trachea to bronchioles. They are stimulated by inflation of the lungs, and their reflex action includes the inhibition of inspiratory activity (the Hering–Breuer inflation reflex) and bronchodilatation. Paintal (1955, 1957) has recorded action potentials from vagal non-myelinated fibres coming from "specific deflation receptors" in the lungs. The receptors have not been identified histologically but they are probably in the alveolar wall close to the capillary endothelium. They are stimulated by pulmonary congestion, micro-embolism and several chemicals, but not greatly or consistently by deflation of the lungs or pneumothorax. Their probable reflex action is apnoea or rapid shallow breathing, hypotension and bradycardia.

These two groups of receptors cannot account for all the respiratory reflexes arising in the lungs—for example the reflex respiratory reponses to bronchial irritation, deflation of the lungs and pneumothorax, and the vagal component of the responses to histamine and anaphylaxis (Karczewski and Widdicombe, 1969a,b).

Histological studies (for example, Larsell, 1921; Elftman, 1943) have demonstrated the presence throughout the intrapulmonary airways of intra-epithelial nerve endings, the terminals of which ramify between the epithelial cells and seem almost to reach the ciliary layer. They resemble closely the "cough receptors" in the tracheal and extrapulmonary bronchial epithelium, which have been studied by recording from single vagal nerve fibres (Widdicombe, 1954b).

This paper describes research on the properties of these lung epithelial irritant receptors, mainly by recording from single vagal fibres, and discusses their role in some respiratory reflexes. Fuller details of the methods and of some of the results will be found elsewhere (Mills, Sellick and Widdicombe, 1969; Sellick and Widdicombe, 1969).

## METHODS

Rabbits were used, because they have strong lung reflexes and are easy to sensitize for anaphylactic studies. They were anaesthetized with pentobarbitone sodium (30–45 mg/kg). Tracheal cannulae were inserted and also jugular venous catheters for the injection of drugs.

The following were measured in various combinations: femoral arterial and right atrial blood pressures (C.E.C. strain gauge, or Southern Instruments capacitance manometer); transpulmonary pressure from a polyethylene catheter in the lower right intrapleural space (differential capacitance manometer, Southern Instruments or I.R.D. Development Co.); tracheal air flow and tidal volume (Godart pneumotachograph and integrator); end-tidal carbon dioxide percentage (Beckman-Spinco LB1); systemic arterial $Po_2$ and $Pco_2$ (Radiometer); action potentials from single vagal fibres (Tektronix 122 preamplifier, platinum electrodes). Records were displayed on an oscilloscope (Tektronix 551) and photographed on 7-cm paper, or recorded on a UV oscillograph (Honeywell). Total lung resistance and dynamic compliance were computed by the subtractor method of Mead and Whittenberger (1953), both during the experiment and subsequently from a tape record (Thermionix T1000).

The following procedures were carried out in various experiments: paralysis by gallamine triethiodide (10 mg) followed by artificial ventilation; previous sensitization to bovine serum albumen (three intraperitoneal injections at 2-day intervals of 0·1 ml of a 20 per cent solution), with a challenging dose of 40 mg after a 3–6-week interval; pneumothorax by injecting air through the catheter in the right intrapleural space; and pulmonary congestion by inflating, with 0·5–2·0 ml of saline, a balloon tied into the left atrium.

## RESULTS

Fibres from lung irritant receptors were identified by the following criteria, which would eliminate slowly adapting pulmonary stretch receptors and "specific deflation receptors": (a) a rapidly adapting irregular discharge to maintained large inflations and/or deflations; (b) a myelinated fibre of small diameter (Group A) on the evidence of conduction velocity (mean: 13 m/sec) or size of action current; and (c) lack of stimulation by an intraluminal catheter inserted into the trachea and extrapulmonary bronchi

TABLE I

RESPONSES OF LUNG IRRITANT RECEPTORS TO VARIOUS STIMULI

| | Number of | | Receptor response (impulses/s) | |
|---|---|---|---|---|
| Stimulus | Fibres | Tests | Control | Change |
| Inflation | 8 | 8 | 8·5±2·84 | +46·0± 8·03* |
| Deflation | 8 | 8 | 8·5±2·84 | +42·5±11·10* |
| Pneumothorax | 11 | 11 | 4·2±1·24 | +9·6± 2·17* |
| Hyperpnoea | 10 | 15 | 6·7±0·94 | +9·3± 3·20* |
| Ammonia | 13 | 13 | 4·7±3·00 | +22·3±10·20* |
| Smoke | 10 | 12 | 11·6±1·42 | +7·6± 3·21† |
| Pulmonary congestion | 9 | 29 | 4·4±0·62 | +3·4± 0·62* |
| Microembolism | 5 | 7 | 8·7±3·88 | +9·4± 2·77† |
| Histamine | 6 | 13 | 3·8±1·21 | +40·0±11·82* |
| Histamine after isoprenaline | 6 | 13 | 6·1±2·65 | +8·5± 2·00* |
| Isoprenaline | 7 | 14 | 4·3±1·82 | +9·6± 1·76* |
| Adrenaline | 10 | 10 | 4·1±1·96 | +6·1± 2·73† |
| Phenyl diguanide | 11 | 13 | 3·9±1·71 | +7·4± 3·03† |
| Anaphylaxis | 9 | 9 | 4·9±7·88 | +8·2± 2·78† |

Values are means ± standard errors.     * $P < 0.01$     † $P < 0.05$.
Discharge frequencies are average rates over at least 3 s.

(which would stimulate extrapulmonary cough receptors). The identification was reinforced if the receptor was stimulated by the inhalation of ammonia, by an intraluminal catheter inserted deep into the right lung and by intravenous injections of histamine acid phosphate.

Nearly 100 receptors have now been studied. Table I summarizes some of the results, for which quantitative analysis was done. Several of the

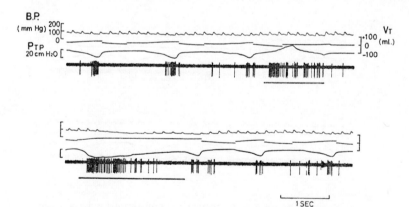

FIG. 1. Responses of a pulmonary irritant receptor to deflation (upper record) and inflation (lower record) of the lungs. From above down: systemic arterial blood pressure (B.P.), tidal volume changes (VT, trace zeroing at points of zero air flow; inflation upwards), transpulmonary pressure (PTP) and action potentials in a single vagal fibre. Deflation and inflation were during the horizontal signal bars. Note the rapidly adapting irregular discharges (Mills, Sellick and Widdicombe, 1969; reproduced by permission of J. Physiol., Lond.).

tests were performed on many or all of the receptors, but the responses were
only reported as a qualitative change in discharge pattern.

### Responses to lung volume changes

Large lung inflations and deflations stimulated the receptors, giving
rapidly adapting and characteristically irregular discharges (Table I; Fig. 1).
It was therefore not surprising that many of the receptors showed a spontaneous discharge with respiratory (usually inspiratory) rhythm, and that

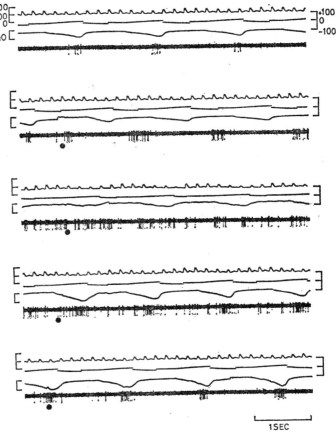

FIG. 2. Discharge of a single irritant receptor during induction and
removal of pneumothorax. Traces as in Fig. 1. Records from above
down: control; injection of 10 ml of air into the right intrapleural
space; increase of pneumothorax from 40–50 ml; decrease of pneumothorax from 40–30 ml; decrease of pneumothorax from 10–0 ml. The
records are examples of progressive induction and removal of pneumothorax in steps of 10 ml. The black dots indicate times of volume changes
in the pneumothorax (Sellick and Widdicombe, 1969; reproduced by
permission of *J. Physiol., Lond.*).

this was increased by left vagotomy (the right vagus being already cut) since this made the rabbits breathe more deeply. When ventilation was increased by rebreathing through an added dead space, impulse frequency also increased (Table I). This was due to mechanical rather than chemical changes in the lungs; when the rabbits were paralysed and artificially ventilated, and the pump was connected to a hypercapnic and hypoxic mixture (5–7 per cent carbon dioxide and 8–10 per cent oxygen in nitrogen), there was no increase in discharge for eight receptors.

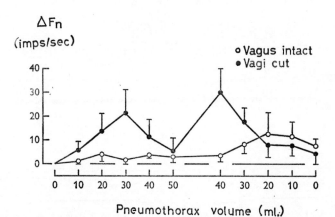

FIG. 3. Sequential plot of mean changes in lung irritant receptor discharge during induction and removal of pneumothorax. —— o ——: means of five experiments on rabbits with left vagus nerve intact. —— ● ——: means of six experiments on rabbits with both vagi cut. Vertical lines give standard errors of the means. Values are expressed as changes from pre-pneumothorax controls. Abscissa: volume of pneumothorax. Ordinate: mean change in impulse frequency ($F_n$) in single vagal nerve fibres from lung irritant receptors (Sellick and Widdicombe, 1969; reproduced by permission of *J. Physiol., Lond.*).

Pneumothorax stimulated the receptors (Table I; Fig. 2), both during the induction of the pneumothorax and during its removal (Fig. 3). The response was present both in rabbits with the left vagus intact, and therefore having vagal reflex changes in breathing, and in rabbits with both vagi cut. During pneumothorax the phase of discharge of the receptor in relation to the respiratory cycle frequently varied (Fig. 2).

Since the frequency and sometimes the pattern of the receptor discharge depended on the pattern of breathing or ventilation, in all the other tests described below it was essential to establish that any change in discharge was not secondary to these mechanical effects. For this reason studies were done with paralysed, artificially ventilated animals, or in rabbits with both vagi cut to eliminate reflex changes in breathing and bronchomotor tone. Tidal volume and frequency and lung mechanics were always recorded to ensure that changes in them could not account for any of the responses of the receptors.

### Responses to epithelial irritants

Inhalation of ammonia vapour or of cigarette smoke (Fig. 4) stimulated the receptors (Table I), as did the inhalation of ethyl ether vapour. The

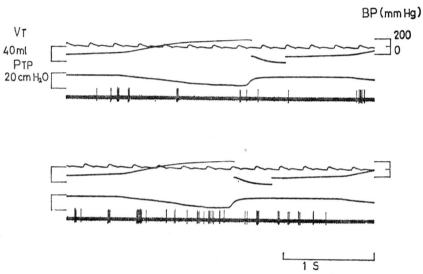

FIG. 4. Response of a lung irritant receptor to inhalation of cigarette smoke in a vagotomized rabbit. Traces as in Fig. 1. The upper record is a control before inhalation of the smoke; the lower record shows the response during inhalation of the smoke.

concentrations of these irritants were adequate to cause moderate respiratory changes in rabbits with intact vagi. Halothane 2·5–4·0 per cent had no significant action on five receptors.

Passage of a polyethylene catheter (0·5–1·0 mm diameter) into the right bronchial tree stimulated seven of the receptors at depths shown by measurements at post mortem to be within the right lung. This procedure eliminated tracheal cough receptors. The receptors that were not stimulated were thought to lie in airways not reached by the catheter.

### Responses to pulmonary vascular changes

In paralysed, open-chest rabbits distension, with 0·5 to 2 ml of saline, of a balloon in the left atrium, stimulated the receptors (Table I; Fig. 5).

The congestion was mild, as judged by changes in femoral arterial blood pressure ($-13 \pm 2 \cdot 1$ mmHg) and in right atrial pressure ($+0 \cdot 8 \pm 0 \cdot 27$ cm-$H_2O$). There was little evidence of pulmonary oedema, since dynamic lung compliance decreased by only $-13 \cdot 7 \pm 2 \cdot 67$ per cent and total lung resistance increased by $+15 \cdot 4 \pm 2 \cdot 81$ per cent. The changes in vascular

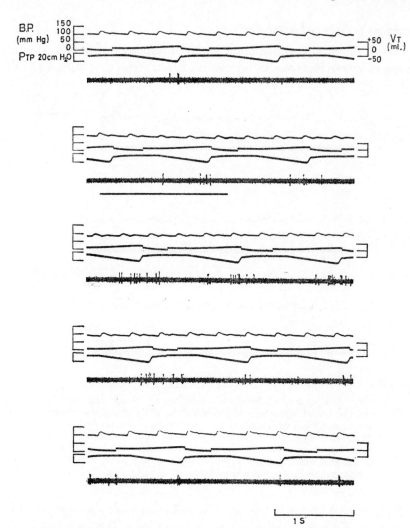

FIG. 5. Response of a lung irritant receptor to inflation of a balloon in the left atrium. Traces as in Fig. 1. Records, from above down: control; inflation of the balloon with 1 ml at signal; continuation of previous record; 20 s later; emptying of balloon. The rabbit was vagotomized, paralysed and artificially ventilated (Sellick and Widdicombe, 1969; reproduced by permission of *J. Physiol., Lond.*).

pressures, lung mechanics and firing frequency were rapidly reversible on removing the left atrial obstruction.

Injection of barium sulphate or starch emboli into the right atrium stimulated the receptors (Table I). The stimulation occurred before there were measurable changes in lung compliance or pattern of breathing.

*Responses to drugs and anaphylaxis*

One of the most consistent and vigorous responses of the lung irritant receptors was to intravenous injections of histamine (50–100 μg/kg of the

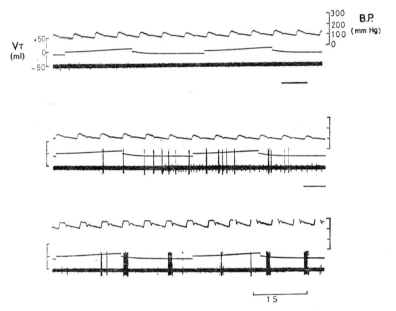

Fig. 6. Response of a pulmonary irritant receptor to injection into the right atrium of histamine acid phosphate 100 μg/kg (at signal in upper-most record) in a vagotomized, paralysed, artificially ventilated rabbit. Traces as in Fig. 1: 5·5 s between upper two traces, 20·5 s between lower two. Histamine caused an increase in blood pressure and a receptor discharge not clearly related to the respiratory phase (Mills, Sellick and Widdicombe, 1969; reproduced by permission of *J. Physiol., Lond.*).

acid phosphate) (Table I; Fig. 6). The receptors were also stimulated by inhalation of aerosols of solutions of histamine. The increases in the discharge were not correlated clearly in time or size with the increases in total lung resistance. However, they were prevented or greatly reduced by previous intravenous injection of isoprenaline sulphate 25–100 μg (Table I; Fig. 7), which also greatly reduced the increases in lung resistance due to histamine; this result suggested that histamine might be acting by contraction of the smooth muscle of the airways rather than by direct chemical action on the receptors. For the experiments summarized in Table I, it was found that histamine caused an increase of $+83 \pm 13 \cdot 7$ per cent (mean and standard error) in total lung resistance, and a decrease in compliance of $-15 \pm 3 \cdot 2$ per cent. After isoprenaline, histamine increased lung

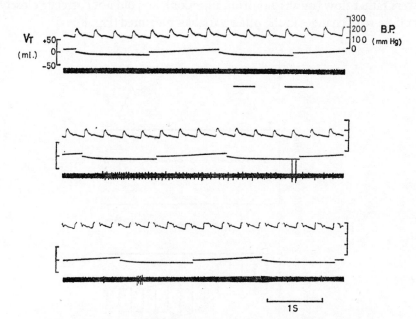

FIG. 7. Response of a single pulmonary irritant receptor to injection into the right atrium of histamine acid phosphate 100 μg/kg (at double signal in uppermost record), about 30 s after intravenous injection of isoprenaline sulphate 50 μg. The rabbit and receptor were the same as those shown in Fig. 6, but in this instance the isoprenaline limited the receptor response to a few impulses in the middle record: 4 s between upper two records, 20 s between lower two (Mills, Sellick and Widdicombe, 1969; reproduced by permission of *J. Physiol., Lond.*).

resistance by $+16 \pm 7 \cdot 1$ per cent and decreased compliance by $-1 \pm 0 \cdot 7$ per cent.

Isoprenaline itself also stimulated the receptors (Table I), and caused a small increase in total lung resistance, but both these effects had practically worn off by the time the second dose of histamine was given. The action of adrenaline, 10–50 μg, on the receptors was similar to that of isoprenaline (Table I).

Phenyl diguanide was tested because it has frequently been used to stimulate specific deflation receptors (Paintal, 1963). It stimulated the irritant receptors in ten out of thirteen tests, the mean response being statistically significant (Table I). This drug also increased total lung resistance (+ 10·9 per cent) and reduced lung compliance (− 5·3 per cent), whether or not the left vagus nerve was intact.

The anaphylactic reaction to albumen in sensitized rabbits stimulated lung irritant receptors (Table I; Fig. 8). The latencies of receptor responses were rather slow (mean: 14 s from injection), and did not correlate closely in time with changes in the other variables measured (Fig. 8).

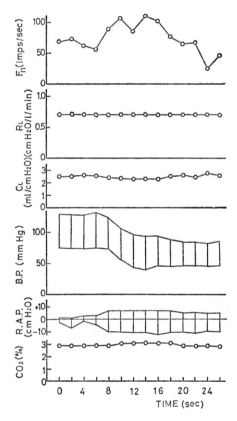

FIG. 8. Time course of changes after the injection of bovine serum albumen, 0·2 ml of a 20 per cent (v/v) solution, into a previously sensitized rabbit, vagotomized, paralysed and artificially ventilated. From above down: impulse frequency ($F_n$) in a single vagal fibre from a pulmonary irritant receptor; total lung resistance ($R_L$), lung compliance ($C_L$), systemic arterial blood pressure (B.P., systolic and diastolic), right atrial pressure (R.A.P., maximum and minimum respiratory variations) and end-tidal carbon dioxide per cent. The injection of albumen was at zero time (Mills, Sellick and Widdicombe, 1969; reproduced by permission of J. Physiol., Lond.).

## DISCUSSION

We have concluded that the irritant receptors form a uniform group and are distinct from pulmonary stretch receptors and specific deflation receptors (Table II). This conclusion is based on the following properties of irritant receptors: (a) action currents and conduction velocities are typical of small myelinated fibres; (b) these receptors have an irregular discharge pattern, sometimes unrelated to respiratory phase; (c) they are stimulated by maintained strong inflations and deflations, with rapidly adapting responses; (d) they are stimulated during pneumothorax (cf. Homberger, 1968) and by asphyxial hyperpnoea; and (e) they are consistently stimulated by inhaled irritant gases, microembolism, anaphylaxis and the injection of such drugs as histamine and phenyl diguanide.

### Histological identity of the receptors

The evidence that the fibres come from receptors shown by histological studies (for example, Larsell, 1921; Elftman, 1943) to lie between the cells of the bronchial and bronchiolar epithelium is as follows. (1) Their physiological properties are qualitatively identical to those of irritant (cough) receptors which have been unequivocally localized in the epithelium of the trachea and *extrapulmonary* bronchi of the cat (Widdicombe, 1954b). Thus receptors of both groups are characterized by rapid adaptation to inflation and/or deflation, connexion to myelinated afferent vagal fibres, irregular discharge of action potentials at high frequency, mechanical stimulation by epithelial contact with a catheter, stimulation by the inhalation of chemical irritants and particles, and by the intravenous injection of histamine (J. A. Nadel and J. G. Widdicombe, unpublished). (2) Histological evidence suggests that the only pulmonary receptors which have myelinated afferent fibres and are appropriately situated to respond to mechanical and chemical irritation are subepithelial or intra-epithelial endings (see, for example, Larsell, 1921; Elftman, 1943; Widdicombe, 1964). (3) The receptor responses collected in Table I can, in general, be explained on the basis of an airways epithelial site, but only with difficulty for other sites or other receptors identified histologically.

### Nature of the stimuli to lung irritant receptors

The endings are mechanoreceptors, as shown by their responses to inflation and deflation of the lungs, and to excitation by an intrabronchial catheter. The discharge of lung irritant receptors in eupnoeic rabbits with both vagus nerves intact would be small or absent. Since the receptors are rapidly adapting their discharge depends not only on the size but also on the rate of change of the mechanical stimulus. Their stimulation during asphyxial hyperpnoea is therefore not surprising. Their response during pneumothorax and its removal is more complicated (Homberger, 1968). Tidal volume decreased throughout most of the pneumothorax, but breathing frequency increased. In addition, the lungs were being ventilated in a more collapsed state, and the receptors may have been responding to this mechanical change; collapsed lung is known to exert a greater pull on the bronchi and bronchioles (Severinghaus and Stupfel, 1955; Caro, Butler and DuBois, 1960). Thus we postulate that the receptors are stimulated mechanically by changes which vigorously distend or collapse the bronchial and bronchiolar walls and thereby deform the epithelial layer of cells in which the receptors lie.

The stimulation of irritant receptors by pulmonary vascular congestion was not due to changes in the pattern of breathing, since the rabbits were paralysed; or to generalized changes in lung mechanics, since these could not be correlated with receptor discharge and were sometimes absent. One possibility is that back pressure along the bronchial vessels might cause vascular congestion in the environment of receptors in the bronchial epithelium. Whatever the mechanism, the results indicate that if pulmonary congestion is caused by, for example, vaso-active drugs this could cause mechanical rather than chemical stimulation of the endings. This may apply to the action of adrenaline, which causes a pulmonary venous constriction in rabbits (Daly and Hebb, 1967) that could lead to increased pulmonary capillary pressure.

With regard to the powerful receptor responses to histamine, these could seldom be correlated in time or size with changes in total lung resistance or compliance, and often occurred in their absence. The fact that the histamine-induced receptor discharge was prevented by isoprenaline is therefore unlikely to be due to the isoprenaline preventing general changes in lung mechanics which had previously stimulated the receptors. It is more probable that the isoprenaline prevented changes in contraction of smooth muscle local to the receptors, which contraction, of course, is one of the contributors to the total mechanical effects in the lung.

We cannot say whether embolism or anaphylaxis induced smooth muscle or mechanical changes near the receptors, and that this is what stimulated them, or whether they released chemicals which had a histamine-like effect, direct or indirect, on the receptors. Neither do we know whether phenyl diguanide acted directly or indirectly. Similarly, although the simplest hypothesis for inhaled irritant gases and smoke is that they have a direct chemical action on the receptor, we cannot rule out the occurrence of stimulation by local mechanical changes in the environment of the receptors due to the irritant chemicals.

The sensitivity of the receptors to several different types of mechanical changes in the lungs (possibly including intraluminal mucus) may explain the considerable variations in discharge of individual receptors during control conditions and during stimulation, variations which could not be correlated with ventilatory or lung mechanical measurements (for example, see Figs. 2, 3 and 6). It is probable, on the basis of histological evidence (Larsell, 1921; Elftman, 1943) that lung irritant receptors are found in the epithelium throughout the bronchi and bronchioles, and receptors in different sites may have different sensitivities to the various tests used.

### Reflex action of lung irritant receptors

The reflex responses in the conditions we have studied undoubtedly include the effects of changes in discharge of other receptors, in particular pulmonary stretch endings, deflation receptors, and cough receptors in the extrapulmonary airways. Activity of these different types of receptor would sometimes have a reinforcing and sometimes an opposing action on breathing and bronchomotor tone (Table II). However, the responses in the various conditions, complicated though they are, point to the probable reflex action of the lung irritant receptor.

It is unlikely that the main respiratory response of the receptors is coughing. This is not the chief change in breathing when mechanical or chemical

TABLE II

RESPONSES OF LUNG RECEPTORS, AND VAGAL REFLEXES INITIATED FROM THE LUNGS

| | Response of | | | Vagal reflex response of | |
|---|---|---|---|---|---|
| Stimulus | Pulmonary stretch receptors | "Specific deflation receptors" | "Lung irritant receptors" | Inspiratory efforts | Bronchial tone |
| Small inflation | ↑ | Nil | Nil | ↓ | ↓ |
| Large inflation | ↑ | Nil | ↑ | ↑ | ? |
| Deflation | ↓ | (↑) | ↑ | ↑ | ? |
| Pneumothorax | ↓ | Nil | ↑ | ↑ | ? |
| Hyperpnoea | ↑ | Nil | ↑ | ↑ | ? |
| Ammonia | (↑) | (↑) | ↑ | ↑ | ↑ |
| Smoke | ? | ? | ↑↑ | ↑ | ↑ |
| Lung congestion | (↑) | ↑ | ↑ | ↑ | ? |
| Microembolism | Nil | ↑ | ↑ | ↑ | ↑ |
| Histamine | ? | Nil | ↑ | ↑ | ↑ |
| Phenyl diguanide | Nil | ↑ | ↑ | ↓ or ↑ | ↑ |
| Anaphylaxis | ? | ? | ↑ | ↑ | ↑ |

"Inspiratory efforts" includes hyperpnoea, hyperventilation and gasping.

irritation of the airways is restricted to beyond the primary bronchi in experimental animals (Larsell and Burget, 1924; Widdicombe, 1954a) or probably in man (Jackson, 1922); and none of the other tests listed in Table II cause prominent (or any) coughing although irritant receptors are stimulated. Hyperpnoea and hyperventilation are the characteristic reflex changes in breathing that occur, in man and other animals, in response to most of the stimuli listed in Table II.

Deflation of the lungs or pneumothorax in experimental animals can cause hyperventilation which is prevented by vagotomy (Binet, Strumza and Leobardy, 1948; Simmons and Hemingway, 1957; Hemingway and Simmons, 1958; Sellick and Widdicombe, 1969), and the same mechanism might exist in man (Richards, Riley and Hiscock, 1932).

In rabbits, anaesthetized or unanaesthetized, bilateral vagotomy lessens the hyperpnoea due to moderate hypercapnia (Wiemer and Kiwull, 1965; Richardson and Widdicombe, 1969). In man, bilateral anaesthesia of the vagus and glossopharyngeal nerves approximately halves the ventilatory response to breathing a mixture of carbon dioxide in oxygen (Guz et al., 1966). Thus, in both species, there can be a vagal reflex drive which potentiates the hyperpnoeic response to hypercapnia. Stimulation of lung irritant receptors could be the mechanism potentiating the hyperpnoea of asphyxia and hypercapnia when the vagi are intact.

Table II indicates that those reflexes induced by mechanical changes in the lungs cannot easily be explained as due to the pulmonary stretch receptors or specific deflation receptors. It therefore seems probable that the lung irritant receptors cause the reflex stimulation of breathing. If so, they may mediate the respiration-excitatory deflation reflex of Hering and Breuer (Hering, 1868, Breuer, 1868).

The other stimuli—lung congestion, anaphylaxis, microembolism, inhalation of ammonia or smoke and injections of histamine and phenyl diguanide—have all been shown to cause vagal reflex hyperpnoea (see Whitteridge, 1950; Widdicombe, 1964; Paintal, 1963; Karczewski and Widdicombe, 1969a,b for references); they are unlikely to exert their vagal reflex actions via the pulmonary stretch receptors, but they all stimulate lung irritant receptors, and several excite the specific deflation receptors. More research is needed to partition the role of these last two afferent pathways in the reflex responses of the conditions studied.

Many of the lung conditions we have studied cause vagal reflex bronchoconstriction, as well as "direct" changes in bronchial calibre (see Whitteridge, 1950; Wyss, 1952; Widdicombe, 1963; Karczewski and Widdicombe, 1969a,b for references). Pulmonary stretch receptors, which cause reflex bronchodilatation, are unlikely to play a primary role in these responses. The reflex action of the specific deflation receptors on bronchial tone has not been established, but there is good evidence that irritant receptors cause a reflex bronchoconstriction (DeKock et al., 1966; Karczewski and Widdicombe, 1969a,b) and they therefore probably play a role in the bronchial responses of the conditions studied.

The correlation between the stimulation of lung epithelial irritant receptors by all these experimental procedures and by vagally-mediated hyperpnoea and bronchoconstriction is strong enough to point to a causal link. If this mechanism exists, the fact that both increased tidal volume and drug-induced bronchoconstriction stimulate the receptors suggests that there could be a positive feedback tending progressively to increase ventilation and bronchomuscular tone.

Finally, it should be pointed out that most of the conditions that are listed in Table II as stimulating lung irritant receptors are also associated with unpleasant respiratory sensation or dyspnoea in human subjects and patients. The correlation is less close for deflation receptors and non-existent for pulmonary stretch receptors. It may be significant that Burger and Macklem (1968) have shown that reinflation of a collapsed lung in healthy subjects causes immediate pain, localized to the chest, and sometimes a cough. The properties of lung irritant receptors indicate that they are the only lung end-organs yet studied which are likely to mediate this unpleasant sensation.

## SUMMARY

"Lung irritant receptors" have been studied in rabbits by recording action potentials from single vagal fibres from the receptors. Their rapidly adapting response to inflations and deflations of the lungs, their irregular pattern of discharge, and their small myelinated fibres distinguish them from the slowly adapting pulmonary stretch receptors and the "specific deflation receptors" of Paintal (1955, 1957).

The receptors are stimulated by strong inflations and deflations of the lungs, pneumothorax, asphyxial hyperpnoea, pulmonary congestion, the inhalation of ammonia vapour or cigarette smoke, pulmonary microembolism, anaphylactic reactions and bronchoconstriction induced by injections of histamine and phenyl diguanide.

It is concluded that the reflex action of the receptors is to cause hyperpnoea and probably bronchoconstriction, and that these receptors may contribute to unpleasant respiratory sensation in human subjects and patients.

4*

REFERENCES

ADRIAN, E. D. (1933). *J. Physiol., Lond.*, **79**, 332–358.
BINET, L., STRUMZA, M. V., and LEOBARDY, H. J. DE (1948). *C. r. Séanc. Soc. Biol.*, **142**, 876–877.
BREUER, J. (1868). *Sber. Akad. Wiss. Wien*, **58**, part 2, 909–937.
BURGER, E. J., and MACKLEM, P. (1968). *J. appl. Physiol.*, **25**, 139–148.
CARO, C. G., BUTLER, J., and DuBOIS, A. B. (1960). *J. clin. Invest.* **39**, 573–583.
DALY, I. DE B., and HEBB, C. O. (1967). *Pulmonary and Bronchial Vascular Systems*. London: Arnold.
DEKOCK, M. A., NADEL, J. A., ZWI, S., COLEBATCH, H. J. H., and OLSEN, C. R. (1966). *J. appl. Physiol.*, **21**, 185–194.
ELFTMAN, A. G. (1943). *Am. J. Anat.*, **72**, 1–28.
GUZ, A., NOBLE, M. I. M., WIDDICOMBE, J. G., TRENCHARD, D., and MUSHIN, W. W. (1966). *Resp. Physiol.*, **1**, 206–210.
HEMINGWAY, A., and SIMMONS, D. H. (1958). *J. appl. Physiol.*, **13**, 165–170.
HERING, E. (1868). *Sber. Akad. Wiss. Wien*, **57**, part 1, 672–677.
HOMBERGER, A. C. (1968). *Helv. physiol. pharmac. Acta*, **26**, 97–118.
JACKSON, C. (1922). *J. Am. med. Ass.*, **79**, 1399–1403.
KARCZEWSKI, W., and WIDDICOMBE, J. G. (1969a). *J. Physiol., Lond.*, **201**, 271–291.
KARCZEWSKI, W., and WIDDICOMBE, J. G. (1969b). *J. Physiol., Lond.*, **201**, 293–304.
LARSELL, O. (1921). *J. comp. Neurol.*, **33**, 105–124.
LARSELL, O., and BURGET, G. E. (1924). *Am. J. Physiol.*, **70**, 311–321.
MEAD, J., and WHITTENBERGER, J. L. (1953). *J. appl. Physiol.*, **5**, 779–796.
MILLS, J., SELLICK, H., and WIDDICOMBE, J. G. (1969). *J. Physiol., Lond.*, **203**, 337–357.
PAINTAL, A. S. (1955). *Q. Jl exp. Physiol.*, **40**, 89–111.
PAINTAL, A. S. (1957). *Q. Jl exp. Physiol.*, **42**, 56–71.
PAINTAL, A. S. (1963). *Ergebn. Physiol.*, **52**, 74–156.
RICHARDS, D. W., RILEY, C. E., and HISCOCK, M. (1932). *Arch. intern. Med.*, **49**, 996–1006.
RICHARDSON, P. S., and WIDDICOMBE, J. G. (1969). *Resp. Physiol.*, **7**, 122–135.
SELLICK, H., and WIDDICOMBE, J. G. (1969). *J. Physiol., Lond.*, **203**, 359–381.
SEVERINGHAUS, J. W., and STUPFEL, M. (1955). *J. appl. Physiol.*, **8**, 81–87.
SIMMONS, D. H., and HEMINGWAY, A. (1957). *Am. Rev. Tuberc. pulm. Dis.*, **76**, 195–214.
WHITTERIDGE, D. (1950). *Physiol. Rev.*, **30**, 475–487.
WIDDICOMBE, J. G. (1954a). *J. Physiol., Lond.*, **123**, 55–70.
WIDDICOMBE, J. G. (1954b). *J. Physiol., Lond.*, **123**, 71–104.
WIDDICOMBE, J. G. (1963). *Physiol. Rev.*, **43**, 1–37.
WIDDICOMBE, J. G. (1964). In *Handbook of Physiology*, sect. III, vol 1, pp. 583–630, ed. Fenn, W. O., and Rahn, H. American Physiological Society. Baltimore: Williams and Wilkins.
WIEMER, W., and KIWULL, P. (1965). *Pflügers Arch. ges. Physiol.*, **283**, R 46.
WYSS, O. A. M. (1952). *Bronches*, **2**, 101–151.

# DISCUSSION

*Dornhorst:* Did you use isoprenaline as an aerosol or intravenously?

*Widdicombe:* Intravenously. We gave 25–100 µg over a period of a few seconds.

*Dornhorst:* What is the evidence that this caused venoconstriction?

*Widdicombe:* Daly and Hebb (1967) have presented pharmacological evidence that when adrenaline and noradrenaline are perfused through an isolated lung they cause pulmonary venoconstriction.

*Dornhorst:* I cannot accept that this applies also to isoprenaline and other members of the catecholamine group without further proof. All the catecholamines do not have the same pharmacological properties. This is important because I know of no evidence that isoprenaline has any venoconstrictive effects in reasonable pharmacological doses.

*Widdicombe:* I agree that isoprenaline, and adrenaline and noradrenaline, may have different actions.

*Fillenz:* By what mechanism does venoconstriction affect epithelial receptors?

*Widdicombe:* There are at least two possible mechanisms. First, pulmonary venoconstriction might decrease compliance of the lung thus producing greater mechanical pull on the airways; we measured lung compliance and, although this was sometimes decreased by the congestion, there was no clear correlation between compliance and impulse frequency. Second, venoconstriction could exert back pressure on the bronchial epithelium via the bronchial circulation.

*Fillenz:* Your comments imply that the irritant receptors have a rather high mechanical sensitivity. Are you postulating a single population of these receptors or might there be two different kinds, one mechanically and the other chemically sensitive?

*Widdicombe:* Most of the receptors respond to all the stimuli we have used.

*Dornhorst:* Does each individual receptor have a wide range of sensitivity to both mechanical and chemical stimuli?

*Widdicombe:* Yes.

*Cotes:* You have described various factors that stimulate your receptors. What inhibits them?

*Widdicombe:* The only inhibiting substance that we found was halothane and, although halothane 2·5-4 per cent inhibited the discharge of four out of five receptors, the mean change was not statistically significant.

*Cotes:* What about local anaesthetics?

*Widdicombe:* We are trying this at the moment*.

*Dornhorst:* Did you try the effect of the inhalation of any inert dusts on the irritant receptors? This would be an interesting experiment because such dusts could hardly stimulate any receptors other than the bronchial ones, which are known to cause reflex bronchoconstriction in man.

* Note added in proof: the receptors can be inhibited by lignocaine (aerosol) 4-20 per cent.

*Widdicombe:* We intend to do this next.★

*Paintal:* Did you find any intermediate endings similar to those you described in the cat (Widdicombe, 1954) in your rabbits, and, if so, do these correspond to the irritant receptors?

*Widdicombe:* We did find some receptors in the rabbit with properties intermediate between pulmonary stretch receptors and irritant receptors, but we cannot state their relationship to similar receptors in the cat because these last were studied only in the extrapulmonary bronchi and the trachea. Intermediate receptors in large and small air passages, and irritant receptors in the lungs, may all be part of one system that extends from the trachea into the lung, but there are some differences between the types of receptor. For example, none of the manoeuvres we used in the rabbit caused coughing, as occurs with stimulation of tracheal receptors; and different receptors may show different mechanical and chemical sensitivities.

*Dornhorst:* How do you decide where these receptors are located?

*Widdicombe:* We pass a bronchial catheter of about 0·5–1 mm external diameter. We use such small catheters so as to bypass cough receptors in the trachea and extrapulmonary bronchi.

*Fillenz:* Is it possible that these various receptors have the same response characteristics but differ from each other in position and in reflex connexions? These differences could account for the circumstances in which they are stimulated and the reflex responses they elicit.

*Widdicombe:* The properties of the receptors and their reflex actions differ according to their position in the respiratory tract.

*Dejours:* Is irritant the best name for these receptors? You have shown that they can be stimulated by physical factors as well as by chemical irritants. Would not a name such as epithelial receptors be more appropriate?

*Widdicombe:* We decided not to call them epithelial receptors because this builds a hypothesis into the name. It was difficult to think of a name that included all the different sorts of stimuli to which they respond, and we reasoned that their most physiological role is to respond to inhaled irritants. If anyone can suggest a better name I shall be delighted!

*Fillenz:* What about calling them mechanoreceptors?

*Dornhorst:* These receptors are inefficient as mechanoreceptors because they fire off so irregularly; aren't they just unspecialized, rather inefficient, general receptors?

---

★ Note added in proof: Dr H. Sellick and I (unpublished material) have tried the effect of "inert" carbon dust on eleven lung irritant receptors; ten were stimulated and the mean increase in discharge frequency was $5·54 \pm 2·54$ impulses/s ($P < 0·05$).

*Widdicombe:* They are unspecialized, general-purpose receptors, but to determine their efficiency one needs to assess their reflex activity.

*Sears:* The irritant receptors seem to adapt fairly rapidly to continuous stimulation but in other ways they differ from the rapidly adapting receptors. It is usual for a rapidly adapting receptor to show a dynamic response at the onset of lung inflation not only at the height of rapid inflation. And such receptors usually respond to the dynamic phase in a mechanical stimulus whereas the receptors you described responded only at the height of inflation. Was this a consistent finding?

*Widdicombe:* The irritant receptors discharged fastest as inflation reached its peak, and then firing tended to decrease although inflation was maintained. Threshold must also influence the pattern of the response. Inflation volume and pressure must reach a given level before these receptors can fire off at all, and this may make the dynamic phase of the response less conspicuous.

*Dornhorst:* It is dangerous to draw conclusions from time sequences like these; we cannot assume that mechanical strain in the bronchi is proportional to the volume of gas inspired.

*Merrill:* Dr Widdicombe, can you comment on the different thresholds that distinguish different sorts of lung receptor? For example, what levels of inflation are needed to stimulate irritant and rapidly adapting receptors respectively?

*Widdicombe:* In the quietly breathing, anaesthetized rabbit most of the lung irritant receptors do not discharge spontaneously; but in conditions in which tidal volume is increased, for example after vagotomy or during asphyxia or hypercapnia, irritant receptors give bursts of impulses. Thus, from the point of view of volume and pressure, the thresholds are below the animal's vital capacity but not usually below the eupnoeic tidal volume. However, the rapidly adapting receptors described by Knowlton and Larrabee (1946) certainly did adapt more rapidly than our irritant receptors.

*Newsom Davis:* For how long is the increased discharge from irritant receptors maintained following pneumothorax?

*Widdicombe:* We have not maintained the pneumothoraces in our rabbits for more than about three minutes so I have no information about what happens after this period of time. But the response starts immediately air is injected and is maintained during the period of pneumothorax.

*Newsom Davis:* Did immobility of the lung increase the response?

*Widdicombe:* We have not seen this in our particular experimental conditions but this needs further study.

*Howell:* You have said that the induction of a pneumothorax stimulates the irritant receptors. If one breathes out voluntarily one may induce similar changes in lung volume. Is it therefore fair to deduce that voluntary deflation of the lung will also stimulate these receptors?

*Widdicombe:* Yes, but the response will depend on the deflation volume threshold.

*Howell:* You have also suggested that these receptors have a sensory component. Burger and Macklem (1968) produced absorption atelectasis in man, and you (this volume, p. 91) have suggested that the accompanying sensation arose from lung irritant receptors. But when I breathe out maximally I do not feel anything. Can you explain this contradiction?

*Widdicombe:* The reason must be that the appreciation of sensation depends on the number of receptors stimulated and their rate of firing during voluntary deflation and reinflation of the collapsed lung. The thresholds and receptor responses may be different in different individuals, and in the rabbit compared with man. This does not surprise me.

*Godfrey:* When my own lungs were shrunk below residual volume I experienced no painful sensation. There was some intensification of the normal breath-holding, crushing sensation but no qualitative differences.

*Widdicombe:* Was the intensification of sensation during shrinking or during reinflation of the collapsed lung? The strongest stimulation of irritant receptors in the rabbit is always seen on reinflation.

*Godfrey:* The crushing sensation occurred during shrinking. There was no abnormal sensation during the first breath after maximal shrinking.

*Dornhorst:* We must be careful about equating changes in overall lung volume with the localized changes in strain that occur, say, during the reinflation of partially atelectatic lung. In these circumstances, intense fine strains may occur locally.

*Cross:* Ernsting (1960) and Green and Burgess (1962) described pilots who centrifuged themselves while breathing oxygen and experienced similar sensations to those described by Burger and Macklem (1968).

*Dornhorst:* This is a rather different situation because these men had radiological abnormalities during these procedures.

*Prys-Roberts:* In a series in which four supine subjects (Prys-Roberts *et al.*, 1967) breathed down to residual volume, thus producing diffuse atelectasis but without X-ray changes, all the subjects, on reinflation, felt a "tearing" sensation, but only one described this as painful. It would be interesting to repeat this and see if the tearing sensation is abolished by vagal block.

*Dornhorst:* Widespread differences between individuals concerning the point at which they experience abnormal sensations as painful are to be expected.

*Cotes:* All the stimuli for J receptors also stimulate the irritant receptors, with the single exception of halothane which stimulates the J receptors only. Does halothane induce reflex tachypnoea or bradycardia through the J receptors?

*Paintal:* A single insufflation of a small volume of halothane (to avoid its causing central effects) induces apnoea and bradycardia through these receptors.

*Cotes:* Do you mean apnoea or tachypnoea?

*Paintal:* I mean apnoea; tachypnoea could not be observed because the lungs were inflated.

*Cotes:* What direct evidence is there that the J reflex affects breathing by any pathways other than the ones through which the irritant receptors act?

*Paintal:* The reflex pathways are quite different. The latent period for stimulation of the respiratory reflex responses to the injection of phenyl diguanide into the right atrium is less than two seconds; excitation of the irritant receptors in response to phenyl diguanide does not occur until some seconds later. Excitation of irritant receptors, therefore, must have a superadded influence on the initial excitation of the J receptors. This might explain the modification of shallow breathing that occurs after intravenous phenyl diguanide. How long after the injection of phenyl diguanide do the irritant receptors start to respond, Dr Widdicombe?

*Widdicombe:* The excitation starts at a mean of 7·1 seconds after the injection; but this was intravenous. I agree that the total of reflex responses to phenyl diguanide must be due to the additive effects caused by stimulation of both sorts of receptor.

*Paintal:* Reflex bradycardia, hypotension and apnoea all start from the J receptors; by the time these responses are well set phenyl diguanide has reached the bronchial circulation, excitation of the irritant receptors starts and the existing response is modified. Is that right, Dr Widdicombe?

*Widdicombe:* I agree in general although it is difficult to be precise when we are dealing with time intervals of a few seconds and overlapping receptor responses. All the methods we have used to stimulate lung irritant receptors probably affect more than one type of nerve ending, and I am not suggesting that the irritant receptors are responsible for the entire reflex response to these interventions, which are "dirty" in the sense that the stimulus is not restricted to a single afferent pathway. Nevertheless, the pathway from lung irritant receptors may be the primary mechanism by which the responses are mediated.

*Guz:* Further direct evidence that the J receptors initiate these respiratory reflexes comes from experiments in which the cervical vagus is differentially blocked with direct current so that only C (that is, non-myelinated) fibres remain active (Guz and Trenchard, 1969). This procedure results in the abolition of the respiratory response to inflation and deflation of the lungs. If phenyl diguanide, a known stimulant of the J receptors, is now injected intravenously, reflex tachypnoea results. This tachypnoea must, therefore, have been mediated through the J receptors and the C fibres in the vagus. Direct evidence that irritant receptors cause tachypnoea is less convincing. How can one separate the effects of these two sorts of receptor?

*Widdicombe:* Two groups of experiments give direct evidence about this problem. We know that neither pneumothorax nor the injection of histamine stimulates J receptors, although both stimulate irritant receptors. Therefore any reflex vagal effects that occur in these two situations cannot be mediated by J receptors but must be due to irritant receptors, possibly with modulation of the response by pulmonary stretch receptors.

*Guz:* When a pneumothorax is present there will be a reduction in pulmonary stretch receptor discharge because the volume of one lung is reduced; this may be excitatory to breathing.

*Widdicombe:* During reinflation after pneumothorax in the rabbit, the irritant receptors fire off more vigorously (and reflex hyperpnoea is consequently greater) than before the pneumothorax or when it is being induced (Sellick and Widdicombe, 1969).

*Guz:* Tachypnoea is greatest in man when the pneumothorax is actually occurring.

*Paintal:* There may be species differences in these reflexes. Dawes, Mott and Widdicombe (1951) showed that when phenyl diguanide was injected intravenously in the rabbit apnoea occurred in the inspiratory position. But in the cat apnoea occurred in the expiratory position. Moreover, apnoea (and tachypnoea) only occurred when the drug was injected intravenously, not when it was injected into the left atrium. These findings suggest that the predominant effect of phenyl diguanide is on the J receptors, but that in the rabbit the irritant receptors may also be involved.

## REFERENCES

BURGER, E. J., and MACKLEM, P. (1968). *J. appl. Physiol.*, **25**, 139–148.

DALY, I. DE B., and HEBB, C. (1967). *Pulmonary and Bronchial Vascular Systems.* London: Arnold.

DAWES, G. S., MOTT, J. C., and WIDDICOMBE, J. G. (1951). *J. Physiol., Lond.*, **115**, 258–291.

ERNSTING, J. (1960). *Proc. R. Soc. Med.*, **53**, 96.

GREEN, I. D., and BURGESS, B. F. (1962). Flight Personnel Research Committee Report No. 1182, January 1962. Internal publication.

GUZ, A., and TRENCHARD, D. (1969). *J. Physiol. Lond.*, **202**, 31–32P.

KNOWLTON, G. C., and LARRABEE, M. G. (1946). *Am. J. Physiol.*, **147**, 100–114.

PRYS-ROBERTS, C., NUNN, J. F., DOBSON, H. R., ROBINSON, R. H., GREENBAUM, R., and HARRIS, R. S. (1967). *Lancet*, **2**, 399–401.

SELLICK, H., and WIDDICOMBE, J. G. (1969). *J. Physiol., Lond.*, **203**, 359–381.

WIDDICOMBE, J. G. (1954). *J. Physiol., Lond.*, **123**, 71–104.

# SENSORY INNERVATION OF THE AIRWAYS

MARIANNE FILLENZ AND R. I. WOODS

*University Laboratory of Physiology, Oxford*

REISSEISEN (1822), in his treatise on the lung, described nerve fibes accompanying the airways as far down as he could follow them by dissection. He suggested that these nerve fibres were a sensory innervation to the respiratory mucosa. Krause (1876) distinguished two kinds of nerve fibres, "pale nucleated" and "double-contoured", distributed respectively to smooth muscle cells and bronchial mucous membrane. He may well have been describing non-myelinated fibres accompanied by Schwann cell nuclei, and myelinated fibres. Berkley (1893), who used the Golgi silver staining method, described nerve endings in the epithelium of the airways and nerve fibre ramifications among the smooth muscle cells and around blood vessels. Larsell (1921, 1922) found nerve fibres throughout the lungs after methylene blue staining. He called the complex terminal arborizations in the epithelium and among smooth muscle cells sensory endings on the basis of their appearance. Similar sensory endings in epithelium and smooth muscle were described by Hayashi (1937) using a modified silver staining method. He comments on the similarity of the sensory endings among the smooth muscle cells and the endings described by Sunder-Plassmann (1933) in the carotid sinus, aortic arch and chambers of the heart. Hayashi's account of the motor innervation of the airways, however, is marred by his description of it in terms of the nerve net theory and the terminal reticulum. The proponents of this concept (Stöhr, Boeke) were still rejecting Cajal's neurone theory as late as 1957 (Stöhr, 1957). A continual source of confusion in this field has been the staining of elastin and reticulin fibres by silver methods and methylene blue. This lack of specificity can lead to doubt about the interpretations made in some papers (Elftman, 1943; Honjin, 1956). In fact, in some recent papers (Hirsch et al., 1968a,b), an extensive afferent innervation of the alveoli has been described on the basis of results obtained with a silver staining method specific for reticulin.

All results that have been obtained with non-specific, nerve fibre stains must be examined with care; only structures made visible by a variety of methods in preparations that are otherwise entirely free of artefacts can be accepted as possible nerve endings. It is remarkable how similar many of the earliest descriptions are to current views, whilst the intervening period has been filled with work that is more imaginative than exact.

Recently Feyrter (1938) has described a system of "pale cells" in various epithelia which he has compared to the argentaffin cells in the gut. However, Fröhlich (1949) has put forward the alternative theory that the pale cells in the bronchial epithelium represent chemoreceptor cells on the grounds that they look like the α cells of the taste buds in the tongue and seem to be associated with nerve terminals.

There have been very few electron microscope studies of airways innervation. Bensch, Gordon and Miller (1965) have described cells containing dense-cored vesicles in the bronchial epithelium of man. They regard these as the counterpart of the argentaffin cells in the gut. They also described nerve endings both between the epithelial cells of the bronchi and in juxtaposition to myoepithelial cells; they conclude that these are cholinergic motor fibres.

In an electron microscope examination of the tracheal epithelium of the rat, Luciano, Reale and Ruska (1968) feel that they are able to distinguish two kinds of nerve process; first, cholinergic motor fibres to ciliated and goblet cells and, second, sensory processes enclosing brush border cells. The status of the various cell types in the respiratory epithelium as sensory receptor cells remains equivocal.

In contrast to the empiric classical staining methods, histochemical methods demonstrate specific enzymes or compounds. This means that with histochemical methods it is possible to identify some cell types with certainty. The methods by which the cholinesterases and catecholamines are localized have produced a much greater understanding of the autonomic nervous system. The presence of catecholamines in peripheral neurones has been correlated with their release as transmitters; thus fluorescent nerve fibres are monoaminergic, that is, sympathetic postganglionic. There is as yet no histochemical method that demonstrates acetylcholine but an indication of the cholinergic nature of nerve fibres can be obtained from the presence of acetylcholinesterase within them. However, this is only an indication, because in other structures the presence of this enzyme clearly does not imply the release of acetylcholine.

Thus sympathetic and parasympathetic postganglionic fibres can be identified by virtue of the chemical compounds within them.

In the autonomic postganglionic neurones the length of axon which is thought to release transmitter is called the terminal fibre. This can be distinguished on morphological grounds from parts that are thought not to release transmitter and are called non-terminal fibres. The distribution of acetylcholinesterase and catecholamines within the nerve fibres, demonstrated histochemically, distinguishes terminal from non-terminal fibres; this is confirmed by electron microscopy. Methylene blue and silver or gold staining methods give rise to appearances which have often been used to identify terminal fibres (beaded appearance with methylene blue; rings, boutons and fibre thickenings or expansions with silver and gold methods). Because exact counterparts to these structures have not been found with the electron microscope they must be at least partly artefacts produced by the staining methods. Hence some of the descriptions of the distribution of terminal fibres obtained with non-histochemical methods are not reliable.

The presence of terminal fibres in a tissue indicates that the tissue is actually innervated by these nerve fibres, whereas the presence of bundles of non-terminal axons has no functional significance.

There is as yet no histochemical method for identifying sensory neurones; their presence can be inferred by subtracting the autonomic fibres from the total number of nerve fibres. Further, there are no well-established criteria for defining sensory nerve terminals and their very existence is questioned by some workers.

PRESENT STUDY

In the present study we have tried to arrive at a picture of the sensory innervation of the airways by a combination of various histological and histochemical methods and electron microscopy. The animals used were guinea-pigs, rabbits and dogs. Some results are included that were obtained on rats and guinea-pigs by A. M. S. White whilst working on a thesis on the innervation of the trachea and lung (1968).

*Results*

The fluorescence method of Hillarp and Falck (see Falck and Owman, 1965) demonstrates the presence of catecholamines and is used to identify sympathetic noradrenergic fibres. In all the species examined fluorescent fibres were seen innervating the bronchial blood vessels. The dog and guinea-pig have a few fluorescent terminal fibres in the smooth muscle layer of the airways also, but the rat does not. The airways epithelium does not fluoresce and there are no fluorescent nerve fibres entering it.

Acetylcholinesterase was located by Karnovsky's method with suitable controls (Woods, 1968). Fibres containing acetylcholinesterase occur in large bundles alongside the largest airways and in smaller bundles around and amongst the smooth muscle of the whole bronchial tree. Apparently terminal fibres are numerous between the smooth muscle cells of airways, and are certainly present, though in smaller numbers, in the adventitia of the blood vessels. Acinar glands, wherever they occur, are heavily innervated. In the rabbit we have carefully examined the respiratory epithelium for a cholinergic innervation. Though there are some acetylcholinesterase-containing fibres in the subepithelial connective tissue none entered the epithelium.

Non-specific cholinesterase demonstrated with butyrylthiocholine substrate occurs in many structures. In the rabbit it is present in the Schwann cells of the postganglionic autonomic fibres throughout the body (Woods, unpublished). In sections of rabbit trachea and lung, all the bundles of postganglionic autonomic fibres shown by the previous two methods were stained (Fig. 1a). However, there were more structures stained than could be explained on this basis. The staining was in fine processes containing nuclei and located at the base of the epithelium and in the subepithelial connective tissue (Fig. 1a,b). These processes were continuous with nerve bundles and penetrated between the epithelial cells. We believe that these are the Schwann cells of sensory fibres, but there may also have been some staining of nerve fibres.

Many of the afferent fibres are identified as myelinated A fibres on the basis of measurements of conduction velocity. We have therefore stained myelin in sections of lung and trachea, some of which had been incubated to show cholinesterase. Large numbers of myelinated fibres run in the bundles alongside the airways. Small bundles and single fibres occur in the walls of the airways down to the respiratory bronchioles in the connective tissue. The myelin ends outside the smooth muscle layer or below the epithelium in connective tissue. The axons of these myelinated fibres did not contain cholinesterase.

We have also examined the lungs from two rabbits killed twelve months after supranodose section of the vagus. Although the number of myelinated fibres in the large bundles was reduced, their distribution in the bronchial walls was apparently normal.

We perfused a rabbit with methylene blue and examined sections of trachea and lung. We confirmed the presence of nerve endings in the epithelium (Fig. 2) similar to those seen by Larsell (1921), but only as far as the resporatory bronchioles. We traced these endings to myelinated fibres in the subepithelial connective tissue. The myelinated fibres

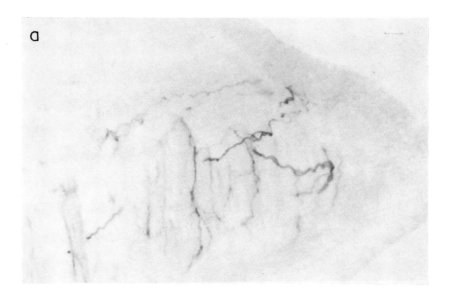

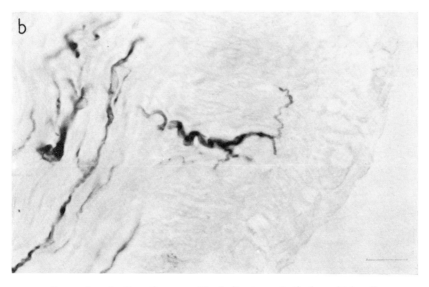

FIG. 1. Localization of non-specific cholinesterase in the bronchial wall of the rabbit. The nerve bundles in smooth muscle, subepithelial connective tissue and processes approaching and entering the epithelium are stained. (Calibration lines: 5 μ.) (*a*) Shows nerve bundles and Schwann cells containing butyrylcholinesterase; (*b*) (higher magnification, see calibration lines) shows a process approaching the epithelial layer and running along the base of the epithelial cells.

[*To face page 104*

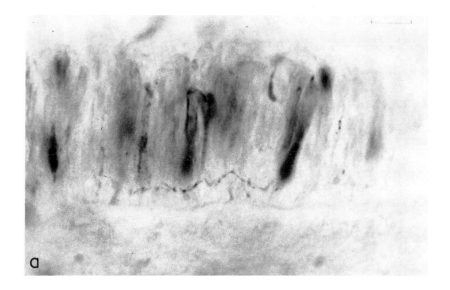

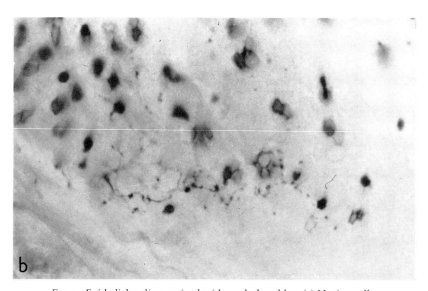

FIG. 2. Epithelial endings stained with methylene blue. (*a*) Horizontally running fibres between epithelial cells of a bronchus; (*b*) widespread arborization seen in horizontal section of epithelium near tracheal bifurcation. Some nuclei of epithelial cells have stained. (Calibration line: 5 μ.)

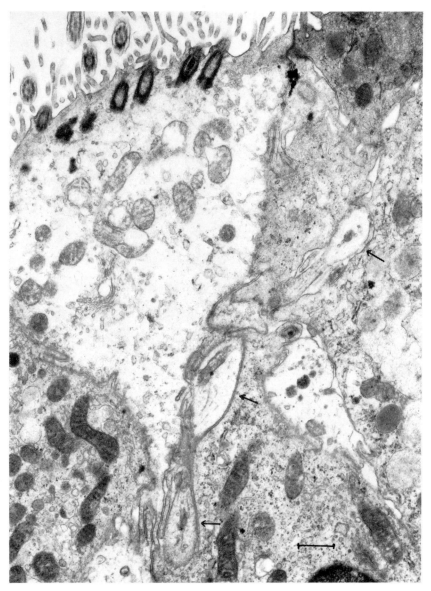

FIG. 3. Epithelial cells with three varicosities (at arrows) of a nerve fibre.
(Calibration line. 0·5 μ.)

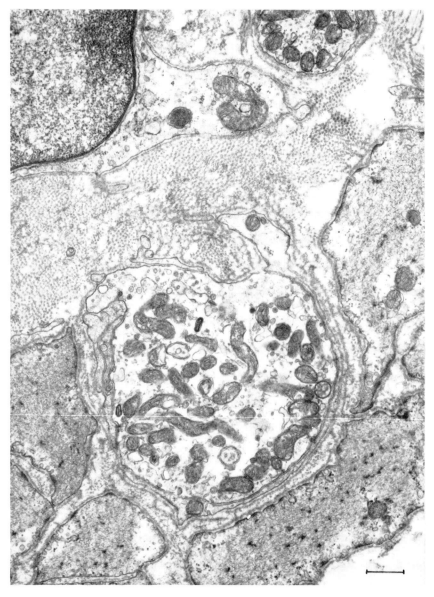

Fig. 4. Non-cholinergic axon varicosity with mitochondria between smooth muscle cells and connective tissue. (Calibration line: 0·5 μ.)

branched repeatedly before non-myelinated twigs entered the epithelium. There is further extensive horizontal branching between the lower parts of the epithelial cells and vertical twigs towards the surface. It appears that a single myelinated fibre may give rise to an ending extending over an area of some mm². We also confirmed Larsell's description (1922) of endings within smooth muscle. With these methods we can add nothing to his descriptions.

We have shown similar nerve arborizations in airways epithelium and smooth muscle with a variety of metal impregnation staining methods on a number of species. Some of these methods preferentially impregnate axons of large diameter, and thus these endings of myelinated fibres are more prominent than the autonomic innervation.

The preliminary results of an electron microscopic study of airways innervation prove that nerve fibres do occur in the epithelium (Fig. 3). Only the tracheal bifurcation in the rabbit and guinea-pig have so far been examined. As expected, there are many subepithelial nerve bundles. These contain nerve fibres of two types: one is typically cholinergic in appearance, and the other is quite different but not monoaminergic. The latter type is also found between the epithelial cells and is generally without Schwann cells at this point. These nerve fibres are seen close to the free surface of the epithelium and they are adjacent to both mucous and ciliated cells. The subepithelial myelinated fibres have accumulations of mitochondria, which makes them somewhat unusual.

Among the smooth muscle cells also, in addition to the characteristic cholinergic fibres, there are axons containing numerous mitochondria and glycogen granules (Fig. 4). These are probably sensory and correspond to the endings described by both Larsell and ourselves using methylene blue and other staining methods.

### CONCLUSIONS

From our results we conclude that in the rabbit there is no motor innervation of the airways epithelium and, therefore, that the nerve fibres in the epithelium are sensory. At least some of the epithelial endings are the terminals of myelinated fibres but we could not determine whether non-myelinated fibres also give rise to epithelial endings.

The epithelial endings which we have seen are scattered and each one covers a large area. Such a discontinuous innervation suggests that only coarse localization exists, possibly confined to levels within the airways.

The evidence for a sensory innervation of smooth muscle is not so good.

The coarse and branched endings within the smooth muscle layers, which are stained by the empiric methods but not by the histochemical methods, appear to be sensory and are clearly distinguishable from the motor innervation. They resemble the endings in the walls of blood vessels and the heart, as shown by the same methods. These latter are considered to be stretch receptors. Thus, by inference, the endings in the airways smooth muscle may also be stretch receptors.

Despite the varied structures described in the literature, our results provide no evidence for any sensory endings in the respiratory tract other than the discrete endings in the smooth muscle layer and the branching fibres between the epithelial cells.

### SUMMARY

1. Histochemical methods for identifying acetylcholinesterase and catecholamines demonstrate the distribution of postganglionic autonomic fibres; these do not enter the airways epithelium in the rabbit.

2. The method for non-specific cholinesterase stains bundles of autonomic postganglionic fibres and, in addition, branching processes entering the airways epithelium; these represent sensory fibres with Schwann cells.

3. Myelinated fibres are found in the walls of the airways after degeneration of the preganglionic fibres in the vagus.

4. Methylene blue and metal impregnation methods stain the motor fibres to the various components of the airways wall and also nerve arborizations in the epithelium and smooth muscle.

5. With the electron microscope, axons with characteristics different from those of postganglionic autonomic fibres are found both among the epithelial cells and among smooth muscle cells.

6. The methods all confirm the presence of sensory endings in epithelium and smooth muscle of the airways. Many of these are the terminals of myelinated fibres.

ACKNOWLEDGEMENTS

We are indebted to Dr A. Guz for the lungs from the two rabbits with supranodose section of the vagus; we wish to thank Miss A. M. Drury for skilled technical assistance.

### REFERENCES

BENSCH, K. G., GORDON, G. B., and MILLER, L. R. (1965). *J. Ultrastruct. Res.*, **12**, 668.
BERKLEY, H. J. (1893). *J. comp. Neurol.*, **3**, 107.
ELFTMAN, A. G. (1943). *Am. J. Anat.*, **72**, 1.
FALCK, B., and OWMAN, C. (1965). *Acta Univ. lund.*, **2**, 7.

FEYRTER, F. (1938). *Über diffuse endokrine epitheliale Organe.* Leipzig.

FRÖHLICH, F. (1949). *Frankf. Z. Path.*, **60**, 517.

HAYASHI, S. (1937). *J. orient. Med.*, **27**, 37.

HIRSCH, E. F., KAISER, G. C., BARNER, H. B., COOPER, T., and RAMS, J. J. (1968a). *Archs Path.*, **85**, 51.

HIRSCH, E. F., KAISER, G. C., BARNER, H. B., NIGRO, S. L., HAMOUDA, F., COOPER, T., and ADAMS, W. E. (1968b). *Archs Surg. Chicago*, **96**, 149.

HONJIN, R. (1956). *J. comp. Neurol.*, **105**, 587.

KRAUSE, C. F. T. (1876). *Handbuch der Menschlichen Anatomie*, 3rd edn., ed. Krause, W. von. Hanover: Hahn'sche Buchhandlung.

LARSELL, O. (1921). *J. comp. Neurol.*, **33**, 105.

LARSELL, O. (1922). *J. comp. Neurol.*, **35**, 97.

LUCIANO, L., REALE, E., and RUSKA, H. (1968). *Z. Zellforsch. mikrosk. Anat.*, **85**, 350.

REISSEISEN, F. D. (1822). *Über den Bau der Lunge.* Berlin: August Rücker.

STÖHR, PH., JR. (ed.). (1957). *Handbuch der Mikroskopischen Anatomie des Menschen*, vol. 4, part 5. Berlin: Springer-Verlag.

SUNDER-PLASSMANN, P. (1933). *Dt. Z. Chir.*, **240**, 249.

WHITE, A. M. S. (1968). *Innervation of trachea and lung.* D.Phil. thesis. University of Oxford, Faculty of Physiology.

WOODS, R. I. (1968). *Innervation of the frog's heart.* D.Phil. thesis. University of Oxford, Faculty of Physiology.

# DISCUSSION

*Dornhorst:* Have you seen any fibres to mucous glands?

*Fillenz:* The mucous glands have only a cholinergic (motor) innervation; the respiratory epithelium, which contains mucous cells, receives a sensory but no motor innervation.

*Dornhorst:* Have you found any ganglion cells?

*Fillenz:* Yes, in the walls of the trachea and bronchi; these ganglion cells are cholinergic postganglionic autonomic neurones.

*Paintal:* Holmes and Torrance (1959) have described sensory fibres travelling in the sympathetic chain. How can you be sure that some of the fibres in your preparations are not of this type?

*Fillenz:* The myelinated fibres which we see in the rabbit lung after supranodose vagotomy are sensory fibres and could travel in either the vagus or the sympathetic chain.

*von Euler:* Are the stretch receptors oriented in any particular way in relation to the way in which the bronchi lie? If these receptors are oriented at right angles to the main axis of the bronchi, that is along the circumference of the tube, one would expect the discharge rate to be proportional to the square root of the volume change of the tube; whereas if they are oriented longitudinally the discharge rate would be directly proportional to the volume. Dr F. Clark and I (unpublished observations) have recently found a straight-line relationship between discharge rate and the square root of the volume, over a volume range of small and moderate inflations. Can any of your data on the orientation of stretch receptors throw light on this square-root relationship?

*Fillenz:* Unfortunately my data cannot contribute to this interesting idea. The receptors I have described are not necessarily smooth muscle receptors; they look more like the stretch receptors in the carotid sinus, aortic arch and the chambers of the heart. Electron microscopically one can show that they lie between smooth muscle cells and collagen fibres and are not intimately related to or coiled round smooth muscle cells. So, from our results (which are still only preliminary), I cannot say if these receptors respond more to deformation of connective tissue or of smooth muscle cells or to a combination of the two.

*Dornhorst:* Are they mechanoreceptors?

*Fillenz:* Yes.

*Dornhorst:* We must try to distinguish between nerve endings which respond in specific and those which respond in non-specific ways to mechanical stimuli. The baroreceptors, for example, fire off in response to pressure changes in such a keyed-in way that they must have a very specialized function. Dr Widdicombe's irritant receptors, on the other hand, seem to respond to various different stimuli, and at different thresholds, and are probably rather non-specialized; and the phase relationship of their response to mechanical stimulation was variable.

*Fillenz:* Are the endings themselves specialized or does their position make them so?

*Dornhorst:* The whole of the terminal complex may be involved, so that it is not the nerve ending only but also its location that is specialized.

*Cotes:* Dr Paintal, you showed a rather curious diagram of the J receptor (this volume, p. 64, Fig. 4). Was this entirely schematic or have you actually seen one of these receptors under the microscope?

*Paintal:* That was a diagramatic representation of a J receptor; I have never seen one. We know that such nerve endings exist, one has to start looking for them somewhere and, as collagen is a convenient sponge, it seemed reasonable to start looking there.

*Cotes:* Are there any known techniques for increasing the number of sensory endings?

*Widdicombe:* Before we start thinking about this sort of approach, we need to devise an accurate method for counting nerve endings in the lung.

*Fillenz:* I do not entirely agree. The J receptors must be so infrequent and scattered that it would be useful to increase their frequency in order to find even one of them.

*Dornhorst:* It might be worth looking for J receptors in immature animals.

*Paintal:* There might be a few more endings per square millimetre in the kitten. Another difficulty is that these receptors are tiny, of the order of 0·1–0·3 μm in diameter.

*Howell:* Chronic bronchitic patients develop hyperactive, hyperirritant bronchi that respond to many non-specific irritants. Could this hyperirritability be due to an increase in the sensory nerve fibre endings in the mucosa? Have you ever studied the bronchial mucosa in such patients, Dr Fillenz?

*Fillenz:* No.

*von Euler:* Would it be feasible to devise a "receptor preparation" of a pulmonary stretch receptor? One could then stimulate nerve endings, mechanically or electrically, with more precision than is possible by just inflating the lung.

*Widdicombe:* Theoretically this sounds fine, but I know of no way of maintaining the bronchial circulation so as to keep the bronchi oxygenated. Action potentials from receptors in the trachea and extrapulmonary bronchi have been studied with an intact circulation (Widdicombe, 1954a) but this sort of preparation has not been used for direct study of nerve endings in the lung itself. Stimulation of receptors by a catheter passed into the bronchus is not a very precise way of localizing them.

*von Euler:* Have you tried to dissect more distally in the lung parenchyma?

*Widdicombe:* I have dissected down on to the endings in the lung to try to localize receptors in airway smooth muscle (Widdicombe, 1954b) but all one sees is (literally) a bloody mess with which one can do little except stimulate the receptors electrically or mechanically. It would be a tremendous asset if we could devise a technique such as you have suggested.

## REFERENCES

HOLMES, R., and TORRANCE, R. W. (1959). *Q. Jl exp. Physiol.*, **44**, 271–281.
WIDDICOMBE, J. G. (1954a). *J. Physiol., Lond.*, **123**, 71–104.
WIDDICOMBE, J. G. (1954b). *J. Physiol., Lond.*, **125**, 226–351.

# GENERAL DISCUSSION

*Petit:* I have some data on the effects of histamine inhalation in man before and after vagal block. This work was done in Dr Guz's laboratory on a mild chronic asthmatic subject, J.P. (myself), in whom the inhalation of a histamine aerosol regularly provokes bronchoconstriction. All these studies were done after the administration of atropine $1 \cdot 8$ mg ($0 \cdot 02$ mg/kg body weight) to block the vagal parasympathetic efferent

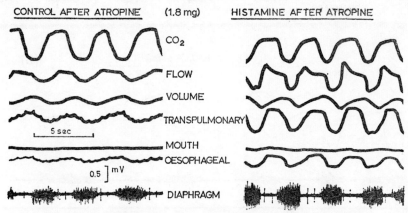

FIG. I (*Petit*). Histamine-induced bronchoconstriction, vagi intact. Effect of the inhalation of histamine aerosol, in the presence of atropine, in subject J.P., a mild, chronic asthmatic. Control traces and traces after histamine are shown. The following parameters are included. $CO_2 =$ end-tidal $PCO_2$ (mmHg); flow (l/min); volume (l); transpulmonary = transpulmonary pressure (cmH$_2$O); oesophageal = oesophageal pressure (cmH$_2$O); diaphragm = diaphragmatic electromyogram. Pulmonary conductance = 169 ml/s/cmH$_2$O (control), 83 ml/s/cmH$_2$O (after histamine).

fibres. Fig. I shows the results from a typical control experiment, in which the vagi were intact. The histamine aerosol provoked bronchoconstriction, tachypnoea, a slight increase in tidal volume, an increase in peak flow rates and a fall in end-tidal $PCO_2$. The results when this study was repeated during bilateral block of the vagus and glossopharyngeal nerves at the base of the skull are shown in Fig. 2. The decrease in pulmonary conductance was comparable in this and the control experiment (Fig. I), but there was no tachypnoea and tidal volume and peak flow rates were decreased after vagal block. Diaphragmatic activity was increased by histamine in the control experiment but showed little change after histamine during vagal block. The hyperventilation associated with the histamine-induced bronchoconstriction when the vagi were blocked seems to be related to the absence of conduction in vagal afferent fibres. The normal sensation of tightness in the chest was not experienced by

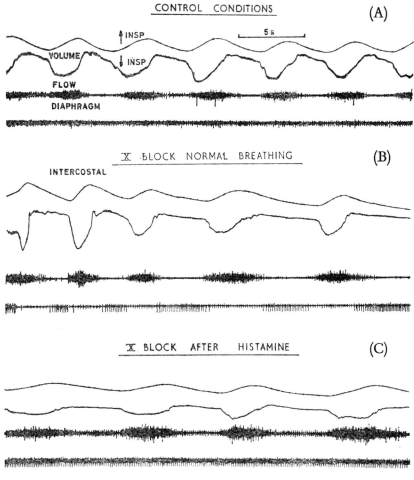

FIG. 2 (*Petit*). Histamine-induced bronchoconstriction during vagal block. Effect of the inhalation of histamine aerosol, in the presence of atropine, in subject J.P. (see legend to Fig. 1 [*Petit*]) after bilateral vagal block at the base of the skull. (A): control, before vagal block; (B): vagal block without histamine; (C): vagal block plus histamine. Note irregular normal pattern of breathing with prolonged expiration in this asthmatic subject. Pulmonary conductance = 288/ml/s/cmH$_2$O (normal breathing), 86 ml/s/cmH$_2$O (after histamine). (For full explanation, see text.)

this subject during histamine-induced bronchoconstriction with vagal block.

In my laboratory in Liège, my colleagues and I repeated the experiment with the addition of local anaesthetic inhaled as an aerosol. We used a solution of lignocaine 20 per cent, adrenaline 1 per cent (to potentiate the lignocaine), ascorbic acid 1 per cent (to avoid oxidation of adrenaline) and N-hydrochloric acid, 2 per cent, as a solubilizing agent. We devised a system whereby bronchoconstriction could be continuously controlled during the inhalation of histamine (Petit, 1966). Fig. 3 shows that this aerosol mixture abolished histamine-induced tachypnoea, the sensation of breathlessness and alveolar hyperventilation, even though pulmonary resistance remained high.

We have done similar experiments in a dog (to exclude bias, the previous subject being a respiratory physiologist), and in nine naive asthmatic patients; the results are essentially similar to those shown in Fig. 3.

*Paintal:* Have you repeated this work using an aerosol containing adrenaline and hydrochloric acid, but without lignocaine, as a control?

*Petit:* Yes. I have given also propranolol 40 mg, by mouth, one hour before the experiment, to block the beta-adrenergic effects of the inhaled adrenaline which would otherwise induce bronchodilatation in these asthmatic subjects.

*Dornhorst:* Does the adrenaline potentiate the action of lignocaine because of local vasoconstriction with consequent delay in absorption, or are you postulating some additional effect?

*Petit:* No, just vasoconstriction.

*Paintal:* Was lignocaine ineffective without adrenaline?

*Petit:* It had no effect except in the mild asthmatic subject. He showed some effects from the inhalation of lignocaine alone (without adrenaline) but as he was already taking orciprenaline this is not a fair example.

*Paintal:* But local anaesthesia in other sites can certainly be achieved without adrenaline.

*Petit:* I used adrenaline to potentiate the effects of lignocaine because the concentrations of lignocaine that can be achieved in an aerosol are usually insufficient to produce anaesthesia of the respiratory tract.

*Dornhorst:* Adrenaline would also increase the reproducibility of your results. It might be easier to use noradrenaline to delay the absorption of lignocaine, rather than adrenaline plus propranolol, because noradrenaline has no bronchodilatory effects.

*Widdicombe:* Professor Paintal, does histamine stimulate the J receptors?

*Paintal:* No.

*Widdicombe:* This and Dr Petit's results confirm that the J receptors are unlikely to be involved in surface responses mediated through epithelial irritant receptors; the latter are strongly stimulated by histamine.

*Noble:* Did local anaesthetic in the airways have any effect on the response to inflation and deflation?

*Petit:* The lignocaine aerosol mixture that I used had no effect on the response to sudden inflation and deflation. Another mechanism must be involved with these responses.

To study the effects of inflation we have used a short stimulus—a sudden "dynamic" inflation by a square wave—of positive or negative intra-oral pressure over a period of 0·5 seconds. We have used this technique in anaesthetized, intubated dogs and man, but have not yet used it successfully in the conscious human subject during vagal block. In two anaesthetized and intubated human subjects this sudden inflation was found to inhibit diaphragmatic activity throughout the corresponding respiratory cycle. In contrast, a sudden deflation, with reduction in lung volume, shortened the expiratory pause. Therefore these effects do not depend on consciousness, nor can they originate in receptors in the respiratory tract above the larynx; they seem to be mediated through the vagi. In two dogs with left pneumonectomies the responses to sudden inflation and/or deflation disappeared after vagotomy and must, therefore, have been mediated through the vagi. The inhalation of lignocaine aerosol in man did not abolish the responses to deflation and inflation but it increased the threshold for these responses. These findings suggest that the tachypnoea of asthma has a different origin from the inflation and deflation responses.

In a patient with a homotransplant of the right lung, the threshold for the response to inflation was increased compared with the threshold in a normal subject under similar experimental conditions. The increase in threshold in the patient may be due either to the denervation of the right lung or to airways obstruction in the left lung. (This patient has been described by Dr P. Vermeire at a meeting of the Thoracic Society, London in December 1969; see Vermeire, 1970).

*Campbell:* Are there any more observations about the respiratory function of this patient who has survived for many months after transplant?

*Petit:* It would be interesting to measure lung function bronchospirometrically in the two separate lungs in this patient but this is impossible because he is too ill.

*Guz:* Interpretation of abnormal lung reflexes in this patient will be difficult. He has had one of his lungs transplanted; the other lung is non-functioning but still present and innervated; thus, the good,

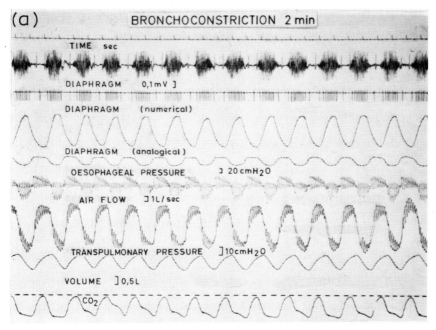

FIG. 3 (*Petit*). Effect of lignocaine aerosol on histamine-induced bronchoconstriction in subject J.P. (see legend to Fig. 1 [*Petit*]). Numerical and analogical traces of diaphragmatic activity indicate the action potential frequency of the diaphragmatic electromyogram (EMG) and were computed electrically; the analogical trace corresponds to integrated diaphragmatic EMG. Pressure and air flow traces show oscillations due to use of interruptor method for measuring pulmonary resistance. Calibrations shown refer to traces immediately above.

(*a*) Record shows changes in breathing two minutes after the administration of histamine. Flow resistance = 16·7 cmH$_2$O/l/s; respiratory frequency = 27/min; tidal volume = 800 ml; air flow = 21·6 l/min; end-tidal P$_{CO_2}$ = 28 mmHg.

*See also Fig. 3(b) overleaf.*

[*To face page 114*

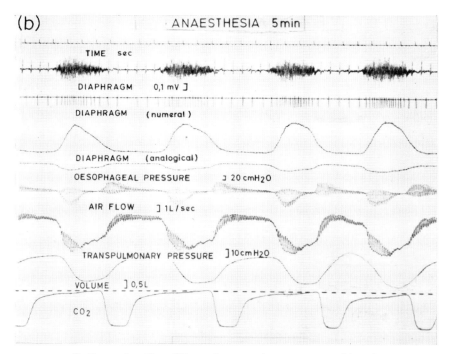

(b) Shows the effect of lignocaine aerosol, 20 per cent, on histamine-induced bronchoconstriction. Flow resistance = 14 cmH₂O; respiratory frequency = 8/min; tidal volume = 1440 ml; air flow = 11·5 l/min; end-tidal $P_{CO_2}$ = 44 mmHg. Note that bronchoconstriction persists but tachypnoea and hypocapnia are abolished by the inhalation of lignocaine aerosol. (See text.)

transplanted, denervated lung and the diseased lung are being assessed together when respiratory function is tested in this man.

*Howell:* Dr Petit, you said that when you blocked the vagus in man the effect of a sudden deflation or inflation on the diaphragmatic response was abolished. I am not sure that your inference that this reflex must therefore involve the vagus is justified. The vagus may play a permissive role without being directly involved in the reflex pathway. We (Campbell *et al.*, 1961) studied the effect of vagotomy on the reflex increase in inspiratory muscle tension which arose when the inspiratory muscles were given an added load; this increase in tension no longer occurred after vagotomy. However, when the central end of the cut vagus was rhythmically stimulated to restore the normal respiratory pattern, the reflex could again be elicited.

*Petit:* The only thing I am trying to say is that block of the whole vagus nerve is necessary to abolish the classical inflation reflex and the dynamic responses to sudden inflation and deflation. The vagally mediated, tachypnoeic response to histamine aerosol inhalation is abolished by surface anaesthesia of the airways mucosa.

*Dornhorst:* Are you saying that classic inflation and deflation reflexes are not inhibited with local anaesthetic?

*Petit:* Yes.

*Dornhorst:* This is important because it must mean that lignocaine aerosol introduced in this way is not sufficiently absorbed to block the classic stretch receptors. But we are not justified in assuming that these receptors therefore play no part in the tachypnoea of asthma. Asthma is not an all-or-nothing syndrome; an attack can be mild, moderate or severe. As the attack gets worse, more and more afferent fibres are recruited. There is good evidence (Widdicombe, 1961) that bronchoconstriction modifies stretch receptor traffic.

*von Euler:* What is the relative importance of higher centres *versus* vagal reflexes in an asthmatic attack? In other words, how important is the emotional component?

*Dornhorst:* Vagal reflexes are probably of primary importance when an attack continues during sleep.

*Petit:* An asthmatic attack during sleep is less severe if the patient is not sedated because he wakes sooner than he would if he had taken a sedative, and can therefore take a bronchodilator drug sooner. In my view, the emotions play an important role in their effects on the behaviour of the asthmatic but not on the bronchoconstriction itself. The emotional component is not important in true allergic asthma.

*Dornhorst:* In all but the most serious attacks the patient is overventilating and has a low $Pco_2$ which is not normalized by keeping the $Po_2$ at normal levels. So there must be a non-chemical factor causing increased respiratory drive.

*Aitken:* I agree with the first of Dr Petit's comments about the role of the emotions in asthma, although this opinion is rarely encountered in the literature on psychosomatic illness. The sensation of asphyxia will be accompanied by anxiety in anyone; the amount of anxiety depends on many factors, including not only the severity of dyspnoea but also the patient's past experience and personality characteristics. This anxiety may be accompanied or masked by physiological activation, such as hyperventilation with resultant hypocapnia and increased muscle activity. This mechanism could explain why some patients hyperventilate despite normal $Po_2$ levels.

## HEAD'S PARADOXICAL REFLEX

*Cross:* Some of my work with Dr Sheila Lewis (unpublished) on newborn infants may help to elucidate the mechanism behind Head's paradoxical reflex. Head (1889), of course, described a rise in inspiratory tone in response to lung inflation in rabbits whose vagi had been frozen and partially rewarmed. We have studied a similar paradoxical effect: the gasp which frequently occurs in the newborn infant when the lungs are inflated. This gasp often interrupts a normal Hering–Breuer apnoeic period and its effect on lung compliance is of particular interest to us. We measure either total compliance or lung compliance in the trunk plethysmograph. The total compliance is the difference between the airways pressure and the pressure on the outside of the baby's body. Fig. 3 shows a trace of an inflation. The baby's total compliances before and after the gasp were $3 \cdot 6$ ml/$cmH_2O$ and $4 \cdot 7$ ml/$cmH_2O$ respectively.

Fig. 4 shows a pressure/volume plot obtained by Bernstein (1957) after maximal inflation of the lungs of a rabbit; pressure/volume measurements from baby S.C. (Fig. 1) are also shown. In this baby there are two populations of points, one of measurements of static compliance which were not preceded by a gasp and the other of measurements which followed a gasp. It seems likely that, as Bernstein postulated for his rabbits, the infant had recruited lung volume, that is opened up more alveoli, after a gasp. If this is so then I would like to suggest, and invite comments on the idea, that the receptor for the gasp reflex is at least related to any situation in which many alveoli are unexpanded.

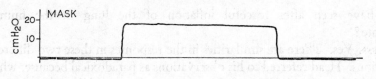

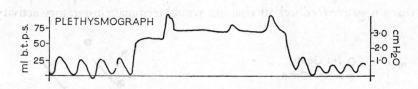

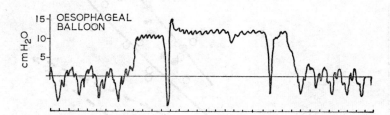

FIG. 3 (*Cross*). Record of inflation of female baby, S.C. Age: 3 days; weight: 2·85 kg. From above downwards the figure shows airway pressure (cmH₂O), plethysmograph trace of tidal volume calibrated for both volume and pressure change, oesophageal pressure (cmH₂O), and time in seconds; b.t.p.s.: body temperature, pressure, saturated with water.

Note that when the baby's lungs are inflated there is a period of apnoea interrupted by a gasp. After the gasp, both lung volume and oesophageal pressure are increased with the same airway pressure.

$$\text{Total compliance before gasp:} \frac{58 \cdot 5}{18 \cdot 8 - 2 \cdot 7} = 3 \cdot 6 \text{ ml/cmH}_2\text{O}$$

$$\text{Total compliance after gasp:} \frac{73 \cdot 1}{18 \cdot 8 - 3 \cdot 2} = 4 \cdot 7 \text{ ml/cmH}_2\text{O}.$$

*Merton:* Are you assuming that the baby is not using its muscles at all during these recordings?

*Cross:* Measurements are made when our records show minimal changes in lung volume, suggesting that the baby is in a static state at this time. Lung volume was static for three or four seconds—a reasonable period.

*Guz:* Professor Cross, could you expand your comments on the similarities of Head's paradoxical reflex and the reflex you have just described in newborn babies? Are you relating what Head described in connexion with cooling and rewarming the vagus in the rabbit to what you have seen after forceful inflation of the lung in the human neonate?

*Cross:* Yes. There are similarities in the responses in these two different situations. Head referred to his observations as paradoxical because, when the rabbit lung was inflated after rewarming the cooled vagi, he expected that a negative feedback mechanism would terminate inspiratory activity

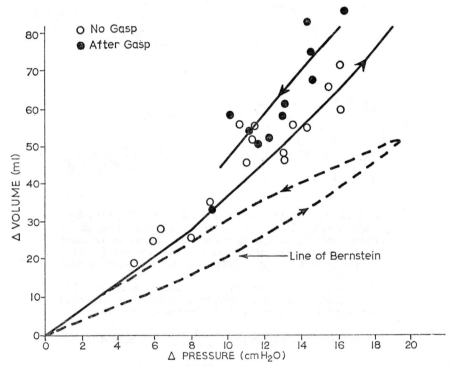

FIG. 4 (*Cross*). Plot of $\Delta V$ (inflating volume, ordinate) against $\Delta P$ (pressure in plethysmograph, abscissa) in female baby, S.C., (continuous lines) and rabbit (discontinuous lines) (Bernstein, 1957, see text). S.C., age: 3 days; weight: 2·85 kg. Open circles: measurements either before gasp or when no gasp occurred during Hering-Breuer apnoea; closed circles: measurements after gasp (Cross and Lewis, unpublished data).

whereas (paradoxically) the rabbit increased its inspiratory activity in these conditions. In our studies, we found it paradoxical that the human neonate gasped when its lungs were inflated; in other words, we found positive instead of negative feedback after inflation. Head and I are thus both using the term "paradoxical" in the same sense, but in connexion with different experiments.

*Widdicombe:* Your studies link up with the mechanism of action of irritant receptors described by Reynolds (Reynolds and Hilgeson, 1965; Reynolds, 1962), who showed that there is an inverse correlation between the sensitivity of the paradoxical reflex (or "gasp reflex") and lung compliance in the cat. As compliance falls the threshold for the gasp reflex also falls (that is, the reflex becomes more sensitive) and the cat gasps; the threshold then rises and the reverse process occurs. We have made sequential plots for lung compliance and irritant receptor discharge. If one either leaves the animal alone (so that its lungs slowly get gummed up) or performs manoeuvres such as forced lung deflation to decrease lung compliance, the volume threshold for the irritant receptors falls and they become more active on inflation of the lungs. If one then either hyperinflates the lung, to increase compliance, or if the animal takes a spontaneous deep breath (this may have an analogous underlying mechanism to the gasp reflex), compliance increases and so does the threshold of the irritant receptors, while their discharge frequency on lung inflation falls. If the central action of the receptors is to stimulate inspiration, then they could be the underlying mechanism for the paradoxical (or gasp) reflex. The other receptors that have been studied in this context— J receptors and the slowly adapting pulmonary stretch receptors—cannot account for this reflex.

*Dornhorst:* Is there a constant relationship between inflation and bronchial stretch?

*Widdicombe:* The amount of pull on a particular bronchus where a receptor is situated becomes less after an inflation which increases lung compliance (Butler *et al.*, 1960). The point I am trying to make is that the threshold and sensitivity of the receptors are directly proportional to the threshold and sensitivity of the reflex, and depend on lung compliance. Professor Cross and co-workers (1960) have shown a similar general relationship between reflex action and lung compliance in newborn babies.

*Dornhorst:* There is a difference between the response of a receptor to a particular method of stimulation and the threshold for that response: the latter suggests something more intrinsic.

*Widdicombe:* The relationship between lung compliance and irritant receptor action applies both to the threshold to an artificial inflation and also to an increase in sensitivity, that is, in the frequency of discharge for different inflation volumes. This can be shown during the animal's own eupnoeic inspiratory efforts.

*Dornhorst:* We may still be confusing two different things: first, the receptor that is firing less in response to similar changes in its own microenvironment and, second, reduced changes in that environment. We must draw this distinction between the threshold of a receptor and the threshold of a reflex.

*Paintal:* Professor Cross, have you done these experiments on tracheostomized infants, thus excluding the influence of nerve endings in the nose and upper respiratory passages?

*Cross:* The only evidence I have that these endings are not involved comes from our experiences with inflation in one baby with an imperforate anus, who was anaesthetized with ether. Whitteridge and Bülbring (1944) have shown that ether blocks tracheal nerve endings.

*Widdicombe:* The situation with ether is rather complicated. It first sensitizes and then inhibits such nerve endings as the slowly adapting pulmonary stretch receptors. It also has central effects and it stimulates lung irritant receptors.

*Godfrey:* In the newborn anaesthetized and intubated rabbit, after recovery from asphyxia, a paradoxical response could be easily evoked at a time when lung compliance was low (Godfrey, 1968). The paradoxical response was accompanied by frequent spontaneous sighs; as the breathing pattern in these baby rabbits returned to normal the frequency of the spontaneous sighs and the ease with which the paradoxical response could be elicited decreased. This paradoxical response is a gasping response to inflation of the lung. It is not, as Professor Cross has said, what Head originally described.

*Prys-Roberts:* This sort of paradoxical response also occurs in adult man during anaesthesia. If a lightly anaesthetized, intubated adult is inadvertently given an overdose of a short-acting opiate, spontaneous ventilation ceases so that controlled ventilation is temporarily necessary. During recovery from the effects of the opiate, a spontaneous inspiration may be triggered by a short, sharp inflation of the lung during the expiratory phase of artificial ventilation, followed after a few minutes by the resumption of normal spontaneous breathing.

*Dornhorst:* You see this also during recovery from barbiturate overdosage.

*Prys-Roberts:* In that situation the whole process is more prolonged; with short-acting opiates the time sequence is very rapid.

*Campbell:* Hering and Breuer first demonstrated that when breathing is suddenly blocked in the rabbit at the height of inspiration, prolonged apnoea occurs. (Whether active expiration occurs or not is still disputed.) If breathing is similarly blocked at the height of inspiration in *man*, he immediately inspires (Campbell *et al.*, 1961). Although I am not suggesting that this is a paradoxical reflex, it is another surprising response in view of man's very weak Hering–Breuer reflex.

*Newsom Davis:* Dr A. Guz and I (unpublished observations) found that the "reflex" you have described is retained after vagal block.

*Dornhorst:* How does this reflex relate to the paradoxical gasp reflex in neonates, Professor Cross?

*Cross:* The experimental procedures in these two situations are different. I am actively inflating the babies' lungs; Professor Campbell was suddenly blocking inspiration in adult man during spontaneous respiration.

*Merton:* And the babies you have studied do not take this inspiratory gasp until several seconds after inflation. Is that right?

*Cross:* Not always.

*Merton:* An anaesthetized man or animal not breathing spontaneously can often be triggered to take an immediate breath by either sudden forced inflation or deflation. But this is quite different from the experiments Professor Cross has described in which a human baby takes an inspiratory gasp some seconds after inflation.

*Cross:* Nevertheless, our observations are certainly related to the reflexes that Head described. He described many happenings during the respiratory cycle. First, at the cessation of the classical Hering–Breuer inflation reflex, he observed that the rabbit often took a big breath; Head called this an interrupting inspiration and showed that the timing of this could be varied by different manoeuvres. The interrupting inspiration could be deferred by giving the rabbit oxygen to breathe, or brought on earlier if the animal inhaled a gaseous mixture rich in carbon dioxide or low in oxygen, and so on. But the gasping we have observed in babies occurs early in the apnoeic response period before the Hering–Breuer reflex would be expected to be "interrupted" (in Head's sense).

*Ullmann:* Rosenthal (1864) wrote: "In an animal rendered asphyxial with H [hydrogen] one frequently sees that insufflation with air from bellows is immediately followed by one deep inspiration. If air is blown in repeatedly there occurs at first a brief stage of dyspnoea, followed by normal breathing. The first single inspiration which follows immediately after inflation is absent if both vagi are sectioned. . . ." (See also this volume, p. 393, note 29.) This reflex should be called "Rosenthal's" not "Head's" paradoxical reflex!

*Paintal:* We have still not clearly defined the two reflexes that Head described. One of these, which he called "paradoxical" is the reflex that Professor Cross described on p. 116: reflex inspiratory excitation occurs in response to lung inflation when the vagi in the rabbit are rewarmed after cooling. But Head also noted that inspiratory excitation occurs if the lungs of a rabbit are inflated very rapidly without previous cooling of the vagi.

*Cross:* Head thought that the rapid large inflation of the second reflex came from the body wall because it persisted after vagal section.

*Howell:* Did he actually use the term "paradoxical"?

*Paintal:* Yes, but only for the first of these two reflexes.

*Plum:* Professor Cross, at what age, that is, at what level of maturity of the nervous system, do the paradoxical events you have described disappear? Could the reason you see this response in neonates be a reflection of the fact that they are, in a sense, functionally decerebrate preparations? In cats with low pontine decerebration we have often been able to elicit gasping in response to various stimuli, including pinching the tail. Is the paradoxical gasp response specific to the stimulus of lung inflation, or might other noxious stimuli induce gasping in a newborn baby as they do in the experimental animal?

*Cross:* One can only do these experiments in human beings who are cooperative. In practice this means that we can only test babies before they are sentient; after that there is a gap of about five years before the child becomes voluntarily cooperative enough for us to elicit any more data. We can study a normal baby immediately after birth until he is about ten days old, premature babies for the first six weeks of life and some abnormal babies, such as those with the respiratory distress syndrome, for about two months. Paradoxical phenomena are still present, but not so frequent, at the age of two months.

*Dornhorst:* Another factor that makes it possible to study very young babies is that their lungs are incompletely inflated.

*Cross:* I agree.

*Cohen:* Professor Cross, the gasp in Fig. 3 (*Cross*) might be interpreted as an interrupting or secondary response, since it occurs only after a period of prolonged apnoea, which of course is an example of the classical Hering–Breuer reflex.

Some of my own observations are relevant to our discussions about Head's paradoxical reflex. These data were obtained in a simplified animal preparation: the decerebrate or anaesthetized cat which is paralysed, artificially ventilated and has bilateral pneumothoraces (to minimize afferent input from chest wall receptors). In this situation, efferent phrenic discharge is used as an indicator of the central respiratory cycle, and the recurring pump inflation acts to excite pulmonary stretch receptors. As shown in Fig. 1, the phrenic discharge-burst locks in with each pump inflation, which starts in the later part of the burst and continues into the early part of the expiratory phase (period of phrenic silence). When the airway is occluded at the peak of inflation, the resulting maintained inflation causes a greatly lengthened expiratory phase, which is the Hering–Breuer reflex effect (Fig. 5, A). If now (Fig. 5, B) the airway is opened to the pump at the proper time, an additional inflation is superimposed on the existing maintained inflation, and the result is an inspiratory-excitatory effect: the production of a premature inspiratory

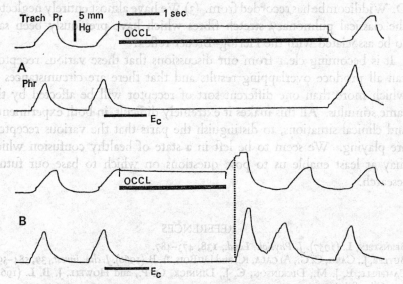

FIG. 5 (*Cohen*). Comparison of inspiratory-inhibitory and inspiratory-excitatory reflexes. Traces show tracheal pressure (*Trach Pr*) and integrated phrenic (*Phr*) discharge (activity upwards). *A*: occlusion (horizontal bar) started at peak inflation and ended at beginning of next phrenic burst; *B*: occlusion started at peak inflation and ended 3·4 s later, during a pump inflation stroke. Note 300-ms latency to start of inspiratory burst (vertical dotted line). $E_C$ (horizontal bar): duration of control expiratory phase.

burst after a latency of 300 milliseconds. This inspiratory-excitatory effect may be considered to be an example of Head's paradoxical reflex, according to the broader definition proposed by Widdicombe (1967). The reflex presumably results from excitation by the additional inflation of higher-threshold receptors which had not been firing during the preceding maintained inflation. These may belong to the group of rapidly adapting vagal receptors which have higher inflation thresholds than the slowly adapting receptors (Knowlton and Larrabee, 1946); or they may be the same as the irritant receptors described by Mills, Sellick and Widdicombe (this volume, p. 77).

5*

*Dornhorst:* Some important topics have emerged from our proceedings so far. (1) The need to postulate the existence of receptors lying in, or very close to, alveolar walls has been demonstrated by Professor Paintal; although no one has yet seen these receptors under the microscope, Paintal's work should stimulate us to look until we do find them. (2) The existence of sensory endings in bronchial epithelium has been shown anatomically, and these may plausibly be identified with the fibres that Dr Widdicombe has recorded from. (3) We have almost entirely neglected the classical pulmonary stretch fibres which have previously been said to be associated with the Hering–Breuer reflex.

It is becoming clear from our discussions that these various receptors can all produce overlapping results and that there are circumstances in which more than one different sort of receptor will be affected by the same stimulus. All this makes it extremely difficult, in both experimental and clinical situations, to distinguish the parts that the various receptors are playing. We seem to be left in a state of healthy confusion which may at least enable us to pose questions on which to base our future research.

## REFERENCES

BERNSTEIN, L. (1957). *J. Physiol., Lond.,* **138**, 473–487.
BUTLER, J., CARO, C. G., ALCALA, R., and DuBOIS, A. B. (1960). *J. clin. Invest.,* **39**, 584–591.
CAMPBELL, E. J. M., DICKINSON, C. J., DINNICK, O. P., and HOWELL, J. B. L. (1961). *Clin. Sci.,* **21**, 309–320.
CROSS, K. W., KLAUS, M., TOOLEY, W. H., and WEISSER, K. (1960). *J. Physiol., Lond.,* **151**, 551–565.
GODFREY, S. (1968). *Q. Jl exp. Physiol.,* **53**, 97–118.
HEAD, H. (1889). *J. Physiol., Lond.,* **10**, 1–70; 279–290.
KNOWLTON, G. C., and LARRABEE, M. G. (1946). *Am. J. Physiol.,* **147**, 100–114.
PETIT, J. M. (1966). In *Breathlessness,* pp. 178–181, ed. Howell, J. B. L., and CAMPBELL, E. J. M. Oxford; Blackwell.
REYNOLDS, L. B. (1962). *J. appl. Physiol.,* **17**, 683–688.
REYNOLDS, L. B., and HILGESON, M. D. (1965). *J. appl. Physiol.,* **20**, 491–495.
ROSENTHAL, I. (1864). *Arch. Anat. Physiol.,* 469.
VERMEIRE, P. (1970). *Clin. Sci.,* **38**, 9–10P.
WHITTERIDGE, D., and BÜLBRING, E. (1944). *J. Pharmac. exp. Ther.,* **81**, 340–359.
WIDDICOMBE, J. G. (1961). *J. Physiol., Lond.,* **159**, 436–450.
WIDDICOMBE, J. G. (1967). *Q. Jl exp. Physiol.,* **52**, 44–50.

# HOW RESPIRATORY RHYTHM ORIGINATES: EVIDENCE FROM DISCHARGE PATTERNS OF BRAINSTEM RESPIRATORY NEURONES

M. I. COHEN

*Department of Physiology, Albert Einstein College of Medicine, Yeshiva University, New York*

THE attempt to explain the origin of respiratory periodicity has occupied many investigators, who have used three major methods. (*a*) *Transections and lesions* (Pitts, Magoun and Ranson, 1939*b*; Breckenridge and Hoff, 1950; Tang, 1953; Wang, Ngai and Frumin, 1957; Tang, 1967). On the basis of studies of this type, a rough anatomical localization of the respiratory mechanisms in the pons and medulla has been obtained, and the existence of several functional sub-systems of the "respiratory centre" has been suggested (Wang, Ngai and Frumin, 1957): an upper pontine inspiratory-inhibitory "pneumotaxic mechanism"; a lower pontine inspiratory-facilitatory "apneustic mechanism"; and a more primitive medullary rhythmic mechanism which, if isolated, produces a "gasping" type of respiration. (*b*) *Electrical stimulation of brainstem regions* (Pitts, Magoun and Ranson, 1939*a*; Brookhart, 1940; Baxter and Olszewski, 1955; Ngai and Wang, 1957; Tang, 1967). In studies of this type, the anatomical localization of various "centres", and in particular the medullary "inspiratory" and "expiratory" centres, has been sought by discrete electrical stimulation. (*c*) *Microelectrode recording from respiratory neurones* (Gesell, Bricker and Magee, 1936; Dirken and Woldring, 1951; Hukuhara, Nakayama and Okada, 1954; Baumgarten, Baumgarten and Schaefer, 1957; Haber *et al.*, 1957; Cohen and Wang, 1959; Salmoiraghi and Burns, 1960; Batsel, 1964; Nesland and Plum, 1965; Carregal, Williams and Birzis, 1967). In most studies of this type, the major emphasis has been on the description of discharge patterns of respiratory neurones and on their anatomical localization.

In my own studies (Cohen, 1968, 1969) the aim has been to explain the origin of respiratory periodicity by the interactions between populations of respiratory neurones. The principle of analysis has been to induce changes in respiratory rhythmicity and to compare the changes in activity of individual neurones with the changes in the overall respiratory cycle, indicated by phrenic discharge. Three major experimental variables have been used: (a) carbon dioxide tension; (b) lung inflation; and (c) brainstem electrical stimulation. On the basis of the differing responses of various classes of neurone, hypotheses have been formulated about the functional role of such neurones; and a preliminary theoretical schema will be presented to explain how the interactions of these classes result in respiratory periodicity.

## METHODS

Observations were made in adult cats. Two main types of preparation were used: (a) animals with intact neuraxis, under either urethane or dialurethane anaesthesia; and (b) midcollicular decerebrate animals, maintained without anaesthesia after surgery had been performed under ether. The cats were paralysed with a neuromuscular blocking agent (succinylcholine or gallamine), were subjected to bilateral pneumothorax and were artificially ventilated with carbon dioxide-oxygen mixtures by a positive-pressure respirator. Thus ventilation-related sensory input not derived from pulmonary stretch receptors was minimized. In different types of experiment the vagi were left intact or were sectioned.

*Electrical recording.* The phrenic nerve, located by a dorsal approach in the neck, was sectioned and recordings were made from the central end with a bipolar hook electrode. The activity of individual respiratory units in pons and medulla (exposed by partial removal of the cerebellum) was recorded extracellularly with glass electrolyte-filled (3M KCl or 4M NaCl) micro-electrodes having 3–6 μm tip diameters. The data were recorded on magnetic tape, and subsequently played back for photography and computer analysis.

*Data processing.* The phrenic potentials and the brainstem unit potentials were subjected to processing (Fig. 1) to derive pulse signals suitable for computer analysis. The phrenic potentials, after half-wave rectification and suitable amplification, were passed through a "leaky integrator" circuit (time constant usually 0·1 s) to furnish a signal whose amplitude was approximately proportional to the amplitude and frequency of the input potentials (Cohen, 1964b). By further processing of the integrated phreni-cogram (Cohen, 1968, appendix 1), pulses were derived marking the start of the inspiratory (I) and expiratory (E) phases; these phases are thus

defined as the periods of phrenic activity and inactivity, respectively. The
unit potentials were processed through an amplitude discriminator to give
a standard pulse corresponding to each unit spike.

The discharge patterns of respiratory neurones were analysed by determining the time distribution of spikes during the central respiratory cycle,
as indicated by phrenic discharge. By means of an average response

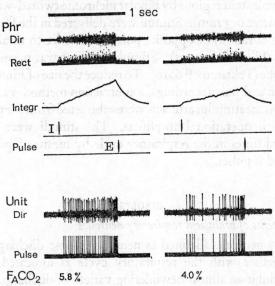

FIG. 1. Successive stages in processing of phrenic (*Phr*) neurogram and
neurogram of medullary inspiratory unit, to derive standard pulses for
start of inspiratory (*I*) and expiratory (*E*) phase, and for each unit spike.
Recordings are of activity at two end-tidal carbon dioxide levels—
$F_ACO_2$,—, where $F_ACO_2$ is the fractional concentration of carbon dioxide
in alveolar gas (Cohen, 1968, Fig. 1; reproduced by permission of *J.
Neurophysiol.*).

computer (Mnemotron CAT 1000), the unit spikes in a sample of respiratory cycles were summed in analysis sweeps whose synchronizing
triggers (reference signals) were either the *I* or the *E* pulses.

*Carbon dioxide tension study* (Cohen, 1968). In this study, performed in
vagotomized cats, the patterns of unit and phrenic discharge were observed
over a range of end-tidal carbon dioxide values (measured with an infrared
analyser) obtained by changing the level of artificial ventilation or the
composition of the input gas mixture.

*Lung inflation study* (Cohen, 1969). In this study, performed on cats with
intact vagi, the artificial ventilation pump was used as a source of sensory

input to the pulmonary stretch receptors. By means of a solenoid-operated valve in the ventilation circuit, the airway could be closed at any chosen inflation level or phase of the central respiratory cycle. The solenoid valve was controlled by timing pulses derived from phrenic discharge or from the airway pressure signal (measured by an attached pressure transducer).

*Electrical stimulation study* (Cohen, 1964a). Electrical stimuli were delivered in brainstem regions by bipolar nichrome twisted-wire electrodes (total tip diameter 0·3 mm). Stimuli were delivered in the form of pairs of pulses (100 μs duration) of opposite polarity in order to minimize polarization effects (Lilly *et al.*, 1955). Stimulus current was measured with an inductive probe (Tektronix P 6016). To reduce the size of stimulus artefacts in the phrenic and unit recordings, a subtraction method was used: pulses time-locked to the stimulus artefacts were subtracted from the physiological signals through operational amplifiers. The stimuli were delivered at predetermined times in the respiratory cycle by means of pulses delayed from the *I* and *E* pulses.

## RESULTS

### Discharge patterns of brainstem respiratory neurones

Respiratory neurones (defined as neurones whose discharge frequency oscillates together with the respiratory cycle as indicated by phrenic discharge) exhibit an almost bewildering variety of discharge patterns. A schematic classification of the major patterns is shown in Fig. 2. On the left are indicated patterns in which the onset or termination of discharge is closely time-locked to one of the phase transitions of the respiratory cycle; and such patterns have therefore been labelled "inspiratory" and "expiratory". On the right are indicated patterns which do not show such clearly defined locking to a phase transition, but nevertheless show respiratory periodicity. Such patterns have therefore been designated as "phase-spanning" in character; they have been further subdivided into "discontinuous" patterns (having a silent period in discharge) and "continuous" (having a relatively smooth variation of interspike intervals).

Although neurones of all the pictured types are found scattered throughout most regions of the pons and medulla, different discharge types are found with greater frequency in some regions than in others. Thus, inspiratory and expiratory neurones are found predominantly in the medulla, that is, in the region caudal to the level of the eighth nerve, with inspiratory neurones more numerous rostral to the obex and expiratory neurones more numerous caudal to the obex (Baumgarten, Baumgarten and Schaefer, 1957; Haber *et al.*, 1957). In contrast, the phase-spanning neurones are found predominantly in the pons, with inspiratory-expiratory neurones more numerous at rostral levels and expiratory-inspiratory neurones more numerous at caudal levels (Cohen and Wang, 1959; Kumagai *et al.*, 1966).

A first step in analysing the functions of neurones having different discharge patterns is comparison with the patterns found in respiratory nerves and muscles. The inspiratory discharge patterns resemble those

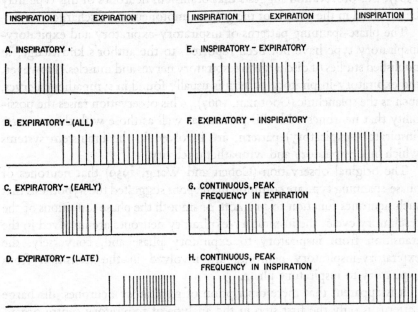

FIG. 2. Schematic classification of major discharge patterns of respiratory neurones. Each pattern is derived from spike counts of a representative neurone (Cohen, 1968, Fig. 2; reproduced by permission of *J. Neurophysiol.*).

found in the phrenic nerve, diaphragm and external intercostal muscles (Gesell, 1936; Gill, 1963; Eklund, Euler von and Rutkowski, 1964; Sears, 1964). The late-expiratory and expiratory-(all) patterns resemble those found in thoracic (internal intercostal) and abdominal expiratory muscles (Gesell, 1936; Floersheim, 1960; Sears, 1964). Finally, the early-expiratory patterns resemble the patterns of recurrent laryngeal expiratory fibres (Eyzaguirre and Taylor, 1963), as well as the expiratory pattern in the discharge of the whole nerve (Rijlant, 1937; Cohen, unpublished observations). These resemblances suggest that inspiratory and expiratory neurones, found predominantly in the medulla, are involved in systems which are relatively near, synaptically speaking, to the motoneurones of corresponding pattern.

By contrast, the relation of the phase-spanning discharge patterns to discharge recorded in the periphery is less obvious. However, patterns of continuous discharge with increased frequency in some portions of the cycle (inspiration or expiration, as the case may be) are typical of intercostal gamma motoneurones (Eklund, Euler von and Rutkowski, 1964; Sears, 1964); this observation suggests that brainstem neurones of this type may be involved in the genesis of the gamma motoneurone discharge.

The phase-spanning patterns of inspiratory-expiratory and expiratory-inspiratory type have not been reported, to the author's knowledge, in published studies of discharge in respiratory nerves and muscles. However, the expiratory-inspiratory pattern is usually found in sympathetic nerves, such as the splanchnic (Gootman, 1967). This observation raises the possibility that neurones with this pattern, as well as those with the converse (inspiratory-expiratory) pattern, are involved in the brainstem systems which link respiratory and sympathetic activity.

The original observation (Cohen and Wang, 1959) that neurones of phase-spanning type are common in the pons suggested the hypothesis that such neurones function to promote or smooth the phase transitions of the respiratory cycle: the inspiratory-expiratory neurones are involved in the transition from inspiratory to expiratory phase and, conversely, the expiratory-inspiratory neurones are involved in the transition from expiratory to inspiratory phase.

It is apparent that mere description of respiratory neurones' discharge patterns is only the first step in the analysis of respiratory centre organization. Therefore, investigations were undertaken to elucidate the functions of these neurones by various experimental manipulations.

*Discharge patterns and carbon dioxide tension (Cohen, 1968)*

In vagotomized cats, the changes in discharge pattern produced by hypocapnia were studied. When the alveolar carbon dioxide level is lowered, the magnitude of phrenic discharge (as seen, for example, in the integrated signal) is reduced; and at a sufficiently low level of carbon dioxide, the discharge disappears or becomes negligible, a condition which is the equivalent of apnoea in terms of neural discharge. At the same time, several kinds of response of brainstem neurones to hypocapnia were observed.

The two major types of response, which have been labelled type 1 and type 2 (Cohen, 1968), are illustrated schematically in Fig. 3. In the type-1 response, the discharge frequency of a neurone is reduced towards zero level by hypocapnia, and its discharge disappears at a sufficiently low level of carbon dioxide. Therefore, a neurone with this response may be designated as "phasic", since it continues to fire in bursts, even though they are sporadic, until the discharge disappears. By contrast, in the type-2 response, a neurone's discharge never disappears, even at the low carbon dioxide levels where phrenic apnoea occurs, but, rather, firing becomes continuous

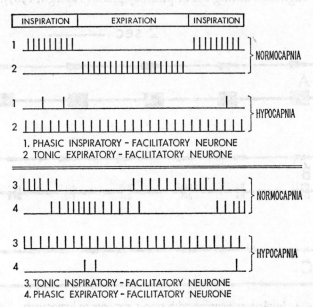

FIG. 3. Schematic representation of contrasting responses to hypocapnia, shown by two pairs of reciprocally firing neurones. *Top pair*: inspiratory neurone (1) with type-1 response; expiratory neurone (2) with type-2 response. *Bottom pair*: expiratory-inspiratory neurone (3) with type-2 response; inspiratory-expiratory neurone (4) with type-1 response.

and without respiratory periodicity. Therefore, a neurone with this response may be designated as "tonic".

In the schema of Fig. 3, two pairs of neurones are shown: the two members of each pair fire in reciprocal portions of the cycle and they also have contrasting responses to hypocapnia. In the first pair, the inspiratory neurone's discharge remains phasic until the lowest carbon dioxide levels, when discharge disappears, while the discharge of the expiratory neurone becomes tonic during hypocapnia. In the second pair, the discharge of the expiratory-inspiratory neurone becomes tonic during hypocapnia, while the discharge of the inspiratory-expiratory neurone remains phasic until disappearance. The schematic diagrams of Fig. 3 are typical of the observations in the cited study (Cohen, 1968); in Figs. 4–7 documentation of these effects will be presented.

The effects of a changed carbon dioxide level on the discharge of an inspiratory neurone with type-1 response are shown in Figs. 4 and 5. This neurone had a discharge pattern which was different from that of phrenic motoneurones and diaphragm motor units, whose discharge frequency augments during the inspiratory phase (Yaşargil, 1967). Rather,

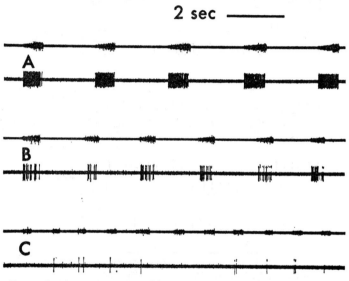

**2 sec** ———

FIG. 4. Inspiratory neurone with type-1 response to hypocapnia. *Top traces*: phrenic potentials; *bottom traces*: unit potentials. End-tidal carbon dioxide: *A*, 5·2 per cent; *B*, 2·7 per cent; *C*, 1·3 per cent.

the neurone's maximum discharge occurred at the start of the inspiratory phase and the frequency then decreased during the phase; its pattern thus resembled the inspiratory discharge of the whole recurrent laryngeal nerve (Cohen, unpublished observations). As the carbon dioxide level was lowered, the neurone's discharge frequency was reduced (Fig. 5, graph) but the general pattern of discharge remained the same (Fig. 5, histograms). Finally, at the lowest carbon dioxide level (1·3 per cent), the neurone's discharge had almost disappeared: it fired only one or two spikes during some inspiratory phases and not at all during others (Fig. 4C).

A most striking observation in this study was that different neurones of similar phase relation to the respiratory cycle showed different responses to hypocapnia. This observation is illustrated in Fig. 6 for two expiratory-(all) neurones. The neurone with type-1 response (top) had almost ceased firing at the lower carbon dioxide level, while the neurone with type-2 response (bottom) fired uninterruptedly at the lower carbon dioxide level, the silent periods having disappeared together with the phrenic discharge.

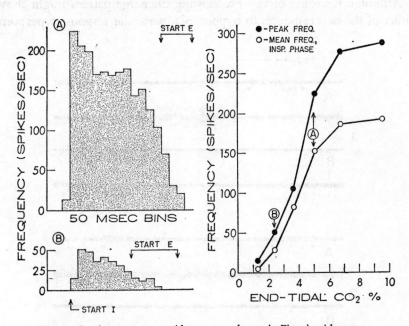

FIG. 5. Inspiratory neurone (the same as shown in Fig. 4) with type-1 response to hypocapnia. *Left*: histograms of spike distribution at two end-tidal carbon dioxide levels: *A*, 5·2 per cent; *B*, 2·4 per cent. In this and subsequent figures, spike histograms show mean discharge frequency in bins falling at fixed times after start of inspiratory (*I*) and expiratory (*E*) phase, indicated by arrows; spike counts are summed in *N* analysis sweeps of the average response computer, with the *I* or *E* pulses (according to the case) as synchronizing triggers. *A*, *N*=20; *B*, *N*=47. Range of bins in which expiratory phase starts is indicated at right of histogram; mean frequencies in these bins were calculated according to number of *I* phases remaining in sample. *Right*: mean frequency in inspiratory phase and peak frequency (in first or second bin of each histogram) at different end-tidal carbon dioxide levels. *A* and *B* are points corresponding to histograms at left.

Finally, the typical response of expiratory-inspiratory neurones to hypocapnia is shown (Fig. 7). When the carbon dioxide level was lowered, the discharge in the high-frequency portion of the cycle (late expiratory and early inspiratory phases) was reduced, but at the same time the discharge in the low-frequency portion of the cycle (late inspiratory and early expiratory phases) was increased, so that the degree of frequency modulation with the respiratory cycle was reduced. In a neurone of this type, when the carbon dioxide level was sufficiently reduced, respiratory periodicity disappeared and the neurone fired with the same frequency in different portions of the cycle (cf. Cohen, 1968, Figs. 14, 15).

Although neurones of any pre-existing discharge pattern might show either of the two responses to hypocapnia, particular response types were

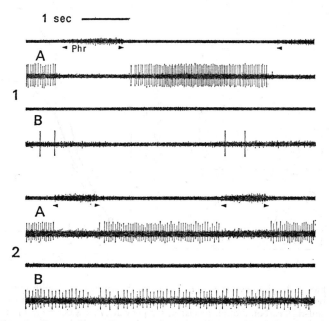

Fig. 6. Comparison of two expiratory neurones (in different cats) showing different responses to hypocapnia (type 1 and type 2). End-tidal carbon dioxide levels: 1: A, 2·9 per cent; B, 1·2 per cent. 2: A, 3·7 per cent; B, 1·2 per cent. Times of phrenic activity (top trace of each strip) are indicated by horizontal arrows.

more common for certain classes of neurone than for others. Thus, almost all inspiratory neurones had type-1 responses; most early expiratory, late expiratory and inspiratory-expiratory neurones had type-1 responses; type-1 and type-2 responses were about equally common among expiratory-(all) neurones; and most expiratory-inspiratory neurones had type-2 responses.

The coexistence of type-1 responses in some neurones and type-2 responses in others supports the idea that respiratory periodicity arises from mutually inhibitory connexions between reciprocal neuronal networks.

As an example, let us take the neuronal pair consisting of (*a*) an inspiratory neurone with type-1 response and (*b*) an expiratory neurone with type-2 response; on the hypothesis that the two types of neurone are members of two mutually inhibitory networks, let us analyse what happens during transition from a hypocapnic to a normocapnic state. During hypocapnia

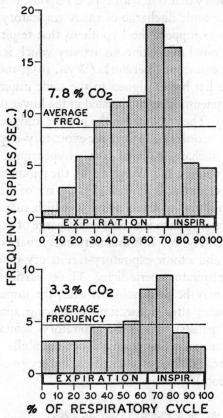

FIG. 7. Expiratory-inspiratory neurone with type-2 response to hypocapnia. End-tidal carbon dioxide: *top*, 7·8 per cent; *bottom*, 3·3 per cent. Spikes are distributed according to occurrence in fractional portion of each respiratory cycle (measured from start of expiratory phase).

many expiratory neurones are firing uninterruptedly, while inspiratory neurones are silent. When the carbon dioxide level is raised, increased chemoceptive input causes some inspiratory neurones to fire and exert inhibitory actions on expiratory neurones, so that some of the latter type now exhibit periods of silence; the consequent reduction of the expiratory neurones' inhibitory input to inspiratory neurones in turn allows greater discharge of the latter group; thus, through a circular process, respiratory periodicity is re-established (for an experimental case, cf. Cohen, 1968, Fig. 4).

An analogous argument can be applied to the neuronal pair consisting of (a) an inspiratory-expiratory neurone with type-1 response and (b) an expiratory-inspiratory neurone with type-2 response (Fig. 3, bottom).

The existence of tonic discharge of many respiratory neurones during hypocapnia tends to support the hypothesis that respiratory periodicity arises on a background of continuous activity which is then periodically inhibited through connecting networks (Wyss, 1954, 1964). In particular, an important role has been assigned to the tonic inspiratory-facilitatory drive from the "apneustic centre" located in the lower pons (Wang, Ngai and Frumin, 1957). The results from the present study tend to support the hypothesis of an apneustic centre since the expiratory-inspiratory neurones, which have tonic discharge patterns during hypocapnia, are found mainly in the lower pons (Cohen and Wang, 1959), the region which, on the basis of transection experiments, is postulated as the site of the apneustic centre.

However, in addition to tonic activity, which may be considered as inspiratory-facilitatory, there is also tonic discharge of expiratory neurones during hypocapnia (Fig. 6). It is therefore likely that both a tonic inspiratory-facilitatory and a tonic expiratory-facilitatory system are important in the genesis of respiratory periodicity. Under particular conditions one or other system may be predominant: thus, the inspiratory-facilitatory system predominates after transections producing apneustic respiration (long inspiratory pauses); while the expiratory-facilitatory system predominates after transection between pons and medulla, which produces a gasping type of respiration (prolonged expiratory pauses interrupted by maximal inspirations).

*Discharge patterns and lung inflation (Cohen, 1969)*

In cats with intact vagi, the periodic lung inflation produced by the artificial ventilation pump was used as a source of afferent input to influence respiratory periodicity. By occlusion at appropriate times in the inflation cycle, the classical Hering-Breuer reflex was produced; and the concomitant changes of respiratory neurones' activity were correlated with the changes in the central respiratory cycle, indicated by phrenic discharge.

In this experimental situation, the central respiratory cycle tends to become synchronized to the cycle of artificial ventilation, usually in a 1:1 or 1:2 relationship. In the text which follows, the phases of the central respiratory cycle will be designated as "inspiratory" and "expiratory" (periods of phrenic activity and inactivity respectively); and the phases of the artificial ventilation cycle will be designated as "inflation" and "deflation" (increase and decrease of lung volume respectively).

The Hering-Breuer reflex produced by lung inflation is expiratory-facilitatory and inspiratory-inhibitory: inflation produces lengthening of the expiratory phase and prevention of inflation produces lengthening of the inspiratory phase. One might therefore expect that the discharge of inspiration-related neurones would be depressed, and of expiration-related neurones facilitated, by lung inflation; and indeed many neurones showed such effects, which are in the same direction as the Hering-Breuer reflex. But, in addition, many neurones had responses which might be considered

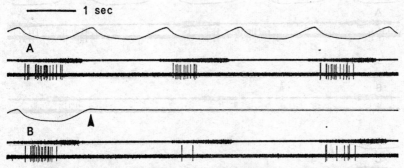

FIG. 8. Inspiratory neurone depressed by inflation. In Figs. 8–11 the traces are: *top*: airway pressure (inflation upward); *middle*: phrenic potentials; *bottom*: unit potentials. *A*: control state (2:1 synchronization of pump and central respiratory cycles). *B*: occlusion at inflation peak in the early expiratory phase (onset of occlusion indicated by arrow).

paradoxical, that is, the responses were in the opposite direction to the Hering-Breuer reflex: inspiration-related neurones were facilitated and expiration-related neurones were depressed by inflation.

In the most usual state of synchronization, the pump inflation stroke started during the phase of phrenic discharge and caused an earlier termination of the inspiratory phase than occurred when the inflation was prevented (by occlusion). Most of the inspiratory neurones depressed by inflation responded in a manner similar to phrenic discharge (cf. Cohen, 1969, Figs. 3, 4). However, some inspiratory neurones were more markedly depressed by inflation than was phrenic discharge; an example is shown in Fig. 8. When occlusion was started at peak inflation (*B*), the maintained inflation resulted in lengthening of the expiratory phase and a reduction of phrenic activity during the next inspiratory phase, but the neurone was more drastically inhibited than was phrenic discharge: the number of spikes in the neurone's burst was reduced to two from the control value of seventeen.

An example of an inspiratory neurone which was also independently excited by inflation is shown in Fig. 9. During the control state of 2:1 synchronization between pump and central respiratory cycles (A) the neurone fired in two bursts, one during the inspiratory phase and one during the expiratory phase coincidently with a lung inflation. Indeed, the lung inflation was producing the latter burst since prevention of the inflation by occlusion (B) resulted in disappearance of the burst. The excitatory effect

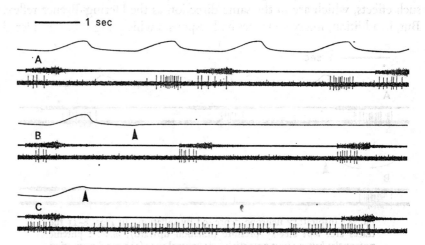

FIG. 9. Inspiratory neurone excited by inflation. *A*: control state (2:1 synchronization). *B*: occlusion at minimum lung volume, which prevents occurrence of the next inflation. *C*: occlusion at inflation peak in the early expiratory phase (Cohen, 1969, Fig. 10; reproduced by permission of *J. Neurophysiol.*). (See also legend to Fig. 8.)

of inflation was further shown by occlusion at peak inflation (*C*); the neurone continued to fire during the lengthened expiratory phase produced by the maintained inflation.

Since maintained inflation results in lengthening of the expiratory phase, one might expect that it would also produce an increase of expiratory neurones' discharge; and this response is observed in thoracic and abdominal expiratory motoneurones and muscles (Sears, 1964; Bishop, 1964). An example of a brainstem expiratory neurone which was excited by inflation is shown in Fig. 10 (1, top). In addition, another expiratory neurone is shown (2, bottom) whose activity was depressed by inflation. Both neurones had somewhat similar discharge patterns (predominantly early-expiratory) and were observed in the same electrode track within a short time of each other; yet they showed opposite responses to inflation. Similarly, these opposite responses (facilitation and depression) were observed in neurones which had late-expiratory or expiratory-(all) patterns (cf. Cohen, 1969, Figs. 7, 8, 11).

Finally, the response to inflation exhibited by many expiratory-inspiratory neurones can be seen in Fig. 11B: a maintained inflation resulted in

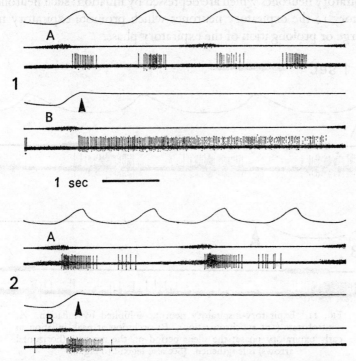

FIG. 10. Comparison of occlusion effects on two predominantly early-expiratory neurones having opposite responses to inflation (*1*, excited; *2*, depressed). *A*: control state (2:1 synchronization); each neurone fires in two bursts. *B*: occlusion at peak inflation in early expiratory phase. The discharge of *1* is increased; that of *2* is decreased. (For further details, cf. Cohen, 1969, Fig. 9.) (See also legend to Fig. 8.)

prolongation of the neurone's silent period (delay from the end of the inspiratory phase to the first spike in the expiratory phase); and this inhibitory effect of inflation was accompanied by the usual prolongation of the expiratory phase. This effect is consistent with the hypothesis that neurones of this type promote the transition from the expiratory to the inspiratory phase, since prolongation of the inactivity of such a neurone is accompanied by a delay in the onset of the next inspiratory phase.

The paradoxical effect of inspiratory neurones being excited by inflation was first observed by Baumgarten and Kanzow (1958), who suggested that such neurones were inhibitory to the inspiratory neurones which promote inspiratory motor discharge. Some of my own ancillary observations (Cohen, 1969) have strengthened this hypothesis. In addition, I have proposed an analogous hypothesis to explain the paradoxical responses of expiratory neurones which are depressed by inflation: such neurones are inhibitory to the expiratory neurones which promote expiratory motor discharge or prolongation of the expiratory phase.

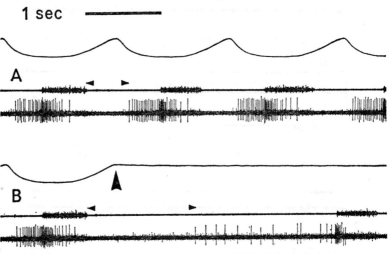

FIG. 11. Expiratory-inspiratory neurone inhibited by inflation. *A*: control state (1:1 synchronization). *B*: occlusion at peak inflation in early expiratory phase; the silent period of the neurone (horizontal arrows) is lengthened. (See also legend to Fig. 8.)

Thus, the most plausible hypothesis to explain the paradoxical responses is as follows: neurones with such responses are interneurones in the reflex arc connecting (*a*) vagal stretch receptor afferents and (*b*) neurones which ultimately promote inspiratory or expiratory motor activity or which promote prolongation of the appropriate phase. According to this view, the inspiratory neurones which are excited by inflation are anti-inspiratory in function, while the expiratory neurones which are depressed by inflation are anti-expiratory in function.

### Discharge patterns during brainstem electrical stimulation

By electrical stimulation of appropriate brainstem regions graded changes in the respiratory cycle can be produced. This method is being used to evaluate the functions of respiratory neurones by correlating the induced changes of their activity with the changes in phrenic discharge. The procedure used is to deliver brief trains of stimuli at predetermined times in the respiratory cycle.

Although respiratory changes can be evoked by stimulation of many brainstem points (Ngai and Wang, 1957; Tan, 1967), in the present study attention is being directed mainly to a region of the dorsolateral rostral

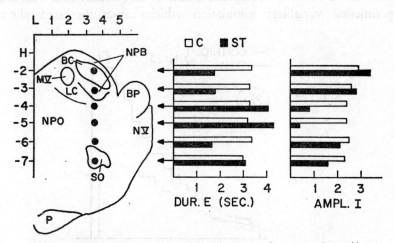

FIG. 12. Effects of electrical stimulation (0·3-ms pulses, 0·5 mA, 250/s) at six points of electrode track in the upper pons (coordinates 3·5 mm lateral, P(3), H(−2) to H(−7)). *C*: control; *ST*: stimulation. *Left graph*: effects on expiratory (*E*)-phase duration; stimulus train started at middle of *E* phase (delay from start of *E* phase equal to half the duration of control *E* phase). *Right graph*: effects on end-inspiratory amplitude (*I*) of integrated phrenic signal; stimulus train started at middle of *I* phase (delay from start of *I* phase equal to half the duration of control *I* phase). Trains were continued to at least the succeeding phase transition. Anatomical diagram constructed from histological sections. *Abbreviations*: *BC*: brachium conjunctivum; *BP*: brachium pontis; *LC*: locus coeruleus; *MV*: motor nucleus of Vth nerve; *NPB*: nucleus parabrachialis; *NPO*: nucleus pontis oralis; *NV*: Vth nerve; *P*: pyramid; *SO*: superior olive.

pons (the "pneumotaxic centre" just caudal to the inferior colliculi) which is known to be important for respiratory periodicity: lesions in this region produce apneustic respiration in vagotomized animals (Tang, 1953; Wang, Ngai and Frumin, 1957). The respiratory effects obtained from stimulation at this level of the pons are shown, together with the anatomical loci, in Fig. 12. Stimulation at more dorsal points has inspiratory-facilitatory effects: delivery during the expiratory phase causes a shortening of the phase, and stimulation during the inspiratory phase causes increased phrenic discharge. Conversely, stimulation at more ventral points has expiratory-facilitatory effects: delivery during the expiratory phase causes a lengthening of the phase, and during the inspiratory phase a shortening of the phase. By variation of time of delivery, current strength and stimulus frequency, it is possible to grade these effects.

The responses of medullary inspiratory neurones to electrical stimulation of the dorsal inspiratory-facilitatory region have been observed. Here again we find a duality of response similar to that already seen with other experimental variables: stimulation which causes increased phrenic

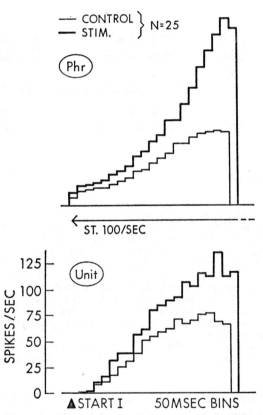

Fig. 13. Inspiratory neurone excited by pontine electrical stimulation which increases phrenic discharge. *Top*: summed phrenic (*Phr*) potentials (after half-wave rectification); histogram (arbitrary scale) constructed from digital readout of average response computer. *Bottom*: mean frequency of unit, from spike counts in average response computer. *ST*: stimulus train started 10 ms after onset of, and stopped at end of, *I* phase; dotted line at right indicates that individual *I* phases end at different times. Histograms are terminated at bin preceding the bin during which shortest *I* phase ends.

discharge produces excitation of some inspiratory neurones and inhibition of other inspiratory neurones. This duality is seen in the opposite responses of two medullary inspiratory neurones recorded in different cats (Figs. 13, 14).

The first inspiratory neurone, which had an incrementing discharge pattern (Fig. 13), was excited by upper pontine stimulation. The stimulus trains (at 100/s), which started at the onset and continued till the end of the inspiratory phase, resulted in a marked increase of phrenic discharge as

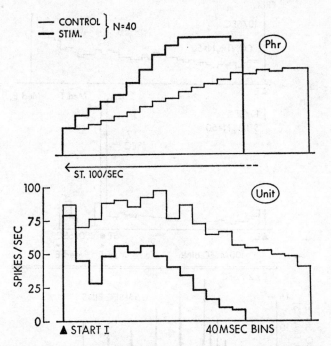

FIG. 14. Inspiratory neurone inhibited by pontine electrical stimulation which increases phrenic discharge. (For explanation of histograms see legend of Fig. 13.)

shown by the histograms of summed phrenic potentials; and the inspiratory neurone also showed a similar increase of discharge. The contrasting response of the second medullary inspiratory neurone, which had a decrementing discharge pattern, is shown in Fig. 14. Here, the neurone's discharge was inhibited by pontine electrical stimulation which produced an increase of phrenic discharge. This effect was not necessarily related to the fact that the neurone had a decrementing discharge pattern, since other inspiratory neurones with decrementing patterns showed increased discharge simultaneously with the increased phrenic discharge produced by stimulation.

The opposite responses of different inspiratory neurones to stimulation undoubtedly indicate differences of function. More detailed investigations are being undertaken to elucidate these differences. For example, it will be of particular interest to compare the response of the same neurone to electrical stimulation and to lung inflation. Thus, it might be expected

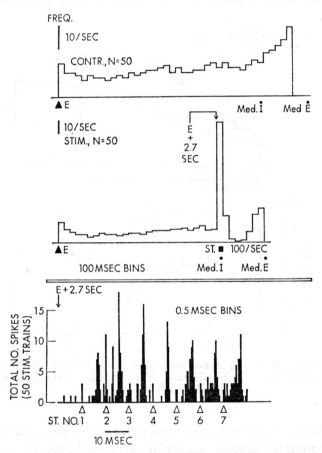

FIG. 15. Lower pontine expiratory-inspiratory neurone excited by upper pontine electrical stimulation which shortens the expiratory phase. Stimulus trains started 2·7 s after onset of E phase and terminated at onset of I phase. *Top and middle histograms*: each histogram is terminated at bin preceding the bin during which shortest respiratory cycle ends. Bin in which median incidence of I or E pulses falls is indicated by dot. Note that frequency scale of stimulus (middle) histogram is half that of control (top) histogram. *Bottom histogram*: incidence of unit spikes in relation to individual stimuli (white arrows).

that an inspiratory neurone which responds to electrical stimuli in a manner opposite to phrenic discharge would also respond oppositely to lung inflation, that is, it would be excited by inflation.

The method of electrical stimulation has also been used to study the mechanism of transition from expiratory to inspiratory phase and the possible role of expiratory-inspiratory neurones in this transition. The response to upper pontine stimulation of a lower pontine neurone with continuous discharge of expiratory-inspiratory type is shown in Fig. 15. This neurone had its lowest discharge frequency in the early expiratory phase; the frequency gradually increased throughout the expiratory phase; and then it rose more sharply during the inspiratory phase (control histogram, top). Upper pontine electrical stimulation (a train of stimuli at 100/s started 2·7 s after the onset of the expiratory phase and terminated by the onset of the next inspiratory phase) produced drastic changes in both the respiratory cycle and the neurone's discharge. The train caused termination of the expiratory phase within 80–100 ms, and thus decreased the duration of the expiratory phase from 3·4 to 2·8 s (median values). During the stimulus train, the neurone's discharge frequency increased more than sevenfold (from 13 to 100/s); this increase was followed by a rebound depression of activity (to the point of almost complete silence) and then by recovery to the control level.

The association of shortened expiratory phase with the large increase of the neurone's discharge is consistent with the hypothesis that this neurone is involved in a system promoting the transition from expiratory to inspiratory phase. However, another possible interpretation is that the neurone's response is related to simultaneously occurring vasomotor changes since: (a) discharge in sympathetic nerves has a respiratory rhythm with a pattern similar to that of the neurone under observation (Gootman, 1967), so that the neurone might be primarily vasomotor in function; and (b) upper pontine electrical stimulation also produces a marked increase of arterial blood pressure. Thus, further investigation must distinguish between effects related primarily to respiratory periodicity and effects related to simultaneous changes of vasomotor activity.

Another type of information obtained from the stimulation studies concerns the time relationship between individual stimuli and unit discharge. This latency relationship is shown in the bottom histogram of Fig. 15. It can be seen that the spikes tended to be concentrated at a time near 6 ms following each stimulus; and this was also the latency for the response to the first shock. Since the onset of phrenic discharge occurred considerably later (80–100 ms after the first shock), the neurone must have been located relatively near, synaptically speaking, the upper pontine centres which were being activated by stimulation.

The isolated observations which have just been presented resulted from an extensive experimental programme using the technique of electrical stimulation. Because this technique enables the experimenter to exert graded control over the characteristics of the respiratory cycle, it should furnish much information about the temporal relationships between

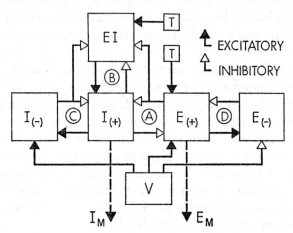

FIG. 16. Schema of hypothetical loops in the respiratory oscillator and their relation to vagal afferent input ($V$). *Black arrows*: excitatory connexions; *white arrows*: inhibitory connexions. $I_M$: inspiratory motor neurones. $E_M$: expiratory motor neurones. $I_{(+)}$: inspiratory-facilitatory system. $I_{(-)}$: inspiratory-inhibitory system. $E_{(+)}$: expiratory-facilitatory system. $E_{(-)}$: expiratory-inhibitory system. $EI$: expiratory-inspiratory system. $T$: tonic input. $A$: master oscillatory loop; $B$: inspiratory-initiatory loop; $C$: inspiratory-inhibitory loop; $D$: expiratory-inhibitory loop.

different neurones in the respiratory centres and about the interactions which generate respiratory periodicity.

## GENERAL SCHEMA OF RESPIRATORY PERIODICITY

A general schema of the origin of respiratory periodicity, based on existing data, will now be presented in an attempt to provide a framework for further research. The respiratory oscillator (Fig. 16) consists of several interrelated subsidiary loops, which in turn consist of operationally defined sub-systems, shown as black boxes with excitatory and inhibitory interconnexions.

In general agreement with the ideas of earlier workers, the schema depicts mutually-inhibitory inspiratory and expiratory "half-centres" (Gesell, 1940): (a) an inspiratory-facilitatory system, $I_{(+)}$, which ultimately produces inspiratory motor discharge ($I_M$); and (b) an expiratory-facilitatory system, $E_{(+)}$, which ultimately produces expiratory motor discharge ($E_M$). Within each of these systems, there probably exist positive-feedback or re-excitant loops which promote maintenance and augmentation of discharge frequency.

The effects of pulmonary stretch receptor input ($V$: vagal) are shown on the basis of results from a previous study (Cohen, 1969). Three destinations of vagal input are shown: (1) excitatory input to the inspiratory-inhibitory system; (2) excitatory input to the expiratory-facilitatory system; and (3) inhibitory input to the expiratory-inhibitory system.

*Master oscillatory loop (A)*

The existence of mutually inhibitory inspiratory-facilitatory and expiratory-facilitatory networks is postulated to account for the alternation of respiratory phases. The master oscillatory loop, consisting of these two networks, is a positive-feedback system, since initiation of activity in one of the constituent systems produces inhibition of the complementary system, which in turn causes a lessening of inhibition of the first system. Thus, activity in one member of the pair will tend to reinforce itself and to diminish activity in the other member; the loop therefore resembles a multivibrator with two stable states.

However, mechanisms must exist to shift the system between the inspiratory and the expiratory states otherwise it would remain indefinitely in one of the two states. It is postulated that such mechanisms are provided by tonic ($T$) inputs to the expiratory-facilitatory and inspiratory-facilitatory systems. The existence of such tonic drives is supported by the observations (Cohen, 1968) that during hypocapnia many expiratory neurones and most expiratory-inspiratory neurones discharge uninterruptedly.

*Inspiratory-initiatory loop (B)*

The original proposal that expiratory-inspiratory (*EI*) neurones have an inspiratory-initiatory function is supported by the finding that inflation simultaneously produces: (a) depression of discharge of many *EI* neurones (lengthened silent period); and (b) prolongation of the expiratory phase. The hypothesis is also supported by the existence of the association between shortening of expiratory phase and excitation of *EI* neurones, both caused by upper pontine stimulation (Fig. 15).

The activity of the inspiratory-initiatory loop can be pictured as follows. Throughout the late expiratory phase, $EI$ discharge is increasing, until at a critical level the discharge of inspiratory neurones is initiated. The discharge of the $EI$ neurones is then inhibited in three ways: (a) by input from $I_{(+)}$ neurones, deduced from the fact that the discharge of many $EI$ neurones starts to diminish well before the end of the inspiratory phase; (b) by input from a portion of the $E_{(+)}$ system, probably the early expiratory neurones, deduced from the fact that the silent period continues well into the expiratory phase; and (c) by vagal afferent input from pulmonary stretch receptors, deduced from the effects of inflation. It is necessary to postulate that inhibitory actions (a) and (b) may be independent of vagal afferent input, since the same basic discharge pattern exists after vagotomy. The resumption of $EI$ discharge in the middle expiratory phase arises in three ways: (a) by decrement of the inhibitory early-expiratory discharge, presumably due to a subsidiary inhibitory loop, or to adaptation, within the $E_{(+)}$ system; (b) in spontaneous breathing, by reduction of the inhibitory stretch receptor discharge when lung volume is reduced during the expiratory phase; and (c) by excitation from tonic ($T$) inputs.

## Inspiratory-inhibitory loop (C)

The existence of an inspiratory-inhibitory loop is supported by the observation that some neurones fire during the inspiratory phase but can also be independently excited by inflation. These neurones are thought to fulfil an inspiratory-inhibitory function; they are shown ($I_{(-)}$) as being excited both by input from pulmonary stretch receptors ($V$) and by input from $I_{(+)}$ neurones, and in turn they act to inhibit $I_{(+)}$ neurones and to terminate the inspiratory phase. Although the discharge of the $I_{(-)}$ neurones is facilitated by vagal afferent input, it must also arise from excitation by $I_{(+)}$ neurones, since it occurs during the inspiratory phase even when there is no lung expansion.

## Expiratory-inhibitory loop (D)

The arguments for the existence of this loop are analogous to those for the existence of the inspiratory-inhibitory loop. It is necessary to postulate a mechanism for bringing expiratory discharge to an end and allowing the $EI$ network to initiate the next inspiratory phase. In addition, there must be pulmonary stretch receptor inputs to the loop, since inflation imposed during the expiratory phase results in facilitation of some expiratory neurones and depression of others. The latter effect is depicted in the diagram as arising from vagal inhibitory input to the $E_{(-)}$ neurones, which are postulated to be expiratory-inhibitory in function; thus inflation lengthens the expiratory phase by disinhibition. In addition, a possible direct excitatory vagal input to $E_{(+)}$ neurones is shown.

## SUMMARY

The origin of respiratory periodicity is being studied through observation of discharge patterns of brainstem respiratory neurones. Microelectrode recordings of pontine and medullary respiratory neurones reveal an almost bewildering variety of discharge patterns. The primary classification of these patterns is based on the phase relation of discharge to the overall respiratory cycle, indicated by phrenic discharge. The functions of the various types of neurone have been studied by observing their responses to several experimental variables: (a) carbon dioxide tension; (b) lung inflation; and (c) brainstem electrical stimulation. The most interesting and perhaps most significant finding of these experiments is that different neurones having similar discharge patterns may have different, and indeed opposite, responses to the same type of stimulus. Thus lung inflation, which evokes the Hering-Breuer reflex, has two classes of action on respiratory neurones: (a) responses in the same direction as the Hering-Breuer reflex (inspiratory neurones depressed and expiratory neurones facilitated by inflation); and (b) responses in the opposite direction to the Hering-Breuer reflex (inspiratory neurones facilitated and expiratory neurones depressed by inflation). On the basis of existing data, a preliminary model is presented which shows how interactions between various classes of respiratory neurone may generate respiratory rhythmicity.

ACKNOWLEDGEMENTS

This work was supported by US Public Health Service Grant NB-03970. The author is Career Scientist of the Health Research Council of the City of New York (Contract I-292).

## REFERENCES

BATSEL, H. L. (1964). *Expl Neurol.*, **9**, 410–426.
BAUMGARTEN, R. VON, BAUMGARTEN, A. VON and SCHAEFER, K.-P. (1957). *Pflügers Arch. ges. Physiol.*, **264**, 217–227.
BAUMGARTEN, R. VON and KANZOW, E. (1958). *Archs ital. Biol.*, **96**, 361–373.
BAXTER, D. W., and OLSZEWSKI, J. (1955). *J. Neurophysiol.*, **18**, 276–287.
BISHOP, B. (1964). *J. appl. Physiol.*, **19**, 224–232.
BRECKENRIDGE, C. G., and HOFF, H. E. (1950). *Am. J. Physiol.*, **160**, 385–394.
BROOKHART, J. M. (1940). *Am. J. Physiol.*, **129**, 709–723.

CARREGAL, E. J. A., WILLIAMS, B., and BIRZIS, L. (1967). *Resp. Physiol.*, **3**, 333–348.

COHEN, M. I. (1964*a*). *Fedn Proc. Fedn Am. Socs exp. Biol.*, **23**, 304.

COHEN, M. I. (1964*b*). *Am. J. Physiol.*, **206**, 845–854.

COHEN, M. I. (1968). *J. Neurophysiol.*, **31**, 142–165.

COHEN, M. I. (1969). *J. Neurophysiol.*, **32**, 356–374.

COHEN, M. I., and WANG, S. C. (1959). *J. Neurophysiol.*, **22**, 33–50.

DIRKEN, M. N. J., and WOLDRING, S. (1951). *J. Neurophysiol.*, **14**, 211–226.

EKLUND, G., EULER, C. VON, and RUTKOWSKI, S. (1964). *J. Physiol., Lond.*, **171**, 139–163.

EYZAGUIRRE, C., and TAYLOR, J. R. (1963). *J. Neurophysiol.*, **26**, 61–78.

FLOERSHEIM, G. L. (1960). *Helv. physiol. pharmac. Acta*, **18**, 17–24.

GESELL, R. (1936). *Am. J. Physiol.*, **116**, 228–238.

GESELL, R. (1940). *Ergebn. Physiol.*, **43**, 477–639.

GESELL, R., BRICKER, J., and MAGEE, C. (1936). *Am. J. Physiol.*, **117**, 423–452.

GILL, P. K. (1963). *J. Physiol., Lond.*, **168**, 239–257.

GOOTMAN, P. M. (1967). *Brain Stem Influences on Efferent Splanchnic Discharge.* Ph.D. thesis, Yeshiva University, Faculty of Physiology.

HABER, E., KOHN, K. W., NGAI, S. H., HOLADAY, D. A., and WANG, S. C. (1957). *Am. J. Physiol.*, **190**, 350–355.

HUKUHARA, T., NAKAYAMA, S., and OKADA, H. (1954). *Jap. J. Physiol.*, **4**, 145–153.

KUMAGAI, H., SAKAI, F., SAKUMA, A., and HUKUHARA, T. (1966). *Progr. Brain Res.*, **21**, 98–111.

LILLY, J. C., HUGHES, J. R., ALVORD, E. C., JR., and GALKIN, T. W. (1955). *Science*, **121A**, 468–469.

NESLAND, R., and PLUM, F. (1965). *Expl Neurol.*, **12**, 337–348.

NGAI, S. H., and WANG, S. C. (1957). *Am. J. Physiol.*, **190**, 343–349.

PITTS, R. F., MAGOUN, H. W., and RANSON, S. W. (1939*a*). *Am. J. Physiol.*, **126**, 673–688.

PITTS, R. F., MAGOUN, H. W., and RANSON, S. W. (1939*b*). *Am. J. Physiol.*, **127**, 654–670.

RIJLANT, P. (1937). *Archs int. Physiol.*, **44**, 351–386.

SALMOIRAGHI, G. C., and BURNS, B. D. (1960). *J. Neurophysiol.*, **23**, 2–13.

SEARS, T. A. (1964). *J. Physiol., Lond.*, **174**, 295–315.

TAN, E.-S. (1967). *Expl Neurol.*, **17**, 517–528.

TANG, P. C. (1953). *Am. J. Physiol.*, **172**, 645–652.

TANG, P. C. (1967). *Resp. Physiol.*, **3**, 349–366.

WANG, S. C., NGAI, S. H., and FRUMIN, M. J. (1957). *Am. J. Physiol.*, **190**, 333–342.

WYSS, O. A. M. (1954). *Helv. physiol. pharmac. Acta*, suppl. X.

WYSS, O. A. M. (1964). *Ergebn. Physiol.*, **54**, 1–479.

YAŞARGIL, G. M. (1967). *Helv. physiol. pharmac. Acta*, suppl. XVIII.

# DISCUSSION

*Dornhorst:* In the group of experiments in which you stimulated the upper pons, where did you record from?

*Cohen:* We recorded mainly in the regions of the medulla near the obex where inspiratory and expiratory neurones are plentiful (Baumgarten, Baumgarten and Schaefer, 1957; Haber *et al.*, 1957). I plan to make more extensive explorations in future experiments.

*Howell:* How do you know that these inspiratory and expiratory neurones are in fact controlling the act of breathing? Could not laryngeal movement, which also has a phasic effect, be the mechanism which is being controlled?

*Cohen:* Aren't laryngeal movements part of the act of breathing?

*Howell:* No, because a laryngeal contraction during expiration does not cause expiratory air flow.

*Cohen:* The glottis normally dilates during inspiration (Bianconi, Corazza and Raschi, 1963) and normally a burst of activity during the inspiratory phase can be recorded in the efferent recurrent laryngeal nerve (Rijlant, 1937; Cohen, unpublished observations). In answer to your question, I have identified the brainstem respiratory neurones in my studies only by inference, for example by comparison of their discharge patterns with those in peripheral nerves. Thus, phrenic discharge has an augmenting pattern (Cohen, this volume, p. 127, Fig. 1), whereas recurrent laryngeal discharge reaches a plateau level early in the inspiratory phase and then decrements (unpublished observations). The latter pattern is very similar to that of the medullary inspiratory neurone illustrated in my Fig. 5 (this volume, p. 133), and one might infer that neurones of this type belong to the system generating laryngeal discharge. Presumably laryngeal mononeurones could be identified by antidromic stimulation of the nerve. Dr Merrill (personal communication) has done this for some medullary neurones. But if one cannot antidromically activate a neurone one must infer that it is an interneurone, and other criteria must be used to specify its function.

*von Euler:* Have you tried to identify these neurones by stimulating them antidromically in their descending path, as was done by Baumgarten and Nakayama (1964)?

*Cohen:* No.

*Sears:* Where in your model is the group of neurones representing the prime mover for inspiratory output? Do the inspiratory and expiratory neurones you showed represent the cells in the medial and lateral parts of the reticular formation in the caudal medulla?

*Cohen:* My model represents functions, and therefore the various blocks do not necessarily correspond to anatomical regions. Reticular neurones located close together are known to respond quite differently to the same stimulus (Amassian, Macy and Waller, 1961). This is also true for respiratory neurones; for example my Fig. 10 (this volume, p. 139) shows that two expiratory neurones in close proximity had opposite responses to inflation.

The greatest concentration of inspiratory neurones is found in two regions of the medulla: (*a*) the lateral reticular formation, about 3-4 mm rostral to the obex (Batsel, 1964; Haber *et al.*, 1957); and (*b*) the region ventral to the tractus solitarius and its nucleus (Baumgarten, Baumgarten and Schaefer, 1957). The greatest concentration of expiratory neurones is found more caudally, in a region 3–4 mm caudal to the obex, near the nucleus ambiguus (Haber *et al.*, 1957; Baumgarten, Baumgarten and Schaefer, 1957). It has also been shown (by antidromic stimulation) that many of the neurones in these regions send axons down the spinal cord (Nakayama and Baumgarten, 1964). In addition, it should be emphasized that respiratory neurones are scattered throughout the lateral reticular formation of the medulla, although less densely than in the two other regions described.

In contrast to the populations in the medulla, which are mainly inspiratory and expiratory, respiratory neurones in the pons (that is, the region from the level of the eighth nerve nucleus to the level of the inferior colliculus) are mainly phase-spanning in discharge pattern (including tonic discharge frequency modulated with the respiratory cycle) (Cohen and Wang, 1959).

*Fillenz:* How can the observations that discharge from the inspiratory unit decreased at the same time as phrenic discharge was not only increased but also shortened be reconciled? Does the increased phrenic discharge indicate an increase in inspiratory neurone activity which is then cut short by inhibition?

*Cohen:* Fig. 14 (Cohen, this volume, p. 143) shows an example of the effect of electrical stimulation in the dorsolateral rostral pons (nucleus parabrachialis): phrenic motoneurone discharge is increased, as shown by the increased slope of the histogram as well as the higher level of discharge at the end of the inspiratory burst. The effect of electrical stimulation on the duration of the inspiratory phase varies from cat to cat: there is sometimes a decrease (Fig. 14) and sometimes an increase; (Fig. 13, this volume, p. 142, shows a slight increase).

*Fillenz:* How are these neurones inhibited in animals whose vagi are cut?

*Cohen:* By entirely central, inhibitory circuits.

*Fillenz:* I still do not understand. You seem to be implying that the inhibitory unit does not inhibit inspiration. What kind of unit is it then?

*Cohen:* One possible interpretation of the fact that a medullary inspiratory neurone is inhibited while phrenic discharge is increased is that this neurone is part of a system which ultimately inhibits phrenic motoneurone discharge, and that inhibition of these inhibitors is contributing to the increased phrenic discharge.

*Fillenz:* Then why is the time of phrenic motor discharge shortened? Is an additional phase of respiration occurring here?

*Cohen:* The shortening of the phrenic burst in this situation may be caused by neurones of other systems which are active near the end of the inspiratory phase. There are at least two variables of phrenic discharge which can be changed: rate of increase (slope) and peak (end-inspiratory) level of discharge; and different systems may act independently on these variables. (For further observations on such independent actions, cf. Hugelin and Cohen, 1963; Cohen and Hugelin, 1965.)

*Karczewski:* Is the particular type of neuronal response permanent? In other words, will any given neurone always show the same response to the same stimulus, or are there several programmes for every neurone so that it may respond differently to the same stimulus in different biological situations? We are currently investigating this problem but our preliminary impressions are that in rabbits there are several types of responses rather than several types of neurones (Bystrzycka *et al.*, 1970). For example, the same medullary or phrenic neurone can respond to hyperventilation (at the same $Pa_{CO_2}$) by continuous discharge or by a complete disappearance of activity, depending upon the level of anaesthesia. In our opinion the type of response is variable and depends upon various general factors, including state of consciousness, integrity of the vagi, metabolism and probably some others.

*Cohen:* We found that the response of each neurone was reproducible in the given experimental conditions. The question of how a neurone would react in other conditions is obviously unanswerable. However, if we always compare a neurone's response with the simultaneous response of the global system (as indicated in phrenic discharge), then we may ultimately generalize by producing different types of phrenic response. A particularly important kind of experiment is to study the same neurone's responses during changes produced by several different procedures (for example lung inflation and brainstem electrical stimulation).

*Newsom Davis:* Scheibel and Scheibel (1965) reported that changes may occur in the sensory responsiveness of individual reticular neurones. When the activity of such neurones is recorded for up to ten hours, responsiveness to stimuli such as a flash or click can be followed by a period of unresponsiveness during which the activity pattern may reflect respiratory rhythms, suggesting that these neurones may show periodic changes of the neural net in which they are involved. Have you looked at any of your units from this point of view?

*Cohen:* I have seen some pontine respiratory neurones showing

A

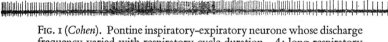

B

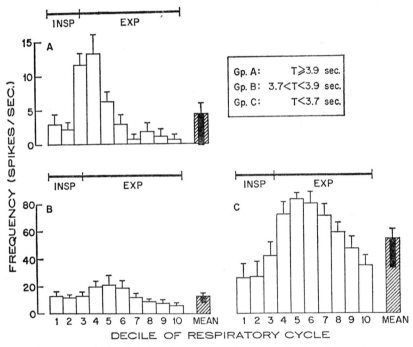

FIG. 1 (*Cohen*). Pontine inspiratory-expiratory neurone whose discharge frequency varied with respiratory cycle duration. *A*: long respiratory cycle (4·0 s) with 10 spikes; *B*: short respiratory cycle (3·4 s) with 217 spikes.

FIG. 2 (*Cohen*). Relation between respiratory cycle duration and discharge pattern of a pontine inspiratory-expiratory neurone. A sample of 21 consecutive cycles was divided into three sub-samples (N=7 each) according to cycle duration (T). In each cycle the spikes were distributed according to the cycle fraction in which they occurred. Each cycle fraction histogram shows mean frequency (white bar) and and standard error (vertical line) for each decile of cycle. At right of histograms, the cross-hatched bar indicates mean frequency per cycle and the black bar indicates RSD (respiratory standard deviation of frequency). Note that frequency scale in B and C is different from that in A. (For further explanation of method of analysis, cf. Cohen, 1968.)

variations of discharge associated with fluctuations in the duration of the respiratory cycle. The upper pontine inspiratory-expiratory neurone shown in Figs 1 and 2 had large variations in the number of spikes per cycle, with a large frequency increase occurring in short cycles (Fig. 1 B). The relation of discharge frequency to cycle length was analysed by dividing the sample of respiratory cycles into three sub-samples according to cycle duration (Fig. 2): thus, it is apparent in Fig. 2 C that the neurone increased its discharge tremendously during the shortest cycles. But it is also apparent that the phase relation of discharge frequency to the cycle remained the same in the three states: the highest frequency was in the early expiratory phase and the lowest frequency was in the late expiratory phase. In addition, increases of the neurone's discharge frequency could be produced by afferent stimuli, although these were not systematically investigated.

*Widdicombe:* The vagal neurones (cardio-inhibitory, bronchomotor and others) also have a respiratory rhythm which often spans the respiratory cycle. How can you be sure that the neurone you are recording from is not a vagal or sympathetic efferent cell rather than a respiratory one? In my view the vagal efferent neurones cannot legitimately be called part of the respiratory motor system (see Widdicombe, 1966).

*Dornhorst:* Your objection is not too important because we are discussing all the neurones showing oscillatory behaviour with a definite rhythm, and what modifies that rhythm.

*Widdicombe:* These objections are fundamental. We are discussing a scheme representing the system that controls the respiratory muscles; the neurones that are being recorded from could be outside this scheme altogether.

*Dornhorst:* We are talking about the main output of this oscillatory system; of course there are other outputs controlling other events such as cardiovascular events.

*von Euler:* I agree with you, Dr Widdicombe. It is important to know if a neurone is secondarily driven in a respiratory rhythm or if it is part of the mechanism which generates the rhythm. Are all the medullary neurones from which we record a respiratory rhythm really part of the generating mechanism? If not, how can we identify those which are essential for rhythm generation, and separate them from the secondary, "driven" neurones and those which represent the output from the system? No one has yet been able to answer this question.

*Cohen:* I should like to comment on the durations of the respiratory phases. In the vagotomized cat I found (unpublished observations) that the duration of the inspiratory phase was much less variable than the duration of the expiratory phase, an observation which implies that the inspiration-generating system is more rigidly programmed than the expiration-generating system. The variability of expiration may be related to the fact that there are two kinds of expiratory discharge: early-expiratory and late-expiratory. Neurones of both types are found in the medulla (Haber et al., 1957) but the discharge in expiratory muscles appears to be mainly late-expiratory in pattern (Floersheim, 1960). This apparent complexity of the expiratory system may result in variability, especially when the feedback control of vagal afferents has been eliminated.

*Paintal:* Dr Cohen, we were stimulated by your work to consider using the integrated phrenic electroneurogram but were put off this because of its sensory discharge; how can this be eliminated?

*Cohen:* In my studies the motor discharge was recorded from the central end of the cut nerves.

*Paintal:* Then how is a diphasic impulse produced? If the nerve is cut the discharge will be monophasic.

*Cohen:* I was not particularly trying to obtain a monophasic recording and therefore the end of the nerve was not crushed. But diphasic recording, with additional processing to give the integrated signal, is perfectly adequate.

*Paintal:* Why do you use the integrated phrenic discharge? What are its advantages compared with tidal volume and air flow, for example?

*Cohen:* Since I am a neurophysiologist and not a respiratory physiologist I prefer to use phrenic nerve discharge! Further, the animals have no tidal volume because they are paralysed! But seriously, the advantage of phrenic nerve recording is that one obtains information on the exact timing of the respiratory cycle. And it is well established that integrated phrenic or diaphragmatic discharge is proportional to tidal volume (Lourenço et al., 1966).

*Merton:* There are two types of theory about respiratory rhythm. One theory postulates that this rhythm is inherent in certain groups of neurones and is merely modified by interconnexions and interactions between them. The other theory is that the rhythm originates because of the interactions, in a way similar to that in which oscillations arise in an appropriately connected feedback system. If the latter theory is correct, rhythmic events will not occur unless there is a time-lag, because a system that is just connected up with pluses and minuses acting without time delay soon reaches static equilibrium. Thus, to produce a rhythm of, say, 20 per minute there must be a delay of several seconds in one of the processes. Which of these two classes of theory does your scheme belong to, Dr Cohen, and if it belongs to the second class, where is the time-lag that is needed to produce the rhythm?

*Cohen:* My scheme fits better with the second theory. As evidence I may cite the observation that during hypocapnia some respiratory neurones lose their rhythmicity and fire tonically (Cohen, 1968; this volume, p. 134, Fig. 6). The existence of a time-lag is implicit in the schema of Fig. 16 (Cohen, this volume, p. 146) since the various blocks are labelled according to the time of discharge of the neurones (inspiratory, expiratory and so on). I agree with you that the millisecond-to-second gap is crucial: how do transient interactions between neurones (individual presynaptic and postsynaptic events) lead to the slower changes of activity within the respiratory networks? A possible answer is that the respiratory networks consist of chains of neurones, both in series and in parallel, in which activity is propagated and in which temporal summation plays an important role.

## REFERENCES

AMASSIAN, V. E., MACY, J., and WALLER, H. J. (1961). *Ann. N.Y. Acad. Sci.*, **89**, 883–895.

BATSEL, H. L. (1964). *Expl Neurol.*, **9**, 410–426.

BAUMGARTEN, R. VON, BAUMGARTEN, A. VON, and SCHAEFER, K.-P. (1957). *Pflügers Arch. ges. Physiol.*, **264**, 217–227.

BAUMGARTEN, R. VON, and NAKAYAMA, S. (1964). *Pflügers Arch. ges. Physiol.*, **281**, 245–258.

BIANCONI, R., CORAZZA, R., and RASCHI, F. (1963). *Archo Sci. biol., Bologna*, **47**, 376–389.

BYSTRZYCKA, E., GROMYSZ, H., HUSZCZUK, A., and KARCZEWSKI, W. (1970). In press.

COHEN, M. I. (1968). *J. Neurophysiol.*, **31**, 142–165.

COHEN, M. I., and HUGELIN, A. (1965). *Archs ital. Biol.*, **103**, 317–334.

COHEN, M. I., and WANG, S. C. (1959). *J. Neurophysiol.*, **22**, 33–50.

FLOERSHEIM, G. L. (1960). *Helv. physiol. pharmac. Acta*, **18**, 17–24.

HABER, E., KOHN, K. W., NGAI, S. H., HOLADAY, D. A., and WANG, S. C. (1957). *Am. J. Physiol.*, **190**, 350–355.

HUGELIN, A., and COHEN, M. I. (1963). *Ann N.Y. Acad. Sci.*, **109**, 586–603.

LOURENÇO, R. V., CHERNIACK, N. S., MALM, J. R., and FISHMAN, A. P. (1966). *J. appl. Physiol.*, **21**, 527–533.

NAKAYAMA, S., and BAUMGARTEN, R. VON (1964). *Pflügers Arch. ges. Physiol.*, **281**, 231–244.

RIJLANT, P. (1937). *Archs int. Physiol.*, **44**, 351–386.

SCHEIBEL, M. E., and SCHEIBEL, A. B. (1965). *Archs ital. Biol.*, **103**, 300–316.

WIDDICOMBE, J. G. (1966). *J. Physiol., Lond.*, **186**, 56–88.

# NEUROLOGICAL INTEGRATION OF BEHAVIOURAL AND METABOLIC CONTROL OF BREATHING

FRED PLUM

*Department of Neurology, New York Hospital-Cornell Medical Center, New York*

BREATHING, the only autonomic function regulated entirely by skeletal muscle, serves two great homoeostatic systems, metabolism and behaviour. The neurologist interested in the neural control of respiration is repeatedly reminded at the bedside of this dual purpose, for many diseases that damage the brain affect the behavioural and metabolic aspects of breathing differently or even selectively. Strengthening these clinical clues is a small but growing body of well-controlled experimental data. Taken together, the clinical and experimental work suggests that the brain controls the behavioural and metabolic functions of respiration by neurological systems that are almost completely separate anatomically although normally closely integrated physiologically. This is still a hypothesis but it explains a great deal about changes in the act of breathing in patients with neurological disease, and it may suggest experimental approaches to such unsolved problems as the high incidence of respiratory symptoms in patients with psychological dysfunction.

Evidence now exists for separate neurological structures mediating behavioural and metabolic influences on the respiratory act at almost every level of the brain, from the cerebral hemispheres to the medulla and even the upper cervical spinal cord. Not unexpectedly, the evidence indicates that the controlling mechanisms for behavioural respiratory function are located largely in the forebrain and the controlling mechanisms for metabolic respiratory regulations lie largely in the hindbrain. However, neither function is exclusively the domain of either territory. It is most convenient to present the evidence for these statements stepwise by anatomic levels, starting with the cerebral hemispheres and proceeding caudally. Since my own knowledge begins from efforts to explain what Hughlings Jackson called the negative symptoms produced by neurological damage, the sections will present the clinical manifestations of impaired function first and buttress these with whatever anatomical and experimental studies are available.

## CEREBRAL HEMISPHERES

Extensive regions of the cerebral cortex influence respiration when stimulated (Spencer, 1894; Smith, 1938; Kaada, 1960), and voluntary control over the respiratory act is everyday knowledge. Altered respiratory patterns are prominent in both pyramidal and extrapyramidal motor diseases (Jackson, 1895; Fluck, 1966; Plum, 1966; Kim, 1968). Indeed, the effects of neurological disease illustrate better than anything else the extensive cerebral influence on respiration. Table I lists the forebrain influences on the respiratory act and the symptoms that result from damaging the different areas. Both behavioural and metabolic influences stem from this level; the former are more profound and are examined first.

TABLE I

FOREBRAIN INFLUENCES ON THE RESPIRATORY ACT

| Function | Clinical defect if damaged | Neuroanatomy |
|---|---|---|
| Verbal communications | Aphasia | Left-hemisphere language area |
| Voluntary deep breathing or breath-holding | Apraxia | Unknown, probably bifrontal |
| | Pseudobulbar palsy | Interruption of corticobulbar tracts |
| Emotional behaviour | Forced, "pseudo-bulbar" laughing and crying | Limbic system and subcortical connexions |
| Voluntary or reflex respiratory inhibition | Epileptic respiratory arrest | Medial temporal lobe: limbic system |
| Wakeful rhythmic breathing | Posthyperventilation apnoea | Unknown |
| Damping response to stimulation | Increased responsiveness to carbon dioxide Cheyne-Stokes respiration | Bilateral pyramidal motor system |

Verbal communication depends on the integrity of the lateral surface of the cerebral cortex (usually in the left hemisphere) which includes the inferior-posterior frontal lobe, the superior temporal lobe and the inferior parietal lobe. The precise boundaries are unclear. Lesions outside this area and its subcortical interconnexions (Penfield and Roberts, 1959; Hécaen and Angelergues, 1964) do not cause aphasia, although bilateral lesions involving the corticobulbar motor pathways anywhere from the cortex to the cranial nerve nuclei can paralyse voluntary laryngeal and chest movements producing severe dysarthria or even anarthria. While not strictly a respiratory function, language behaviour subordinates respiratory control to its purpose although not to the point of overcoming metabolic or reflex stimulation of the system. Below the cortex, descending pathways for vocalization are bilateral (interruption of either one does not cause aphasia) and travel, via the corticobulbar tracts, to the brainstem.

Voluntary deep breathing or breath-holding is a learned act and clinical evidence indicates that specific and more or less circumscribed cerebral mechanisms initiate and control it. A selective abnormality of voluntary breathing arising at the cerebral level is observed as *respiratory apraxia*, an inability to take a deep breath or hold the breath as a specific act, despite being able to understand the command and the presence of functionally normal corticobulbar pathways and lower brainstem respiratory control mechanisms. Respiratory apraxia is sometimes accompanied by the inability to initiate voluntarily the act of swallowing, less often by other behavioural apraxias. The abnormality is most often identified during routine physical examination when it is noted that the patient cannot follow the command to breathe deeply or to hold the breath, although he speaks clearly and easily and carries out other simple commands. We have records of 15 subjects who demonstrated this phenomenon. All were elderly, and had evidence of mild to moderate arteriosclerotic vascular disease in both the general and cerebral circulations. Clinically their mental acuity had declined so that several of them were easily confused by the pressures of hospital examinations; but none were so demented that they were incapacitated and they easily comprehended and carried out other commands requiring them to move their bodies, although most of them had difficulty in swallowing voluntarily unless first given a bolus of food or water. None of these patients have yet died so the anatomic lesions can only be inferred. However, at the time that respiratory apraxia was present, none of them had Cheyne-Stokes respiration, dysarthria or any signs of disease of the corticobulbar tract. The subjects had mild, prehensile, suck and snout reflexes and a diffuse paratonic resistance, or *Gegenhalten*, in the extremities, but no paralysis or pathological reflexes. At least clinically, therefore, their defect could not be explained as a selective pseudobulbar palsy and was more consistent with a diffuse extrapyramidal dysfunction.

*Pseudobulbar palsy* can interrupt voluntary control over the respiratory act in a fairly selective way, but the lesions always involve the corticobulbar pathways to adjacent motor structures which clinically distinguishes the defect from respiratory apraxia. The lesions that can affect voluntary respiration could, theoretically, lie anywhere from the internal capsule to the pons as long as they interrupted the appropriate pathways. However, relatively selective defects in the voluntary control of breathing are produced by lesions in the base of the pons, an example of which is shown in Fig. 1. The abnormality in voluntary breathing is accompanied often by uninterruptable Cheyne-Stokes respiration and always by pseudobulbar dysarthria as well as a voluntary paralysis of swallowing. Abnormal stretch reflexes and other signs of corticobulbar and, sometimes, corticospinal dysfunction are present. It seems likely that the voluntary breathing defect that Hebertson, Talbert and Cohen (1959) called apraxia in patients with Cheyne-Stokes respiration was, in fact, pseudobulbar palsy since all their autopsied patients were found to have bilateral lesions of the brain (Talbert, Currens and Cohen, 1954).

*Cerebral respiratory inhibition*

Influences from the cerebral hemispheres can profoundly inhibit the behavioural functions of the respiratory act. In wakeful man, transient voluntary breath-holding and its relation to metabolic respiratory drives have been well studied by respiratory physiologists, but breath-holding has seldom diverted much attention to breathing's behavioural aspects, largely because metabolic stimuli produce an intolerable urge to breathe long before asphyxia develops.

The results of electrical stimulation of the hemispheres make a stronger case for inhibitory influences on respiration arising at this level (Kaada, 1960). Only a limited number of cerebral points, located mainly in the classic somatic motor and premotor areas, facilitate respiration; in contrast to this modest facilitatory influence, large areas of the hemispheres inhibit breathing (Fig. 2). The stimulation of some of these areas in experimental animals produces apnoea or respiratory suppression that lasts as long as the stimulus, even though accompanied by severe asphyxia. The inhibiting areas lie largely on the medial and inferior surfaces of the hemispheres and include the orbital surface of the frontal lobe, the adjacent insular region, the medial surface of the temporal lobe, the cingular gyrus, the septal region, the amygdaloid nucleus, the adjacent uncus and the fornix. Taken together these inhibitory structures comprise most of the hemispheric contribution to the limbic system, which is now believed to mediate the main forebrain contribution to emotional and autonomic behaviour.

According to Kaada (1960), Nelson and Ray (1968) and others, electrical stimulation of limbic structures in man stops breathing, usually in quiet expiration, with the longest duration of arrest thus far reported being 56 s. However, much longer periods of apnoea or hypoventilation have been reported from limbic stimulation in animals, and in humans with epileptic seizures arising from these regions. In this regard, Reis and McHugh (1968) observed that electrical stimulation of the amygdala in squirrel monkeys

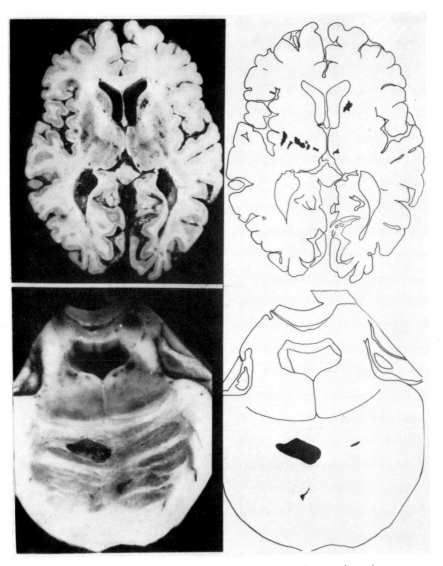

FIG. 1. Diagram of lacunar infarcts in cerebral hemispheres and pontine base of a 62-year-old male with a selective voluntary paralysis of breathing and swallowing. He had dysarthria and uninterruptible Cheyne-Stokes breathing, but good voluntary movement in the extremities.

[To face page 162

anaesthetized with chloralose produced hypoventilation or apnoea accompanied by asphyxial changes in blood gases sufficient to induce cardiac slowing and hypertension. A striking part of these experiments was that the asphyxiated animals lay quietly without resistance during amygdala stimulation but, if equal blood gas abnormalities were induced by tracheal

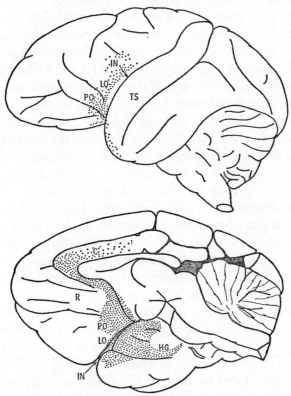

FIG. 2. Points on the anterolateral (above) and ventromedial cerebral cortex of *Macaca mulatta* where electrical stimulation elicited inhibition of respiration. Drawn from Kaada (1960). C: cingulate gyrus; HG: hippocampal gyrus; IN: insula; LO: lateral orbital gyrus; PO: posterior orbital gyrus; R: gyrus rectus; TS: superior temporal gyrus.

occlusion, respiratory effort was increased and the animals struggled to escape.

Several patients have been reported with seizures apparently arising from temporal lobe limbic structures in whom attacks have included quiet respiratory arrest. Jackson (1899) first reported such a patient, and Rovner and Barron (1966) and Nelson and Ray (1968) have studied others. As is usual with electrical stimulation to limbic structures, breathing in the affected patients ceased with the chest in the end-expiratory position. The subjects were inertly unconscious from the seizure and did not struggle despite progressive cyanosis. Nelson and Ray's patient was the most interesting for he remained apnoeic and needed artificial ventilation for some 30 hr during one attack that appeared to be an episode of limbic-system status epilepticus by electroencephalographic criteria.

Although the adaptive benefits to behaviour of being able briefly to suppress breathing are obvious, it is less clear whether the prolonged apnoea of electrical stimulation or seizures has any functional significance in behaviour. Reis and McHugh (1968) suggested that the inhibition may be part of the diving reflex; this is well developed in aquatic mammals and seems to have at least rudiments in man. Whatever its roots, cerebral respiratory arrest illustrates that, in extreme circumstances, cortical mechanisms closely related to behavioural functions can suppress automatic respiration to the point of disrupting metabolic homoeostasis.

Other inhibitory effects of the hemispheres on behavioural respiratory acts can be inferred from the *excessive laughing* or *excessive crying* that sometimes accompanies bilateral damage to the cerebral hemispheres. These are examples of respiratory behaviour released from the natural inhibitions of higher cerebral control. In such patients, cerebral limbic structures that project to the thalamus and hypothalamus are frequently damaged or their connexions interrupted, but the exact anatomy of the relevant pathways is unknown.

Some cerebral effects appear to influence mainly the metabolic functions of respiration, although it cannot be determined from presently available studies in man or animals how much these may be conditioned responses. Jackson's early (1895) clinical observation was that involuntary chest movement increased after hemiplegia. Quantified evidence that metabolic respiratory functions could be enhanced by the removal of cerebral influences was first offered when Heyman, Birchfield and Sieker (1958) reported that patients with bilateral cerebral infarction had an increased respiratory responsiveness to carbon dioxide stimulation. Brown and I (Brown and Plum, 1961) found the same thing. Both these studies were done without reference to the acid-base status of the serum or cerebrospinal fluid (CSF). Since many of the patients studied were elderly and had vascular disease, an unsuspected bicarbonate depletion in the CSF and the fluids bathing the respiratory centre might have explained the results. Accordingly, Dr John Lee and I recently re-examined this problem in patients with bilateral cerebral lesions producing hemiparesis or hemiplegia, and in similarly aged, neurologically intact controls. Ventilation was measured under steady-state conditions at three different levels of inspired carbon dioxide, and respiratory gases and acid-base balance were measured in direct samples of both the arterial blood and the lumbar CSF. As Fig. 3 illustrates, carbon dioxide responsiveness was greater in patients with bilateral cerebral motor dysfunction than in the controls, although there was no significant difference in CSF hydrogen ion concentration in the two groups.

The neuroanatomy of this effect is known only in very general terms.

RELATIONSHIP OF VENTILATORY RESPONSIVENESS TO BRAIN DAMAGE
AND TO CSF $[HCO_3^-]$.

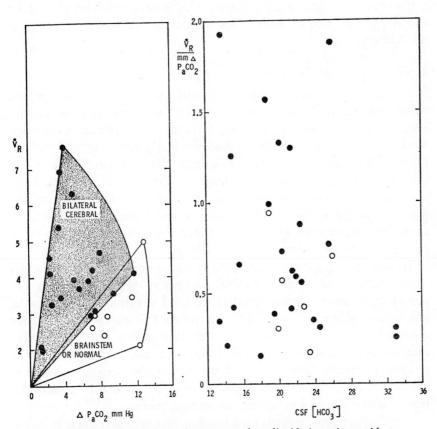

FIG. 3. Ventilatory responsiveness to carbon dioxide in patients with bilateral damage to cerebral hemispheres (solid dots) and age-matched controls (open dots). There is no significant difference in $[HCO^-_3]$ in the CSF between the two groups, although the subjects with cerebral damage have significantly greater responsiveness.

Brown and Plum (1961) studied at autopsy the brains of several patients with measured increases in carbon dioxide responsiveness. All had bilateral infarctions or traumatic damage to the cerebral hemispheres but the lesions were in many different sites and it was not possible to identify a small common area of injury. The phenomenon was always accompanied clinically by at least some abnormality of the corticospinal tract and the change may be related to other cerebral mechanisms which, when damaged, "release" hyperactive, skeletal-muscle stretch reflexes. Normally such damping of respiratory responses by cerebral influences is an important factor protecting the system against such oscillations as Cheyne-Stokes breathing. It is of interest that the normal cerebral damping of respiratory responses is paralleled in experimental animals by cerebral damping of the blood pressure responses to reflex stimulation of baroreceptors (Reis and Cuénod, 1965).

*Cerebral respiratory stimulation*

The cerebral hemispheres normally contribute an important component to the volume of breathing during wakefulness, and in most healthy subjects this cerebral drive maintains the rhythm of respiration even when metabolic stimuli are temporarily removed (Fink, 1961). Several findings illustrate this effect: the resting $Pa_{CO_2}$ level climbs 2–5 mmHg or more during sleep (Birchfield, Sieker and Heyman, 1958) and, following actively or passively induced overbreathing, most awake normal subjects and patients who are free of neurological disease will continue to breathe fairly rhythmically, even though the $Pa_{O_2}$ levels are supernormal and the $Pa_{CO_2}$ tensions are subnormal for at least the next 20–30 s.

This cerebral, respiratory-activating system is easily damped by natural sleep, sedatives, illnesses which dull alertness or produce delirium and neurological illnesses which produce bilateral structural damage to the hemispheres (Plum, Brown and Snoep, 1962). Post-mortem studies have disclosed diffuse or multifocal cerebral damage but not reproducibly localized cerebral lesions. In neuroradiological and surgical studies, the smallest anatomical lesions in awake patients with prolonged post-hyperventilation apnoea have been localized in and around the medial basal frontal region adjacent to the anterior diencephalon.

Whether cerebral respiratory activation during wakefulness is linked more to the behavioural or the metabolic aspects of the act of breathing is not known. Mills (1945) noted that expected exercise was preceded by respiratory acceleration and Dudley, Martin and Holmes (1964) found that respiratory changes during anger or anxiety resembled those of exercise.

The findings imply that cerebral mechanisms are conditioned to anticipate the respiratory needs of increased muscle metabolism. If this is so, then cerebral respiratory activation during wakefulness could be part of the same conditioned anticipation. A neural influence which continues to activate breathing when blood-gas stimuli are temporarily low exerts considerable damping against oscillation in the respiratory system (Brown and Plum, 1961).

## HYPOTHALAMUS

Contributions of the hypothalamus to the control of breathing in man are unknown and are almost impossible to estimate because clinical disease never isolates the hypothalamus from all higher influences or damages it without also extensively injuring adjacent tissues. In lower animals, Redgate (1960) concluded that the hypothalamus exerted a tonic stimulating influence on inspiration. Hypothalamic stimulation in cats, who pant to lose heat, leads to marked polypnoea without true hyperventilation (Ranson and Magoun, 1933). Although Ward (1948) described a large projection from the cingulum to the hypothalamus, Wall and Davis (1951) found that the main descending pathway from the orbital cortex bypassed the hypothalamus.

## FOREBRAIN–BRAINSTEM PATHWAYS

These are practically unknown in man and only partially studied in animals. Jackson (1895), Kolb and Kleyntjens (1937) and Fluck (1966) all noted that after cerebral hemiplegia the voluntary chest movements were less on the paralysed side, implying that their control travelled, via the internal capsule or cerebral peduncles, with other voluntary movements. These pathways apparently travel with the corticospinal tracts at least as far as the upper pons (Fig. 1). Whether other cerebral influences on breathing follow the same tracts is unknown.

In animals, cortical areas concerned with the inhibition of respiration have been traced anatomically to the homolateral medullary reticular formation (Rossi and Brodal, 1956) and stimulation of the orbital cortex evokes short latency responses from the same area (Newman and Wolstencroft, 1959). Ward (1948) traced a pathway from the anterior portion of the cingulate gyrus via the internal capsule and cerebral peduncles at least as far as the rostral pons. Whether other pathways exist is unknown.

## MIDBRAIN

The midbrain does not appear to influence breathing directly, although descending stimulation from the midbrain reticular formation indirectly affects the act of breathing, and the descending cerebral respiratory pathways pass through the midbrain peduncles. Plum and Swanson (1959) attributed central neurogenic hyperventilation in man to damage to the medial reticular formation of the midbrain and upper pons, and other clinicians have reached the same conclusion from clinical pathological studies (Lange and Laszlo, 1965). The hyperpnoea that follows lesions of the midbrain and upper pontine reticular formation has certain features which are poorly understood and several considerations suggest that more than one mechanism may be involved. A problem is that neither we nor other investigators have been able to produce hyperventilation in experimental animals by circumscribed destructive midbrain-pontine lesions. We and others (Berman, Ducker and Simmons, 1969) have produced hyperpnoea with a lowered $Pa_{CO_2}$ in monkeys during the course of experimental midbrain compression, but the over-breathing was always accompanied by a fall in $Pa_{O_2}$ as well as by post-mortem evidence of increased pulmonary congestion. In keeping with this observation, blood gas studies on most but not all patients with what was thought to be central hyperventilation have disclosed a low $Pa_{O_2}$ relative to the degree of hypocapnia; (the hyperventilating patient of Lange and Lazlo [1965] and a child with an upper pontine glioma that we are presently studying have had normal arterial oxygen values and are the best documented exceptions). Therefore present evidence indicates that while true hyperventilation occasionally follows midbrain damage, the more frequent response is that of a reflex hyperpnoea stimulated by pulmonary receptors, with the initial step being that damage to the midbrain reticular formation evokes intense descending sympathetic activity which, in turn, induces pulmonary congestion and hypoxia.

### PONS AND MEDULLA OBLONGATA

In man, as in lower animals, the lower third of the pons and the medulla oblongata contain the crucial central structures that regulate automatic respiration. A disease or experiment that destroys these regions destroys breathing. Smaller, more restricted damage to the region has less devastating results and discloses that different areas exert distinctive effects on the respiratory rhythm. When interpreting these data, clinical and animal experimental studies each have their own special limitations. Thus a great many patients with brainstem infarction or destruction have received clinical and pathological analysis but only in a few are the ante-mortem observations on respiratory function sufficiently careful, or the post-mortem localizations of the lesion sufficiently precise, to provide physiological information comparable to the data from animal experiments. Conversely, although animal studies are invaluable from the standpoint of quantitative measurements and exact anatomy, they are all limited by the effects of anaesthesia, acute brain surgery and brief observation.

The most immediately evident aspect of pontomedullary influences is that destruction of the corticobulbar and corticospinal pathways in the base of the pons has an entirely different effect on breathing from that of even partial injury to the tegmentum. Many clinical-pathological studies on man indicate that disease can destroy most of the base of the pons and interrupt all voluntary control over the respiratory act without interfering with automatic or metabolically controlled breathing, as long as the lesion spares the tegmentum.

Below the pons, descriptions of selective anatomical material are harder to find, but observations on the well-studied patient of Meyer and Herndon (1962) imply that the pyramidal tracts in the medulla can be destroyed without destroying the metabolic, automatic control of breathing. This patient had complete bilateral infarction of the pyramids and the adjacent ventromedial portion of the medulla. Despite quadriplegia and pharyngeal and hypoglossal paralysis, he had only a brief period of respiratory insufficiency requiring artificial respiration immediately after the infarction and he breathed spontaneously and regularly from the fifth day after the infarct until his death from pneumonitis on the seventh week. He was unable to initiate any kind of voluntary movement below the neck, including breathing. The point was not investigated specifically but, according to Dr Meyer, the man had no detectable decline or irregularity in the breathing pattern while asleep and did not need artificial respiration to sleep.

Destruction of the tegmentum of the pons or of the medulla produces different clinical features. With lesions above the trigeminal outflow no consistent effect is observed in the metabolic regulation of respiration. We have studied five patients with basilar artery occlusion who had essentially complete transection of the pontine base and tegmentum just rostral to the trigeminal motor nucleus. Two had transient apneusis immediately after the lesion, but this disappeared within hours, and thereafter they remained eupnoeic for at least several days (as did the other three patients from the time of the occlusion) until they all developed terminal pneumonitis.

At or below the trigeminal level, medial and lateral tegmental injuries produce very different effects. Paramedian destruction can extend well down into the lower third of the pontine tegmentum and leave respiratory rhythm intact. An example is given in Fig. 4 of a man with the basilar artery acutely occluded where it is joined by the vertebral arteries. Despite a failing heart and progressive bronchopneumonia he maintained a normal respiratory rhythm with a rate of 30/min until he died five days later. Blood gases included a $Pa_{CO_2}$ of 28 mmHg and a $Pa_{O_2}$ of 68 mmHg. These negative effects on respiratory rhythm of high pontine transection and paramedian destruction are very similar to what is known from animal experiments (Ngai and Wang, 1957). However, with lateral pontine tegmental injury in man, the changes are more far-reaching and have some effects very similar to but others very different from those seen in animals.

Clinical, and a limited number of pathological, studies from our laboratory indicate that unilateral injuries to the lateral pontine tegmentum have no grossly detectable effect on the control of breathing, except insofar as supranuclear  and nuclear bulbar palsy create mechanical difficulties, allowing secretions to obstruct the airways. However, bilateral lateral lesions at and below the level of the trigeminal nucleus predictably disrupt the rhythm of breathing as well as the respiratory responsiveness to carbon dioxide stimulation (Plum and Alvord, 1964). Lesions of this area, which in animals has been called the pontine pneumotaxic region, result in a pattern of irregular breathing in which tonic inspiratory cramps (apneusis) alternate with tonic expiratory cramps, and with totally irregular breathing in between. The differences from animal experiments are several: the humans live for days with the abnormal rhythms and maintain normal blood gases, whilst apneustic animals rarely survive more than a very few hours and fail to maintain respiratory gas homoeostasis (Katz, 1961); also, in humans, the vagus is anatomically intact while in animals the abnormal rhythm often but not always requires vagotomy plus brainstem transection (Lumsden, 1923; Monnier, 1939).

We have estimated carbon dioxide responsiveness in five subjects with apneustic or irregular respiratory rhythm stemming from pontine injury and have found it markedly below normal in every case. A similar reduction in ventilatory responsiveness to carbon dioxide has characterized every appropriately studied patient with pontomedullary disease impairing the respiratory rhythm. Partly because of this, partly because carbon dioxide stimulates many levels of the ascending reticular formation (Gellhorn, 1953) and partly because direct experimental studies seemed to demonstrate that carbon dioxide directly stimulates the medullary respiratory areas

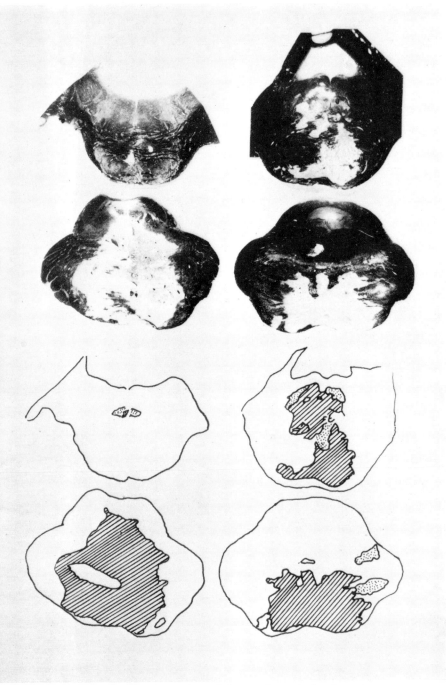

FIG. 4. Paramedian destruction of the pontine reticular formation; no evident effect on respiratory rhythm. The cross-hatched zones were completely and the stippled zones partially destroyed.

[To face page 170

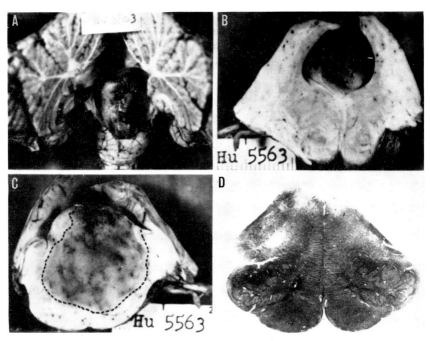

Fig. 5. Anatomical lesions from patients who had lost the ability to breathe automatically while asleep but could satisfy respiratory requirements while awake by voluntary breathing; (A), (B) and (C): views of a glioblastoma of the medulla oblongata; automatic breathing ceased five weeks before death and all voluntary breathing stopped thirteen days before death; (D) medullary necrosis in a patient with poliomyelitis who lost automatic breathing but preserved the voluntary act (Plum and Swanson, 1959).

(Comroe, 1943; Euler von and Söderberg, 1952), the pontomedullary centres are widely believed to be intrinsically sensitive to carbon dioxide. The view is probably still justified although the full significance of carbon dioxide responsiveness and the degree to which it depends on influences reflexly mediated from intracranial chemoreceptors (Mitchell et al., 1963) and from stretch receptors lying outside the pontomedullary respiratory areas is still not fully known. Vagotomy, for example, slows the respiratory rhythm and blunts carbon dioxide responsiveness. Since the Hering-Breuer reflex is relayed through the pons (Wang, Ngai and Frumin, 1957) this may imply central interaction between chemical and reflex stimuli to ventilation comparable to the interaction that may occur between peripheral chemoreceptor reflexes and central chemical respiratory drives (Nielsen and Smith, 1952; Hornbein, Griffo and Roos, 1961).

Ever since Legallois (1812) demonstrated that breathing depended on a circumscribed region of the medulla, numerous experimental studies have confirmed that destruction of the paramedian reticular formation in the medulla oblongata destroys the central control of respiration. However, animal studies on the medullary centres have invariably been done after anaesthesia or decerebration, thus eliminating any chance of determining whether higher nervous pathways still influenced the act of breathing. Well-studied material from man in this context is rare but provides the only information available.

Many clinical studies indicate that medullary depression or compression disproportionately damages the metabolic or automatic control of breathing, so that respiratory homoeostasis can be maintained during wakefulness but not during sleep. However, only a very few anatomical studies (Brown and Baker, 1949; Plum and Swanson, 1959) have confirmed that direct lesions of the medulla have this effect, and none really indicates the location or maximal size of a lesion that will destroy the metabolic control of breathing yet spare the voluntary, behavioural pathways. The mere observation that the medullary lesions can selectively impair the automatic and voluntary control of respiration implies that these two functions travel through the lower brainstem by at least partially separate routes. However, in many illnesses, such as poliomyelitis or with the brain tumour illustrated in Fig. 5, failure of automatic respiration was shortly followed by a total inability to initiate the respiratory act. From this and from the physiological and anatomical studies of Ward (1948), Rossi and Brodal (1956) and Newman and Wolstencroft (1959), it was generally assumed that descending forebrain influences on respiration projected to areas in the medullary reticulum, which areas integrated the metabolic and behavioural influences, programmed the respiratory act and transmitted the fixed programme to the spinal respiratory motor neurones. Some recent observations on breathing after spinal lesions make one question this assumption.

The strongest evidence that behavioural and metabolic influences on respiration can travel at least partially separate paths through and below the medulla comes from studies in man. Neurosurgeons (Belmusto, Brown and Owens, 1963; Rosomoff, Krieger and Kuperman, 1969) have reported that bilateral ventrolateral incisions into the second cervical segment of the

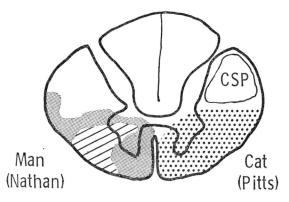

Man
(Nathan)

Cat
(Pitts)

Fig. 6. Descending respiratory pathways in the spinal cord as described by Nathan (1963) in man and by Pitts (1946) in the cat. In Nathan's diagram the cross-hatched area was common to two cordotomies interrupting descending respiratory pathways. CSP: corticospinal pathway. Any control of breathing descending the spinal cord after bilateral lesions of this type must necessarily descend more dorsally, in other pathways.

spinal cord can destroy automatic breathing during sleep even though eupnoea and blood-gas homoeostasis is maintained during wakefulness. Such incisions interrupt not only the ascending spinothalamic but also the descending reticulospinal pathways (Nathan, 1963). In detailed studies of these patients, two groups of investigators (Severinghaus and Mitchell, 1962; Rosomoff, Krieger and Kuperman, 1969) have found that the metabolic respiratory function of carbon dioxide responsiveness is greatly reduced even when the voluntarily controlled vital capacity and maximal breathing capacity show an insignificant decline. The results have been variously interpreted but, in view of Pitts' (1946) finding in cats and Nathan's (1963) in man that the main projection from the medullary respiratory centre to the respiratory motor neurones of the spinal cord is in the ventrolateral quadrant (Fig. 6), we suggest that ventrolateral cordotomy interrupts the metabolic or automatic reticular spinal, respiratory pathway but not the voluntary, behavioural one.

Other studies indicate that voluntary and automatic pathways may travel different routes to the spinal cord, and also that spinal neurones can sometimes coordinate the respiratory act. Most investigators (Wade, 1954; Campbell, 1958) have concluded that man cannot voluntarily fractionate the respiratory muscles in the act of breathing and that these muscles are recruited in stereotyped order according to a programme transmitted from supraspinal levels. However, Stigol and Cuello (1966) reported that one out of eight healthy subjects was able to inspire voluntarily without contracting his diaphragm. If this observation is confirmed it would favour the existence of direct corticospinal pathways to respiratory motor neurones.

Sears (1966), in experimental studies, reported dual spinal descending influences on respiratory motor neurones in the cat. By stimulating the pyramidal decussation at the medullary-cervical junction Sears evoked a powerful and coordinated expiratory apneustic response that presumably descended via corticospinal fibres independent of the more ventral pathway that carries the descending reticulospinal respiratory influences. Working in our laboratory, Newsom Davis (unpublished observations) has confirmed this response and demonstrated that it persists after bilateral ventrolateral cervical cordotomy, a section which abolishes both spontaneous respiration and the inspiratory response to stimulation of Pitts' medullary inspiration region. The evidence is so far not enough to equate corticospinal with *behavioural* or *voluntary* and reticulospinal with *metabolic* or *automatic*, but Sears and Newsom Davis each provide evidence that purely spinal neural mechanisms can integrate descending motor influences into a coordinated breathing act.

### SUMMARY AND CONCLUSIONS

There is considerable evidence, as reviewed here, that the act of breathing serves two functions—metabolism and behaviour—and the nervous system regulates these through different pathways. The more primitive metabolic system is located in the reticular formation of the lower pons and medulla, receives its input from chemoreceptors, vagus nerves and proprioceptive reflexes and is responsible for blood-gas and acid-base homoeostasis; it automatically regulates its own intrinsic rhythm when stimulated and transmits its impulses to the spinal cord via ventral reticulospinal pathways. The behavioural system is located mainly in somatomotor and limbic forebrain structures, adapts man to vocalization and complex behavioural acts and conditions him for the expected metabolic demands of activity and exercise. This system is completely functional only when the forebrain is activated by full wakefulness and it transmits its descending impulses at least partly to the medullary reticulum but also partly to the spinal cord via direct corticobulbar and corticospinal pathways. Studies of this latter system would provide a rewarding field for the analysis of respiratory symptoms, such as breathlessness, anxiety and hyperventilation, which in the past have been so difficult to link to purely metabolic abnormalities.

ACKNOWLEDGEMENT

Aided by Grant NIH ROI NB-06386 from the US Public Health Service.

REFERENCES

BELMUSTO, L., BROWN, E., and OWENS, G. (1963). *J. Neurosurg.*, 20, 225–232.
BERMAN, I. R., DUCKER, T. B., and SIMMONS, R. L. (1969). *J. Neurosurg.*, 30, 532–536.
BIRCHFIELD, R. I., SIEKER, H. O., and HEYMAN, A. (1958). *Neurology, Minneap.*, 8, 107–112.
BROWN, H. W., and PLUM, F. (1961). *Am. J. Med.*, 30, 849–860.
BROWN, J. R., and BAKER, A. B. (1949). *J. nerv. ment. Dis.*, 109, 54–78.
CAMPBELL, E. J. M. (1958). *The Respiratory Muscles and the Mechanics of Breathing.* Chicago: Year Book Medical Publishers.
COMROE, J. H., JR. (1943). *Am. J. Physiol.*, 139, 490–498.
DUDLEY, D. L., MARTIN, C. J., and HOLMES, T. H. (1964). *Psychosom. Med.*, 26, 645–660.
EULER, U. VON, and SÖDERBERG, U. (1952). *J. Physiol., Lond.*, 118, 545–554.
FINK, B. R. (1961). *J. appl. Physiol.*, 16, 15–20.
FLUCK, D. C. (1966). *Clin. Sci.*, 31, 383–388.
GELLHORN, E. (1953). *Electroenceph. clin. Neurophysiol.*, 5, 401–413.
HEBERTSON, W. M., TALBERT, O. R., and COHEN, M. I. (1959). *Trans. Am. neurol. Ass.*, 84, 176–179.
HÉCAEN, H., and ANGELERGUES, R. (1964). In *Ciba Fdn Symp. Disorders of Language*, pp. 223–245. London: Churchill; Boston: Little, Brown.
HEYMAN, A., BIRCHFIELD, R. I., and SIEKER, H. O. (1958). *Neurology, Minneap.*, 8, 694–700.
HORNBEIN, T. F., GRIFFO, Z. J., and ROOS, A. (1961). *J. Neurophysiol.*, 24, 561–568.
JACKSON, J. H. (1895). *Lancet*, 1, 476–478.
JACKSON, J. H. (1899). *Lancet*, 2, 79–80.
KAADA, B. R. (1960). In *Handbook of Physiology*, sect. III, vol. 2, pp. 1345–1372, ed. Magoun, H. W. American Physiological Society. Baltimore: Williams and Wilkins.
KATZ, R. L. (1961). *Fedn Proc. Fedn Am. Socs exp. Biol.*, 20, 431.
KIM, R. (1968). *J. Neurol. Neurosurg. Psychiat.*, 31, 393–398.
KOLB, L. C., and KLEYNTJENS, F. (1937). *Brain*, 60, 259–274.
LANGE, L. S., and LASZLO, G. (1965). *J. Neurol. Neurosurg. Psychiat.*, 28, 317–319.
LEGALLOIS, J. J. C. (1812). *Expériences sur le Principe de la Vie.* Paris: D'Hautel.
LUMSDEN, T. (1923). *J. Physiol., Lond.*, 57, 153–160.
MEYER, J. S., and HERNDON, R. M. (1962). *Neurology, Minneap.*, 12, 637–642.
MILLS, J. N. (1945). *J. Physiol., Lond.*, 104, 15P.

MITCHELL, R. A., LOESCHKE, H. H., MASSION, W. H., and SEVERINGHAUS, J. W. (1963). *J. appl. Physiol.*, **18**, 523–533.

MONNIER, M. (1939). *Pflügers Arch. ges. Physiol.*, **242**, 168–179.

NATHAN, P. W. (1963). *J. Neurol. Neurosurg. Psychiat.*, **26**, 487–499.

NELSON, D. A., and RAY, C. D. (1968). *Archs Neurol., Chicago*, **19**, 199–207.

NEWMAN, P. P., and WOLSTENCROFT, J. H. (1959). *J. Neurophysiol.*, **22**, 516–523.

NGAI, S. H., and WANG, S. C. (1957). *Am. J. Physiol.*, **190**, 343–349.

NIELSEN, M., and SMITH, H. (1952). *Acta physiol. scand.*, **24**, 293–313.

PENFIELD, W., and ROBERTS, L. (1959). *Speech and Brain Mechanisms*. Princeton: Princeton University Press.

PITTS, R. F. (1946). *Physiol. Rev.*, **26**, 609–630.

PLUM, F. (1966). In *Breathlessness*, pp. 203–222, ed. Howell, J. B. L., and Campbell, E. J. M. Oxford: Blackwell.

PLUM, F., and ALVORD, E. C., JR. (1964). *Archs Neurol., Chicago*, **10**, 101–112.

PLUM, F., BROWN, H. W., and SNOEP, E. (1962). *J. Am. med. Ass.*, **181**, 1050–1055.

PLUM, F., and SWANSON, A. G. (1959). *Archs Neurol. Psychiat., Chicago*, **81**, 531–549.

RANSON, S. W., and MAGOUN, H. W. (1933). *Archs Neurol. Psychiat., Chicago*, **29**, 1179–1193.

REDGATE, E. S. (1960). *Am. J. Physiol.*, **198**, 1299–1303.

REIS, D. J., and CUÉNOD, M. (1965). *Am. J. Physiol.*, **209**, 1267–1279.

REIS, D. J., and MCHUGH, P. R. (1968). *Am. J. Physiol.*, **214**, 601–610.

ROSOMOFF, H. L., KRIEGER, A. J., and KUPERMAN, A. S. (1969). *J. Neurosurg.*, **31**, 620–627.

ROSSI, G. F., and BRODAL, A. (1956). *J. Anat.*, **90**, 42–62.

ROVNER, R. N., and BARRON, K. D. (1966). *Neurology, Minneap.*, **16**, 328.

SEARS, T. A. (1966). In *Muscular Afferents and Motor Control*, pp. 186–196, ed. Granit, R. Uppsala: Almqvist and Wiksell.

SEVERINGHAUS, J. W., and MITCHELL, R. A. (1962). *Clin. Res.*, **10**, 122.

SMITH, W. K. (1938). *J. Neurophysiol.*, **1**, 54–68.

SPENCER, W. G. (1894). *Phil. Trans. R. Soc.*, **185**, 609–757.

STIGOL, L. C., and CUELLO, A. C. (1966). *J. appl. Physiol.*, **21**, 1911–12.

TALBERT, O. R., CURRENS, J., and COHEN, M. I. (1954). *Trans. Am. neurol. Ass.*, **79**, 226–228.

WADE, O. L. (1954). *J. Physiol., Lond.*, **124**, 193–212.

WALL, P. O., and DAVIS, G. D. (1951). *J. Neurophysiol.*, **14**, 507–517.

WANG, S. C., NGAI, S. H., and FRUMIN, M. J. (1957). *Am. J. Physiol.*, **190**, 333–342.

WARD, A. A. (1948). *J. Neurophysiol.*, **11**, 13–23.

# DISCUSSION

*Cohen:* Your finding that patients with cerebral lesions showed increased responsiveness to carbon dioxide is similar to some of my observations on the cat (Cohen, 1964). I found that diencephalic decerebration (division of the neuraxis at the level of the hypothalamus) produced a lower apnoea point; that is, the $Pa_{CO_2}$ had to be reduced to a lower level than in the intact animal to abolish phrenic discharge.

*Plum:* Ranson and Magoun (1933) evoked polypnoea in the cat by inducing haemorrhage in the lateral hypothalamus, and many of Bard's animals (1929) with decerebration above the hypothalamus had polypnoea. Fink and co-workers (1962) consistently induced polypnoea in the cat by precollicular decerebration; since $Pa_{CO_2}$ was normal or near normal in many of Fink's animals the defect was not really comparable to central hyperventilation.

*Cohen:* All these effects are probably produced by a similar mechanism: elimination of cerebral inhibition.

*Dornhorst:* Pharmacological evidence in favour of the dual system of control of respiration comes from the reports that phenoperidine induces a state in which the patient can breathe to order but not spontaneously. These findings were reported during the initial clinical trials of phenoperidine in anaesthesia (Garden and Mackenzie, 1963).

*Dejours:* I would like to ask you two questions, Professor Plum. First, we know that changes in ventilation during exercise are related to humoral and neurogenic factors, the latter probably controlled by both reflex and cortical mechanisms. What is the relative importance of these two mechanisms? My second question is related to this. Have you studied the control of ventilation during exercise in your paralysed patients and, if so, what changes have you observed?

*Plum:* We have not measured the ventilatory response to exercise because we have not devised a satisfactory method for simulating exercise in paralysed patients. Information in the literature on animals is contradictory. Leibowitz, Korczyn and Bergmann (1965) state that stimulation of the sciatic nerve in the decerebrate cat does not evoke hyperpnoea, implying that hyperpnoea is reflexly conditioned. Koizumi, Ushiyama and Brooks (1961) reported exactly the opposite effect, namely that the hyperpnoeic response to sciatic nerve stimulation was unchanged in the decerebrate cat, indicating that the exercise response is unconditioned and mediated from the metabolic centres in the brainstem.

*Dornhorst:* Nathan (1963) described patients with bilateral anterior cordotomies whose lesions occurred serially, one after the other. These subjects had temporary intercostal paralyses but were finally left with normal intercostal respiratory movements, suggesting considerable plasticity in the motor tracts. Is that right, Professor Plum?

*Plum:* The implication from Nathan's (1963) and Pitts' (1940) work was that the lack of paralysis immediately after ventrolateral cord section on one side was related to the decussation of descending motor fibres across the spinal cord at the level of the respiratory motoneurone. This was the suggested mechanism for the crossed-phrenic phenomenon (Porter, 1895) in which, when the descending tracts on one side of the spinal cord were cut, the impulses passed down the other side of the cord and crossed at the level of the transection. It was not suggested by Nathan or Pitts that the descending impulses might travel in the posterior part of the cord. Rosomoff and his group (Rosomoff, Krieger and Kuperman, 1969), however, suggested that transection of the anterior part of the cord interferes with the afferent pathways and, therefore, with automatic breathing. I have reservations about this interpretation of Rosomoff as I know of no ventrally placed afferent pathways other than the traditional anterior spinothalamic tracts.

*Newsom Davis:* Some of my current (unpublished) experiments, working in Professor Plum's laboratory, are of interest in this context. I have studied, in the cat, the effects on respiratory muscle discharge of localized lesions in the ventral part of the cervical spinal cord. My results indicate that the descending pathways serving certain respiratory tract reflexes (for example, cough) lie in the medial part of the ventral funiculus and are independent of the pathways which mediate rhythmic breathing.

*Dornhorst:* Did Nathan's patients have bilateral or unilateral cordotomies?

*Plum:* Unilateral. Severinghaus and Mitchell (1962) and Rosomoff, Kreiger and Kuperman (1969) described patients with bilateral lesions of the cord. Surprisingly, these patients showed no defect in vital capacity and a significant, but small, defect in maximal breathing capacity.

*Sears:* Dr Newsom Davis and I have some data (unpublished) on breath-holding experiments on conscious man which are relevant to this discussion. Breath-holding provides an opportunity to study the interaction between willed and spontaneous breathing movements. On breath-holding to break-point, a period of apnoea is followed by the resumption of spontaneous breathing. If, at the limit of breath-holding, a maximal inspiratory or expiratory effort is made against the closed glottis (the respiratory rate by this time may be as fast as 60–80/minute) then, during this steady maximum effort, spontaneous breathing movements persist but the respiratory rate falls to about 25/minute. In electromyographic studies on two subjects, we now have good evidence that during the period of steady inspiratory effort, although the diaphragm shows the expected tonic discharge needed to support the negative intrathoracic pressure, the rhythmic pressure changes are due to the abdominal and probably also the internal intercostal muscles. These findings suggest that during willed (voluntary) action the breathing input to groups of motoneurones is partially if not completely suppressed according to the corresponding motor pathways that the subject is "willing" into action. But, simultaneously, some control is exerted on the rhythm-generating mechanism, as evidenced by the slow respiratory frequency. These observations provide evidence in favour of separate cortical pathways to different respiratory motor nuclei and of a cortical influence on the rhythm of breathing.

*Aitken:* It is attractive to discuss the control of breathing in terms of its neurophysiological and metabolic parts, but a psychological part should also be included. Brainstem or limbic lesions induce a variety of symptoms which themselves alter the behaviour that is being observed. For example, *angor animi* is usually accompanied by physiological activation which, as with dyspnoea, may show itself as hyperventilation.* Professor Plum, have you studied the psychological concepts of this complex servo-system—such factors as non-organic abnormalities in perception, memory, emotion, motivation or adaptation—in your patients? This system contains many feedback loops which cannot yet be assessed solely in neuro-physiological or metabolic terms.

*Plum:* I have to think of behaviour in neurophysiological terms because I am not sufficiently familiar with other behavioural mechanisms that could supplant the neurophysiological ones. What we have done is to observe a certain form of behaviour—respiration—and try to relate abnormalities in it to anatomical lesions in the brain. Pseudobulbar laughing and crying, which are excessive emotional responses to trivial stimuli, have occasionally been reported in association with injuries of the upper part of the brainstem (Cantu and Drew, 1966), but typically the lesions lie in the projection pathways that interconnect the cerebral hemispheres and the limbic system rather than between the limbic system and the brainstem (Davison and Kelman, 1939). One might speculate that this provides indirect evidence that the higher centres, in some unknown way, modulate or inhibit limbic expressions.

It is easier to appraise or remove the influence of emotional factors on breathing in patients with spinal cord lesions than in those with medullary pathology. Patients with primary medullary disease are too ill for emotional changes to be easily assessed. They are nearly always normally oriented mentally, they can respond to commands and their memory and judgement are unimpaired, but they are sick and frightened people who know that their illness is potentially fatal. They often have a foreboding of impending death or disaster (the *angor animi* you have mentioned). All these factors make it difficult to make as meaningful estimates of their behaviour as one can in patients with cord lesions who are still awake and responsive but have a stable respiratory defect.

*Campbell:* Weinstein and his group (Freedman and Weinstein, 1965;

* See also p. 116.

Weinstein and Fowle, 1966; Weinstein, 1967; Annau and Weinstein, 1968) have investigated the response of the central nervous system (CNS) to chemical and sensory stimulants. In birds and rodents they have found that the respiratory responses elicited by chemical stimuli within the physiological range (increased carbon dioxide or decreased oxygen) cannot be classically conditioned, whereas the effects of sensory stimuli, electric shock and threshold or elastic loads can. On the other hand, primitive escape responses can readily be formed to both classes of stimuli. These observations indicate that the CNS representations of sensory and chemical stimuli are quite distinct—although having a final common path—and, as Fowle and Weinstein (1966) have demonstrated, are additive in their effects on total ventilation.*

*Plum:* Do you mean that the birds changed their pattern of breathing but not their chemical response to a given stimulus?

*Campbell:* No. What this work implies is that although both chemical and sensory stimuli affect total ventilation, their interrelationship with cortical activity and thus their susceptibility to behavioural modification are quite distinct. Respiratory alterations produced by changes in metabolism or inspired gas composition are not likely to become contingent upon psychological effects, whereas respiratory changes produced by startle, increased airways resistance and so on would eventually become intertwined with other external environmental sensory factors (Weinstein, personal communication).

*Cotes:* Observations on man under hypnosis are also relevant to our discussions; the influence of the cerebral cortex on specific responses of the respiratory system is now well documented (see, for example, Daly, Overley and Ross, 1964).

*Plum:* Medullary and limbic lesions, and hypnosis, have similar effects: breathing becomes a fixed, metabolic event (as it also does during sleep) although other partially voluntary functions are not similarly suppressed.

*Aitken:* The way in which man utilizes breathing as an available source of energy in order to communicate is interesting. Not only can he express strong emotion by weeping or laughing and with speech, but he can communicate nuances of feeling with, for example, a sigh or a yawn. These mechanisms are easily disturbed by either neuropathology or neurotic defence, and by the induction of a dissociative state such as hypnosis.

*Paintal:* The respiratory responses during sexual intercourse are another

* Weinstein, personal communication. The Editor wishes to thank Professor Weinstein for his help in preparing these comments after the meeting.

important way of assessing communication. In the rabbit coitus can still be carried out when almost the entire cerebrum is removed (Brooks, 1937).

*Dejours:* Abnormalities of speech may be considered as a behavioural phenomenon. Professor Plum, how is articulation affected in patients with respiratory apraxia, the condition we have already discussed in which the subject can only breathe to order?

*Plum:* They have no dysarthria clinically. None of the patients with respiratory apraxia that we have examined have died, so no post-mortem material is available to me. The relationship of respiratory apraxia to fixed anatomical lesions is not clear in the neurological literature. But the patients with this syndrome can be differentiated from patients with breathing and swallowing defects due to pseudobulbar palsy because they have none of the other clinical features of disease of the descending motor pathways. They show no abnormalities of the prehensile, oral reflex and they can carry out other acts involving breathing quite satisfactorily. They can readily blow out a match, for example, but cannot voluntarily take a deep breath or hold their breath. The patients with respiratory apraxia speak without dysarthria, in contrast to the patients with pseudobulbar palsy who experience difficulty in using the descending motor respiratory pathways for speaking; this difficulty is characteristic of patients with supranuclear lesions. The clinical differences between patients with pseudobulbar palsy and respiratory apraxia are distinct but I have not yet been able to study the anatomical differences between them.

*Dejours:* Where is the lesion in these patients? Is it in the corticospinal tracts or the brainstem?

*Plum:* The only available evidence suggests that the pathways involved are in the corticospinal tracts. No descending respiratory pathways from cerebrum to brainstem other than the upper ends of the pontine corticospinal tracts and the tracts in the peduncles of the midbrain have been described, although they may exist. The fibres that probably mediate the cerebral influence on breathing have been traced in the corticospinal system as far as the pons (Tower, 1936); distal to this level they disappear. This may simply be a quantitative problem due to the small number of specific respiratory impulses descending from the pons in the corticospinal system.

*Dornhorst:* What is known about the anatomical lesions in patients with encephalitis lethargica? These subjects may show the most extraordinary isolated respiratory disabilities, including interrupted respiration and the need to breathe in a certain way before they speak—the so-called respiratory tics.

*Plum:* Disabilities in patients with encephalitis lethargica are all paroxysmal; brief paroxysms of hyperventilation may occur (Kim, 1968). We have not studied these patients and I know of no data on patients in whom sustained hypoventilation has been sufficient to produce respiratory insufficiency. It has been suggested that patients with alveolar hypoventilation had subclinical encephalitis which was producing lesions in the medulla, but histological material from these patients is scant and only Naeye's (1961) case showed changes that were clearly the residue of an earlier lesion. In other instances the changes have been non-specific and no anatomical areas were consistently affected.

## REFERENCES

ANNAU, Z., and WEINSTEIN, S. A. (1968). *Commun. behav. Biol.*, **2**, 1–6.

BARD, P. (1929). *Archs Neurol. Psychiat., Chicago*, **22**, 230–246.

BROOKS, C. M. (1937). *Am. J. Physiol.*, **120**, 544–553.

CANTU, R. C., and DREW, J. H. (1966). *J. Neurosurg.*, **24**, 1024.

COHEN, M. I. (1964). *Am. J. Physiol.*, **206**, 845–854.

DALY, N. J., OVERLEY, T. H., and ROSS, J. C. (1964). *Physiologist, Wash.*, **7**, 112.

DAVISON, C., and KELMAN, H. (1939). *Archs Neurol. Psychiat., Chicago*, **42**, 595.

FINK, B. R., KATZ, R., REINHOLD, H., and SCHOOLMAN, A. (1962). *Am. J. Physiol.*, **202**, 217–220.

FOWLE, A. S. E., and WEINSTEIN, S. A. (1966). *Am. J. Physiol.*, **210**, 293–298.

FREEDMAN, S., and WEINSTEIN, S. A. (1965). *J. appl. Physiol.*, **20**, 469–472.

GARDEN, J., and MACKENZIE, A. I. (1963). *Br. J. Anaesth.*, **35**, 731–735.

KIM, R. (1968). *J. Neurol. Neurosurg. Psychiat.*, **31**, 393–398.

KOIZUMI, K., USHIYAMA, J., and BROOKS, C. M. (1961). *Am. J. Physiol.*, **200**, 679–684.

LEIBOWITZ, U., KORCZYN, A. D., and BERGMANN, F. (1965). *J. neurol. Sci.*, **2**, 241–252.

NAEYE, R. L. (1961). *Am. J. Cardiol.*, **8**, 416–419.

NATHAN, P. W. (1963). *J. Neurol. Neurosurg. Psychiat.*, **26**, 487–499.

PITTS, R. F. (1940). *J. comp. Neurol.*, **72**, 605.

PORTER, W. T. (1895). *J. Physiol., Lond.*, **17**, 455

RANSON, S. W., and MAGOUN, H. W. (1933). *Archs Neurol. Psychiat., Chicago*, **29**, 1179–1193.

ROSOMOFF, H. L., KRIEGER, A. J., and KUPERMAN, A. S. (1969). *J. Neurosurg.*, **31**, 620–627.

SEVERINGHAUS, J. W., and MITCHELL, R. A. (1962). *Clin. Res.*, **10**, 122.

TOWER, S. S. (1936). *Brain*, **59**, 408.

WEINSTEIN, S. A. (1967). *Cond. Reflex*, **2**, 118–126.

WEINSTEIN, S. A., and FOWLE, A. S. E. (1966). *Cond. Reflex*, **1**, 117–124.

# PATTERNS OF MOTOR ACTIVITY IN BREATHING IN RESPONSE TO VARYING SENSORY INPUTS

A. A. VILJANEN

*Department of Physiology, University of Helsinki, and Department of Pulmonary Diseases, University Central Hospital, Helsinki*

IN the regulation of breathing the central nervous system integrates afferent information concerning several different variables. Determination of the magnitude of minute ventilation is based on both chemical and neural afferent inputs. The regulation of breathing can be considered in terms of a block diagram, the principle of which was presented by Campbell and Howell in 1962. The "black boxes" represent functional units. After the minute ventilation demand has been established the information passes to another black box, which determines the tidal volume and respiratory frequency which are appropriate under the existing mechanical conditions. The demand for tidal volume passes, via $\alpha$ motoneurones, to the extrafusal fibres of the diaphragm and external intercostal muscles. When the inspiratory muscles contract, the thoracic cage and the lungs will expand. At least part of this demand is transmitted by the gamma system (cf. Campbell and Howell, 1962).

Several workers have shown that in animals the electrical activity of the phrenic nerve bears a linear relationship to the electromyographically recorded activity of the diaphragm (Dittler, 1910; Dittler and Garten, 1912; Gasser and Newcomer, 1921). Likewise it has been shown that a close relationship exists between the electrical and mechanical activities of the respiratory muscles in animals (Fink, Ngai and Duncan, 1958; Bergström and Kerttula, 1961) and in man (Campbell and Green, 1953a, b; Delhez, Petit and Milic-Emili, 1959; Agostoni, Sant'Ambrogio and del Portillo Carrasco, 1960; Petit, Milic-Emili and Delhez, 1960; Delhez et al., 1965; Delhez, Petit and Bottin, 1965; Viljanen et al., 1965; Viljanen, 1966, 1967a, b; Sears and Newsom Davis, 1968). Observation of the electrical activity of the respiratory muscles, therefore, can give information about the efferent output of the respiratory centres and also about the mechanical activity of the respiratory muscles.

In our earlier studies we established that, in man, a linear relationship exists between (a) the total number of electromyographic (EMG) impulses recorded from the inspiratory muscles during inspiration and the first-time integral of the muscular inspiratory work; (b) EMG impulse frequency at the end of inspiration and the muscular inspiratory work; (c) alveolar relaxation pressure and EMG impulse frequency determined four seconds after the end of inspiration when the subject was breath-holding with the glottis open; (d) the number of EMG impulses and the pressure impulse produced by the inspiratory muscles during one and the same inspiration (Viljanen, 1967a, b); and (e) the electrical activities of the diaphragm and the external intercostal muscles during one and the same inspiration (Viljanen and Halttunen, 1967). This last-mentioned relationship can be voluntarily regulated (Viljanen and Poppius, 1968). It has also been shown that intercostal electrical activity in the cat increases linearly with diaphragmatic electrical activity during any one inspiration. The proportion of external intercostal electrical activity decreases with deepening anaesthesia (ether) (Viljanen et al., 1968). Preliminary experiments suggest the same behaviour in cats anaesthetized with pentobarbitone sodium.

The first object of our present work was to study the effect exerted by the afferent discharge of the vagus nerve on the output of the respiratory centres in the pentobarbitone-anaesthetized cat. The activity of the vagus was recorded from one to four nerve fibres whose central connexions were cut, leaving the rest of the nerve intact. The activity of the external intercostal muscles and the diaphragm were recorded simultaneously, using concentric needle electrodes. The electrical activities were conducted to a tape recorder preceded by preamplifiers. The respiratory flow was recorded by a pneumotachograph; the mouth pressure was also recorded, using a differential pressure transducer. The data were analysed with a Linc computer.

Vagal activity was altered by closing the airway at functional residual capacity (FRC) and rapidly inflating the lungs with a known volume of gas, using a piston pump. During the apnoeic period following inflation we determined the average action potential frequency of the vagus. This average frequency was approximately linearly related to the degree of inflation; but in several cases it also increased linearly with the EMG frequency of the inspiratory muscles when the airway had been closed at FRC; these results are in agreement with the studies of Davis, Fowler and Lambert (1956). Vagus nerve activity—the activity of vagal afferent fibres from the slowly adapting pulmonary stretch receptors—was compared to the total number of EMG impulses and also the the highest EMG impulse frequency recorded from the diaphragm and from the external intercostal muscles during the respiratory cycle following the apnoeic period. The total number of EMG impulses recorded from the diaphragm decreased in some instances almost linearly with increasing average action potential frequency recorded from the vagus nerve (Fig. 1). This was also found to be true for the total number of EMG impulses recorded from the external intercostal muscles. The highest EMG impulse frequency often showed a

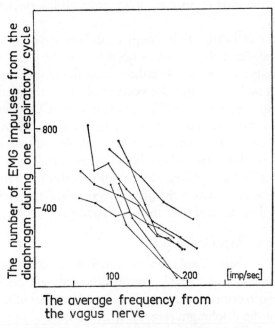

FIG. 1. The total number of EMG impulses recorded from the diaphragm during the respiratory cycle following on inflation-induced apnoea shown as a function of the average action potential activity of the vagus.

much less marked decrease. In many cases, therefore, only the duration of the discharge seemed to have decreased.

In most cases the apnoeic period increased in length exponentially with the average action potential frequency recorded from the vagus, which is in agreement with the studies of Widdicombe (1961); sometimes, however, an almost linear relationship between these two variables was observed. After vagotomy no such decrease in the electrical activity of the inspiratory muscles during inflation was noted, nor was there any apnoeic period.

We have also been able to observe a change in the total number of EMG impulses when the airway was closed at FRC and the lungs deflated by removing a known volume of air: the total number of impulses increased with increasing deflation. The level of anaesthesia that had been induced greatly affected the electrical activity but not the EMG frequency of the diaphragm. After cutting the vagus, no increase in the total number of EMG impulses from the inspiratory muscles was seen. The changes in electrical activity just described for the inspiratory muscles were also found in the external intercostal muscles, but these changes were markedly dependent on the level of anaesthesia so that their interpretation is somewhat difficult.

Inflation and deflation of the lungs in the cat were produced by the following procedure: the cat was placed in a body plethysmograph of 30 litres capacity; the animal breathed from the atmosphere through a pneumotachograph head, and the volume of air in the plethysmograph was altered with a piston pump. The total number of EMG impulses from the inspiratory muscles during the respiratory cycle following apnoea decreased almost linearly with the volume of air drawn from the box. The injection of additional air into the box after withdrawal increased the total number of EMG impulses. These results are similar to those obtained in the experiments in which the airway was closed and the lungs were directly inflated or deflated with the piston pump.

*Carbon dioxide and hypoxic stimulation*

The effect of carbon dioxide stimulation on the electrical activity of the inspiratory muscles was studied. Stimulation with 4·1 per cent carbon dioxide in oxygen caused no changes in the total number of EMG impulses recorded from the diaphragm (Fig. 2), whereas the total number of EMG impulses recorded from the external intercostal muscles increased under these conditions. The highest EMG frequency recorded during one respiratory cycle increased during stimulation, both in the diaphragm and in the external intercostal muscles (Fig. 3). Plotted over a time period, the discharge recorded on the EMG on stimulation with carbon dioxide had its highest impulse frequency but its shortest duration in the diaphragm, the highest impulse frequency approximating to the maximum air flow. The corresponding graph obtained for the intercostal muscles displayed an even more powerful relative increase. After vagotomy, also, carbon dioxide stimulation caused an increase in the highest EMG frequency recorded during one respiratory cycle, but this change differed from that seen before vagotomy: the burst showed a relatively slow initial increase in the frequency, which then remained for a longer time at the new elevated level. During carbon dioxide stimulation, the total number of action potentials recorded from the vagus during one respiratory cycle decreased but the highest frequency increased.

The total number of EMG impulses observed after closure of the airway at FRC was lower if this closure was preceded by carbon dioxide stimulation but the recorded impulse frequency was higher. The increase in the total number of EMG impulses on deflation was much greater under conditions of carbon dioxide stimulation.

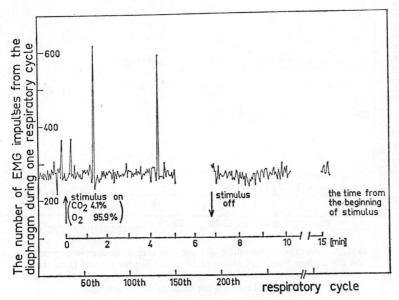

Fɪɢ. 2. The effect of breathing 4·1 per cent carbon dioxide in oxygen on the total number of EMG impulses recorded from the diaphragm during one respiratory cycle.

Stimulation with 4·6 per cent carbon dioxide in air elicited a different response from that obtained with a similar percentage of carbon dioxide in oxygen. Characteristically, the response to carbon dioxide in air occurred much earlier than the response to carbon dioxide in oxygen. The total number of EMG impulses recorded from the diaphragm also increased during the stimulation. The same effects occurred on stimulation with 6 per cent oxygen in nitrogen. During hypoxic stimulation, the highest frequency recorded from the diaphragm during one respiratory cycle did not increase so much as it did with carbon dioxide stimulation but the effect occurred very quickly, usually appearing during the second respiratory cycle after the start of stimulation. The total number of EMG impulses and the highest

7*

impulse frequency both decreased immediately stimulation was discontinued. Since the response to stimulation is different at different levels of anaesthesia, further study is needed to confirm the results of the stimulation experiments just described and for their more detailed analysis.

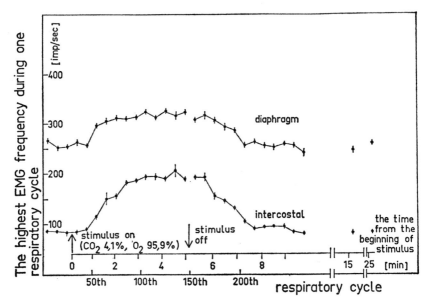

FIG. 3. The effect of breathing 4·1 per cent carbon dioxide in oxygen on the highest frequency recorded from the diaphragm and from the external intercostal muscles during one respiratory cycle. Each point (with standard error) is the mean of ten observations.

### DISCUSSION

Considerable caution is necessary in drawing conclusions about the regulation of breathing from the results in anaesthetized animals. However, the present findings seem to justify the conclusion that the functional unit in which the determination of tidal volume and respiratory frequency takes place (the tidal volume-frequency unit) requires a given amount of "neural energy" before its discharge can occur. If the output to this unit from the minute ventilation unit, for example, increases by the same order of magnitude as probably occurs with carbon dioxide stimulation, the threshold will be reached sooner and the discharges become more frequent; but our results show that the total number of impulses remains constant whereas, in contrast, the impulse frequency increases and the duration of the discharge decreases. The level of the energy threshold in the tidal volume-frequency unit can be changed by, for example, inhibitory and excitatory drives of the vagus. If the output from the minute ventilation unit is maintained constant and the inhibitory drive of the vagus is increased, the threshold increases and a longer time is needed for the requisite energy level at which apnoea occurs to be reached. The first discharge following apnoea occurs at a lower energy threshold than the second and third discharges. The system obviously tends to find a new balance. But if the inhibitory activity is abruptly removed, the discharge begins at once because the threshold in the tidal volume-frequency unit falls rapidly. The vagal excitatory drive probably either lowers the level of the energy threshold or puts the required neural energy into the tidal volume-frequency unit directly. These events take place during deflation of the lungs and probably also at the beginning of inspiration. The setting of the respiratory system is naturally also affected by information arriving from elsewhere in the organism.

Although the diaphragm and intercostal muscles are controlled by the same regulatory system, it seems that they are at least partly separately regulated. The idea of this separate control is supported by the observation that the activity of the intercostal muscles, compared to that of the diaphragm, decreased with increasing depth of anaesthesia. It should also be noted that, even in our preliminary results, the effects of anaesthesia on the intercostal muscles before and after vagotomy were different. Further, we found in our human studies that the relationship between the electrical activities of the diaphragm and the external intercostal muscles can be changed voluntarily. In some preliminary studies we have also observed that on closure of the airway at FRC, with the subject trying to inspire against the closed airway, activity in the external intercostal muscles (measured with surface electrodes), even at airway pressures lower than $-20$ cmH$_2$O, was absent or minimal. The slightest inflation of the lungs resulted in electrical activity in the external intercostal muscles. But in the anaesthetized cat subjected to the experiment just described, activity in the external intercostal muscles was not reduced. Carbon dioxide and hypoxic stimulation produced different responses. The response to hypoxia, as measured by the electrical output of the respiratory centres, appeared much earlier than the response to 4·1 per cent carbon dioxide in oxygen; the former response could usually be detected at the second inspiration after stimulation. The response to discontinuation of the stimulus was usually also seen during the second inspiration.

More positive and detailed inferences will only be possible when additional quantitative studies have been done. Such studies should contribute to the clarification of the mechanisms involved in the regulation of breathing.

SUMMARY

The effect of vagal activity and of carbon dioxide and hypoxic stimuli on the efferent output of the respiratory centres was studied in the pento-barbitone-anaesthetized cat. The output of the respiratory centres was measured by recording the electrical activity of the inspiratory muscles. The total number of impulses recorded electromyographically during the respiratory cycle that follows inflation-induced apnoea decreased almost linearly with the increasing average action potential activity of the vagus nerve.

During stimulation with $4 \cdot 1$ per cent carbon dioxide in oxygen, no change in the total number of impulses recorded from the diaphragm was found although the total number of impulses from the external intercostal muscles increased. In both groups of inspiratory muscles the highest frequency during any one respiratory cycle increased.

Stimulation with $4 \cdot 6$ per cent carbon dioxide in air also produced an increase in the total number of EMG impulses recorded from the diaphragm during the stimulation; the response occurred much earlier than when $4 \cdot 1$ per cent carbon dioxide in oxygen was used. A response similar to that obtained with $4 \cdot 6$ per cent carbon dioxide in air was also found during hypoxic stimulation. Discontinuation of the stimulation was immediately followed by a decrease in both the total number of EMG impulses and in the highest EMG impulse frequency recorded from the inspiratory muscles.

ACKNOWLEDGEMENTS

These studies have been aided by grants from the Paavo Nurmi Foundation, the Finnish Anti-Tuberculosis Association and the Paulo Foundation, Helsinki.

REFERENCES

AGOSTONI, E., SANT'AMBROGIO, G., and DEL PORTILLO CARRASCO, H. (1960). J. appl. Physiol., 15, 1093–1097.
BERGSTRÖM, R. M., and KERTTULA, Y. (1961). Suomal. Tiedeakat. Toim., A, V, 79, 1–12.
CAMPBELL, E. J. M., and GREEN, J. H. (1953a). J. Physiol., Lond., 120, 409–418.
CAMPBELL, E. J. M., and GREEN, J. H. (1953b). J. Physiol., Lond., 122, 282–290.
CAMPBELL, E. J. M., and HOWELL, J. B. L. (1962). In Ciba Fdn Symp. Pulmonary Structure and Function, pp. 29–45. London: Churchill.
DAVIS, H. L., FOWLER, W. S., and LAMBERT, E. H. (1956). Am. J. Physiol., 187, 558–566.
DELHEZ, L., PETIT, J. M., and BOTTIN, R. (1965). J. Physiol., Paris, 57, 598–599.
DELHEZ, L., PETIT, J. M., and MILIC-EMILI, J. (1959). Quoted in PETIT, J. M., DELHEZ, L., and TROQUET, J. (1965). J. Physiol., Paris, 57, 7–113.
DELHEZ, L., PETIT, J. M., SNEPPE, R., and BOTTIN, R. (1965). Revue électrodiagn. thérap., 2, 303–317.
DITTLER, R. (1910). Pflügers Arch. ges. Physiol., 131, 581–588.

DITTLER, R., and GARTEN, S. (1912). *Z. Biol.*, **58**, 420–450.
FINK, B. R., NGAI, S., and DUNCAN, H. A. (1958). *J. Am. med. Ass.*, **168**, 2245–2249.
GASSER, H. S., and NEWCOMER, H. S. (1921). *Am. J. Physiol.*, **57**, 1–26.
PETIT, J. M., MILIC-EMILI, J., and DELHEZ, L. (1960). *J. appl. Physiol.*, **15**, 1101–1106.
SEARS, T. A., and NEWSOM DAVIS, J. (1968). *Ann. N.Y. Acad. Sci.*, **155**, 1, 183–190.
VILJANEN, A. A. (1966). *Acta physiol. scand.*, **68**, suppl. 277, 212.
VILJANEN, A. A. (1967a). *Acta physiol. scand.*, **70**, 54–56.
VILJANEN, A. A. (1967b). *Acta physiol. scand.*, suppl. 296, 1–61.
VILJANEN, A. A., and HALTTUNEN, P. K. (1967). *Acta neurol. scand.*, **43**, suppl. 31, 191.
VILJANEN, A. A., and POPPIUS, H. (1968). *Scand. J. clin. Lab. Invest.*, **21**, suppl. 101, 63–64.
VILJANEN, A. A., POPPIUS, H., BERGSTRÖM, R. M., and HAKUMÄKI, M. (1965). *Acta neurol. scand.*, **41**, suppl. 13, 237–239.
VILJANEN, A. A., SALORINNE, Y., LAITINEN, L. A., and PALOHEIMO, M. (1968). *Scand. J. clin. Lab. Invest.*, **21**, suppl. 101, 64.
WIDDICOMBE, J. G. (1961). *Clin. Sci.*, **21**, 163–170.

# DISCUSSION

*Campbell:* Will you clarify some of the points you discussed about the relationship between impulse frequency and volumes and pressures? First, was the total number of impulses per breath correlated with inspiration?

*Viljanen:* Yes, this number was correlated with the first time integral of the inspiratory muscular work.

*Campbell:* What was impulse frequency correlated with in mechanical terms?

*Viljanen:* Impulse frequency at the end of inspiration was correlated with the work done by the inspiratory muscles during inspiration. Impulse frequency, incidentally, is usually lower than peak frequency.

*Campbell:* What about alveolar pressure?

*Viljanen:* Impulse frequency, four seconds after the end of inspiration with the subject holding his breath and the glottis open, was linearly correlated with the corresponding alveolar relaxation pressure. Further, the impulse frequency during deepening of inspiration was linearly related to inspiratory muscular force. In other words, in each quiet inspiration, impulse frequency is directly proportional to the pressure produced by the inspiratory muscles, and impulse frequency at the end of inspiration is linearly related to inspiratory muscular work. This means that, at the end of inspiration, muscle force and muscle work are directly proportional. Calculations from our equations show that under constant conditions there is a logarithmic relationship between the impulse frequency recorded at the end of inspiration and tidal volume. We suggest that the respiratory centres may not only programme each inspiration to reach a predetermined end-state but also pre-set the next inspiration.

*Campbell:* Are you suggesting that when inspiration starts, a store of pre-set impulses is present somewhere and that these cannot be modified during a breath?

*Viljanen:* Yes. It seems that the functional unit controlling impulse sequence contains a number of impulses and once this number is fixed it is difficult to change it.

*Dornhorst:* I am still not quite clear about the first-time integral of inspiratory muscular work. Is this a measure of respiratory power?

*Viljanen:* Yes. *W*, the integral of pressure and volume during one breath, represents work or power.

*Newsom Davis:* Or is *W* the total amount of work done per breath?

*Viljanen:* That is just another way of putting it; the integral of pressure/ volume is the total amount of work done during inspiration.

*Campbell:* Attempts to work out the relationship between neural and mechanical events in terms of force, work, degree of shortening of muscle fibres and the duration for which force is sustained have been used for other systems, and must certainly now be applied to breathing.

*Viljanen:* We have tried to make calculations based on such mechanical entities as volume and pressure, and to correlate these with electrical events. The relationships between electrical and mechanical activities in voluntary muscles and in the cardiovascular system have also been studied in our Institute. Bergström (1959) found a linear correlation between the number of motor impulses from the muscle and integrated electromyogram activity.

*Campbell:* When one breathes in, the lungs expand to a certain volume; this takes a certain time and the process occurs at a certain speed. Your analysis suggests that the duration, force and amount of work done per breath can be directly correlated to certain electrical events. From this correlation you have concluded that the mechanical implication of the information that is unleashed at the start of a given breath cannot be modified once that breath has started. Is this a reasonable general interpretation of your findings?

*Viljanen:* Yes, at least under the conditions of my experiments.

*von Euler:* The notion that the number of impulses available for a given breath is constant and unalterable may be true with intact vagi, when the Hering-Breuer mechanism is in operation, but it is certainly not true after vagotomy, when the duration of the respiratory cycle is constant and independent of any increase in drive which, however, will increase the neural output by recruitment of new neurones and by increasing the impulse frequency of each neurone.

Concerning the relationship between vagal discharge and lung volume I should like to refer again to our finding (see p. 107) that vagal discharge is linearly related not to lung volume itself but to its square root, within a range of about one and a half to twice eupnoeic tidal volumes. Did you see this square root relationship in your curves, Dr Viljanen?

*Viljanen:* I do not have enough data to answer this question.

*Dornhorst:* The relationship between afferent vagal discharge and lung volume is probably neither strictly linear nor parabolic. The degree of approximation to either form is not a fundamental problem.

*Zechman:* It is interesting and useful to try to make correlations between mechanical events and neural activity. We are currently studying the effects of transient loading on the respiratory system, so I was particularly interested in your comments on the relationship between the total number of impulses per breath and the peak impulse achieved during that breath. Both these parameters can vary. The total number of impulses per breath is dependent on both frequency and duration of discharge. In other words, both slope and/or duration can vary. I wonder, Dr Viljanen, how useful your models are for describing what is happening during respiration unless one takes account of these two parameters. Would you comment on this point and also tell us what you mean by "neural energy"?

*Viljanen:* It is difficult to say what neural energy really is, but it may be an entity which can be related to the number of impulses that are fired in a certain time. There must be some such time entity, because every functional unit has its own time constant, and the energy level of the functional unit depends on the relationship between its input and discharge.

We too have tried to study the effect of transient loading on the respiratory system, but with our methods it has been difficult to determine the part played by the spindle system in the changes in impulse activity. Our main project has been to study correlations between mechanical events and electrical activities in the respiratory muscles. At the same time we have gained some clues about the regulation of breathing and have now begun to study this by constructing an operational model. But this work is too preliminary for me to say anything yet about the regulation of breathing.

REFERENCE

BERGSTRÖM, R. M. (1959). *Acta physiol. scand.*, **45**, 97–101.

# GENERAL DISCUSSION II

*Dornhorst:* Interest seems to be crystallizing around the independent modulation of the frequency and the total number of neuronal discharges on the one hand, and different patterns of correlation of diaphragmatic and intercostal events on the other. Dr Cohen has presented some of his ideas on how the frequency and number of impulses could be independently modulated, and Professor Plum showed clinical examples of grosser dissociations in respiratory patterns. Could we now make our discussion of these subjects more general?

*von Euler:* Concerning the timing of the different phases of the respiratory cycle, when the durations of the inspiratory phases ($T_I$) are plotted (ordinate) against the durations of the corresponding expiratory phases ($T_E$, abscissa) in a rebreathing experiment, the regression line appears to be linear over a fair range of cycle durations and intercepts the abscissa

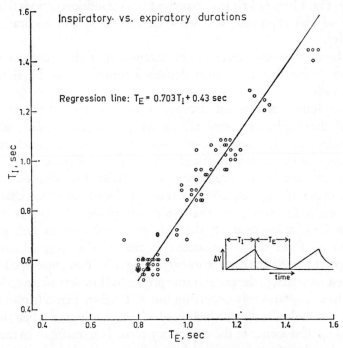

FIG. I (*von Euler*). Inspiratory durations ($T_I$: ordinate) plotted against the corresponding expiratory durations ($T_E$: abscissa) of a series of breaths during a rebreathing experiment. Cat under light pentobarbitone anaesthesia. (Clark, F., and Euler, C. von, unpublished).

at about 300–500 milliseconds, as shown in Fig. 1 (Clark and Euler von, unpublished observations). The same slope and intercept of the regression line also obtains if a breath is cut short by a sudden inflation, but if inflation is maintained during the expiratory phase expiration is prolonged; the latter result supports the idea that expiratory time varies more than inspiratory time. It may also be important that some inspiratory activity usually continues at the beginning of the expiratory phase. Any such activity, by maintaining a somewhat higher lung volume during the early part of the expiratory phase, prolongs the expiratory phase which in turn alters the $T_I$–$T_E$ relationship.

*Dornhorst:* Does the interception point of the regression line with $T_E$ represent a minimum resetting time after which the programme cannot be altered however small the previous inspiratory time? In other words, does it take at least 300 milliseconds before another cycle can be initiated?

*von Euler:* I cannot answer that question because we have not yet studied rapid breathing and our data thus come from a rather restricted range of cycle durations. The time corresponding to the interception point (0·43s in Fig. 1 [*von Euler*]) may represent both transition periods (between inspiration and expiration and between expiration and inspiration repectively).

*Dornhorst:* It would certainly be interesting if the duration of the transition bursts that Dr Cohen described turned out to be about 300 milliseconds.

*Cohen:* Some observations relevant to the problem of the programming of the inspiratory burst are shown in Fig. 2. In the paralysed, vagotomized cat, the dorsolateral rostral pontine region (nucleus parabrachialis) was stimulated electrically. Short stimulus trains were applied at different times in the expiratory phase. With low stimulus current (Fig. 2, upper traces) the stimulus train produced either no change or only a slight shortening of the expiratory phase. At higher current strengths (Fig. 2, lower trace) the train produced a premature phrenic burst whose form was very similar to that of the spontaneous burst (as is apparent in the trace of the integrated signal). Thus, once the inspiratory burst was started, the programme proceeded in a way almost identical to that in a spontaneously occurring burst. Further, Fig. 2 (right) shows that the threshold for the production of a burst was higher when stimulation was applied earlier in the expiratory phase but, again, once the burst was produced its form was then almost the same as that of other bursts.

*Mitchell:* What was the shortest latency period for these responses?

*Cohen:* For stimulus trains delivered in the last quarter of the expiratory

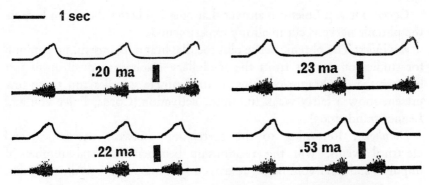

FIG. 2 (*Cohen*). Effects of stimulus trains, applied in nucleus parabrachialis, on the duration of the expiratory phase. In each strip the bottom trace is the original phrenic recording and the top trace is the integrated phrenic signal. Durations of stimulus trains (0·16 s, 0·2 ms pulses, 200/s) are indicated by vertical bars; current strengths indicated in captions. *Left:* stimulus trains start 0·8 s (50 per cent of control expiratory phase duration) after end of phrenic bursts. *Right:* stimulus trains start 0·4 s (25 per cent of control expiratory phase duration) after end of phrenic burst.

phase, the shortest latency was about 100 milliseconds (time from first stimulus to start of phrenic burst).

In recent experiments (unpublished) on the programming of the inspiratory burst I have studied the Hering–Breuer reflex in the naturally breathing, decerebrate cat. When the airway is occluded at the time of minimum lung volume (just before the start of inspiratory movement), the inspiratory phase is lengthened by 50–100 per cent (because prevention of lung expansion lessens the afferent input from pulmonary stretch receptors; the effect of this input is inspiratory-inhibitory). However, there is no change in the *slope* of the integrated phrenic signal during a time equivalent to the duration of the control inspiratory phase; in other words, the global phrenic discharge continues to augment at the normal rate but the burst lasts for a longer time. (This observation was also verified by summing the phrenic potentials in an average response computer.) Thus, pulmonary stretch receptor input does not affect the detailed programming of the phrenic burst but only determines, through a trigger action, the time of termination of the burst. Similar results, obtained by a somewhat different technique, were reported by Larrabee and Knowlton (1946) for individual phrenic motor fibres.

*Dornhorst:* Are your results affected if the phrenic nerve is cut or the diaphragm is paralysed? In other words, does the presence or absence of spindle afferents in the diaphragm affect the results?

*Cohen:* Dr von Euler can answer that question better than I can because the phrenic nerve is cut in all my experiments.

*von Euler:* The phrenic nerve plus the diaphragm is a useful preparation for studies on output from the medullary respiratory mechanism just because the diaphragm contains so few muscle spindles and those few present show a fairly weak fusimotor activation (Corda, Euler von and Lennerstrand, 1965).

*Dornhorst:* Returning to the correlations between mechanical and electrical events, will the relationship between the total number of impulses and tidal volume be destroyed in some pathological conditions, as when airways resistance is increased in asthma?

*von Euler:* Yes. As soon as mechanisms involving spinal (reflex) control of the intercostal muscles come into play the conditions in the lung, and hence the relationships, may be changed.

*Zechman:* But even with considerable increases in airways resistance the correlation between end-tidal $P_{CO_2}$ and inspiratory work remains (Milic-Emili and Tyler, 1963).

*Flenley:* The mechanical conditions under which the diaphragm operates are important in assessing relationships between the mechanical and electrical events connected with breathing. These conditions can be altered by changes in lung volume as well as by airways obstruction. Agostoni (1962) showed clearly in conscious man that the diaphragmatic electromyogram will persist despite large increases in lung volume produced by positive pressure breathing, which reduces tidal volume. In this situation there is a marked dissociation between electrical activity and mechanical function of the diaphragm.

*Campbell:* We need to remind each other that correlations between neural and mechanical events are necessarily crude; more work of the sort carried out by Dr Viljanen is needed to bridge the gap between studies of the respiratory centres and of the behaviour of the respiratory muscles—the mechanics of breathing.

*Zechman:* Our approach has been to study respiratory control by imposing a step-change in inspiratory resistance (Wiley and Zechman, 1968). By comparing the first loaded breath with subsequent breaths one can gain information about the contributions of the primary neural and secondary chemical drives. We are relating the activity of some primary outputs (that is, external intercostal and diaphragm units) of the respiratory system to inspiratory power and work. Roger Shannon, in my laboratory, is currently examining the effect of interrupting the neural feedback loops (vagus, cervical and thoracic dorsal roots and so on) on these relationships. Through these studies we hope to obtain a more quantitative description of the system's behaviour.

*Dornhorst:* Dr Cohen's work, although limited by his experimental model of a paralysed, vagotomized, decerebrate cat, shows fairly conclusively the existence of a pre-set inspiratory pattern that can be fired by an electrical stimulus. It is also known that neural output from the respiratory centre responds rapidly to events at the periphery. Both these approaches seem necessary at this stage.

*von Euler:* Chemical, electrical (or neural) and mechanical parameters are all important in working out these quantitative correlations. Dr Cohen's and Dr Merrill's method of studying impulses from limited samples of neurones is one of the ways of tackling these problems; Dr Zechman's approach is another.

*Godfrey:* Dr Cohen, could you clarify the evidence about the time in the respiratory cycle when its programming is set? The clear relationships between impulse frequency and work in one breath have been nicely demonstrated, but I wonder if the programme for a given cycle could be set in the preceding one or even two or three breaths?

*Cohen:* There is good evidence that a pre-set programme for the inspiratory burst exists (this volume, p. 197, Fig. 2). The observation that the threshold for producing a premature inspiratory burst depends on the time of delivery of the stimulus in the expiratory phase suggests that excitability in some part of the inspiration-generating system is changing continuously. Presumably the rate of change of excitability determines the duration of the expiratory phase and can vary according to the experimental conditions.

*Merrill:* The programme is not necessarily pre-set in the inspiratory period of that particular cycle. Although the respiratory system appears to make a decision early in the inspiratory phase about the desired tidal volume for that inspiration, this decision is not irrevocable. For example, if the carbon dioxide content of the inspired air changes drastically during the inspiration, one occasionally sees a sudden alteration in the rate of change of diaphragmatic tension during that inspiration, as well as a different volume threshold for the termination of the inspiration. These observations indicate that decisions about the shape and duration of a particular inspiration are altered as respiratory movement proceeds and afferent states change. This also appears to be true for decisions about expiration.

*von Euler:* The cycle can also be altered by volume information during the expiratory phase.

*Dejours:* Changes in the pattern of breathing may depend on the type of stimulus. I have observed the effects of various minimal stimuli on this pattern. If the fingers are moved slightly, during either inspiration or expiration, changes in the breathing pattern occur within 0·1 seconds (unpublished data). But, on the other hand, in the cat we have sometimes observed (Leitner *et al.*, 1965) that, following a sudden change of chemo-receptor activity, changes in ventilation do not usually start until the cycle *after* the one in which the stimulation was changed. These findings may mean that the programme for any one cycle is pre-set at the beginning of the previous inspiratory phase. The stimulus from muscular work cannot be exclusively cortical because we have also observed these immediate changes on passive movement of the leg in anaesthetized man (Dejours, 1959).

*Mitchell:* I have recently studied the latency of responses for some afferent inputs to respiratory neurones in the medulla (unpublished results). We first tried to establish the simplest (and shortest) reflex arcs through the medulla. We recorded responses in the nucleus of the tractus solitarius after stimulating the superior laryngeal, glossopharyngeal, the pharyngeal branch of the glossopharyngeal, and the vagal and aortic nerves, in order to establish their fields of activity. Our results show that 80 per cent of the medullary units we stimulated could be affected by more than one afferent input. It has been suggested that there may be a primary afferent pathway for polarization responses, which would allow a large overlap and possibly also some presynaptic inhibition. In view of this, we planned to study the effects of stimulation of the nerve to the carotid sinus with simultaneous lung inflation. This would test the presence of presynpatic inhibition of impulses arriving in the nerve from the carotid sinus. (We do not yet know if the afferent pathway involved is coming from baroreceptors or chemoreceptors.) We recorded from individual inspiratory units in the nucleus of the tractus solitarius and found that, with all these inputs, the latency of response was between four and six milliseconds (the impulses reach the phrenic motor pool in six to ten milliseconds), which means that the reflex arc in this region is very short. We are also using orthodromic and antidromic stimulation (in the medulla and cervical spinal cord) to work out the exact anatomical site of each arc. We hope to map the course of the upper motoneurones to respiratory muscles and to differentiate these neurones from the phase-spanning ones. Incidentally, the latency from the pons to the phrenic motoneurone pool is about 100 milliseconds.

*Widdicombe:* Most of the afferent pathways you have stimulated include fibres that mediate respiratory tract reflexes, which could interfere very dramatically with the normal pattern of breathing. Therefore in your experiments you may have superimposed very abrupt and vigorous respiratory acts on eupnoeic activity and cancelled out the normal pattern of breathing. The picture you have described is probably a composite. The pharyngeal branch of the glossopharyngeal nerve, for example, contains very powerful afferent pathways for stimulating the inspiratory motoneurones (Tomori and Widdicombe, 1969). Phrenic motoneurones can be made to fire off at a rate of over 300 impulses per second for short bursts by stimulating the epipharynx and its nerve (Nail, Sterling and Widdicombe, 1969).

*Newsom Davis:* Hiccup is a disorder usually precipitated through vagal afferents. Its characteristics suggest that the neural structures from which

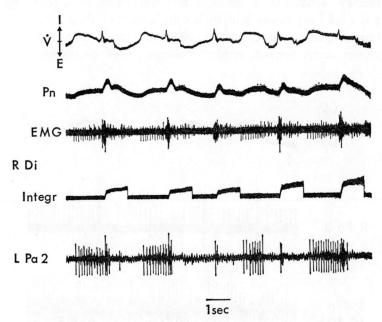

FIG. 3 (*Newsom Davis*). Hiccup during quiet breathing. Single unit EMG activity is present during quiet inspiration. Hiccup is indicated by the intense EMG discharge, brief inspiratory air flow followed by cessation of flow (glottal closure), and peak on pneumograph trace. $\dot{V}$: differentiated air flow (time calibration, 1 s) to emphasize high flow of component hiccup; Pn: abdominal pneumograph; R Di: right diaphragm EMG; L Pa 2: left second parasternal (inspiratory) intercostal EMG; Integr: integration of diaphagmatic EMG for a 1-second period initiated when the level of EMG activity just exceeded that of quiet breathing. EMG recorded with indwelling bipolar electrodes.

it arises are largely independent of the mechanism responsible for rhythmic genesis (Newsom Davis, to be published), so that it provides a means of studying the interaction between separate central drives to the respiratory motoneurone. In Fig. 3 the electromyogram (EMG) has been recorded from the right diaphragm and left parasternal (inspiratory) intercostal muscle with indwelling electrodes. During a normal quiet inspiration, single unit activity is present in both muscles, contrasting with the more intense, brief discharge of hiccup, which occurs almost synchronously in the two muscles. An integrating circuit, opened for a one-second period close to the onset of the hiccup, provided a measure of the amplitude of the hiccup discharge. The hiccup amplitude at peak inspiration was not consistently greater than during expiration. Further, the amplitude and frequency diminish with increasing $Pco_2$ and tend to increase after hyperventilation, in contrast to rhythmic inspiratory discharge. During "voluntary" activation of the expiratory muscles, as in singing (Fig. 4), there is a brief expiratory inhibition coincident with the hiccup, but this inhibition becomes progressively less effective as the drive to the expiratory muscles increases towards residual volume. These events are observed

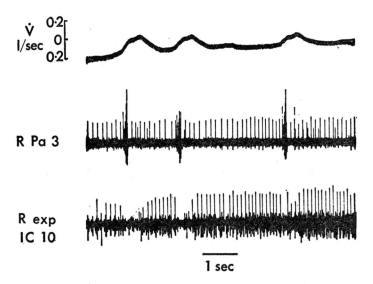

FIG. 4 (*Newsom Davis*). Hiccup during activation of expiratory muscles. Subject is singing a sustained note. Brief inhibition of expiratory EMG activity can be seen coincident with hiccup, becoming less marked as expiratory activity increases. $\dot{V}$: air flow; R Pa 3: right third parasternal (inspiratory) intercostal EMG; R exp IC 10: right tenth internal (expiratory) intercostal EMG, recorded in mid-axillary line.

even when the magnitude of the hiccup, measured from the inspiratory EMG or the air-flow record, has not diminished. These features of hiccup indicate that its interaction with rhythmic or "voluntary" drives to the respiratory motoneurone is at least as likely to be occurring at spinal level as centrally.

*Dornhorst:* The figures show bursts of discharges from the inspiratory intercostal muscles. Is that usual in hiccup?

*Newsom Davis:* Yes.

*Dornhorst:* This is surprising because the chest wall collapses in the antero-posterior direction during an uninhibited hiccup, whereas if you make a sharp inspiratory effort mimicking a hiccup the chest wall does not collapse in this way. Why is the balance between the intercostals and the diaphragm so upset?

*Newsom Davis:* I think the reason for this is that, in hiccup, the glottis closes about 40 milliseconds after the onset of inspiratory muscle discharge, the muscle discharge continuing for a further 500 or more milliseconds. Sometimes the subject even closes his glottis before the hiccup as if he had warning of its approach. The distortion of the chest is a mechanical consequence of a strong inspiratory contraction, against a closed airway, which causes a reduction of the antero-posterior diameter of the chest wall and an increase in the lateral diameter (see Agostoni and Mognoni, 1966).

*Plum:* We have studied a patient with brainstem infarction and a tracheostomy in whom sustained hiccup provided enough air to ventilate him for many hours and keep his $Pa_{CO_2}$ levels below 30 mmHg.

*Sears:* For a given level of diaphragmatic activation the transdiaphragmatic pressure decreases as lung volume increases. This has a profound effect on the mechanical interaction between the intercostal muscles and the diaphragm with regard to whether or not the chest wall collapses.

*Dornhorst:* Do the accessory muscles of respiration, for example the sternomastoids, contract during hiccup?

*Newsom Davis:* Sometimes, but not until about 100 milliseconds after the onset of the diaphragmatic discharge.

*Cross:* May I return to a general problem? How valid are conclusions drawn from sampling from the respiratory centre? It seems to me, Dr Cohen, that there may be a danger that you are sampling from rather few non-typical neurones that give the responses you are looking for, and then generalizing from these "particular" responses.

*Cohen:* The responses shown in the figures in my paper are "typical" in the sense that they were found in many neurones; the actual numbers of recorded neurones having each response are stated in the original papers (Cohen, 1968, 1969). Of course we do not know the precise influence of the various types of neurone since we do not know their input-output relationships, but the frequency of occurrence of the responses suggests that they are important in the total system.

*Merrill:* The total number and the size of the sub-populations that you are recording from is not clear. The question of the validity of the sample sizes you use is therefore difficult to answer. In a cat partly anaesthetized

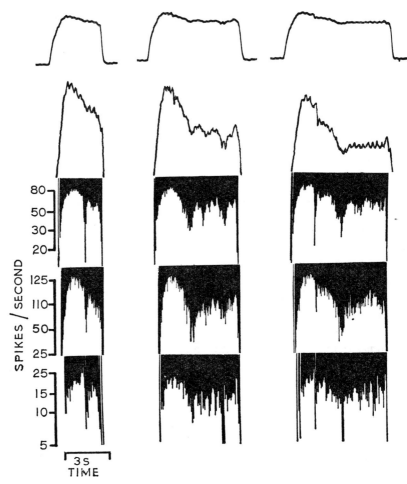

FIG. 5. (*Merrill*). Firing rates from three inspiratory units, recorded simultaneously. Calibration: 3 s. (For explanation see text.)

with pentobarbitone and spontaneously breathing room air, the active inspiratory population is uniform and cannot be meaningfully divided into sub-populations like those described by Dr Cohen. I believe that additional groups become active only with elevated respiratory drives.

Fig. 5 shows the firing rates of three inspiratory units, simultaneously recorded, in an anaesthetized cat. The ordinate is the number of spikes per second and the abscissa is time. The top two traces are chest tension, with the top trace at low gain. Tension was measured from the penultimate rib and thus had intercostal and diaphragmatic contributions. The frequency display is the minus logarithm of the duration of the interval between spikes, with every interval displayed as a descending, dark bar. The three inspirations illustrated came from a series which followed the rapid incremental injection of pentobarbitone, 15 mg. It can be seen that each inspiratory unit accurately mirrors all the details in the tension measure. The activity correlates in very great detail from unit to unit in this population and a few recordings characterize the activity of the whole population.

*Plum:* Does the phase-lag lie between the discharge of the nerve cell and chest movement, or *vice versa*?

*Merrill:* It is difficult to say because I am describing events that occur in a few hundred milliseconds but with latency periods of only 20–30 milliseconds. In my view mechanical changes lag behind neural firing.

*Dornhorst:* If one imposes no limits on a sample it is no longer a sample but the whole population. Another way of stating this problem is to inquire if neurones that are programmed in a particular way for one experiment might behave differently under different conditions. And this sort of question is unanswerable because unless a neurone behaves in a recognizable way one cannot study it.

*Aitken:* In various parts of our discussions so far we have also been drawing general conclusions from observing one or very few subjects. Breathing, like other physiological systems which have psychological aspects, is strikingly prone to individual differences, both within and between even healthy subjects. This variability cannot be discounted in conscious man, though it is less important during sleep or anaesthesia and in lower animals. The object of study should be to determine which factors contribute how much variance. Although neurophysiological and metabolic mechanisms will remain the most important, psychological factors do contribute considerable variance and unknown factors remain as a notable residue.

## REFERENCES

AGOSTONI, E. (1962). *J. appl. Physiol.*, **17**, 215–220.
AGOSTONI, E., and MOGNONI, P. (1966). *J. appl. Physiol.*, **21**, 1827–1832.
COHEN, M. I. (1968). *J. Neurophysiol.*, **31**, 142–165.
COHEN, M. I. (1969). *J. Neurophysiol.*, **32**, 356–374.
CORDA, M., EULER, C. VON, and LENNERSTRAND, G. (1965). *J. Physiol., Lond.*, **178**, 161–177.
DEJOURS, P. (1959). *C.r. hebd. Séanc. Acad. Sci., Paris*, **248**, 2129–2131.
LARRABEE, M. G., and KNOWLTON, G. C. (1946). *Am. J. Physiol.*, **147**, 90–99.
LEITNER, L. M., PAGÈS, B., PUCCINELLI, R., and DEJOURS, P. (1965). *Archs int. Pharmacodyn. Thér.*, **154**, 421–426.
MILIC-EMILI, J., and TYLER, J. M. (1963). *J. appl. Physiol.*, **18**, 497–504.
NAIL, B. S., STERLING, G. M., and WIDDICOMBE, J. G. (1969). *J. Physiol., Lond.*, **200**, 137–138P.
TOMORI, Z., and WIDDICOMBE, J. G. (1969). *J. Physiol., Lond.*, **200**, 25–49.
WILEY, R. L., and ZECHMAN, F. W. JR. (1968). *Resp. Physiol.*, **6**, 105–112.

# THE SENSE OF EFFORT

P. A. MERTON

*Physiological Laboratory, University of Cambridge*

EVERYBODY is familiar with the idea that stimulation of sense organs causes nervous signals to travel to the brain, where they give rise to a subjective sensation. The detailed problems of coding of information in the nerve fibres, of pattern recognition in the cortex and so on are under active investigation in many laboratories. What goes on in the motor system when we make a voluntary movement has attracted much less discussion. In our most deliberate acts we are aware of making a decision to do something, which is followed, when the movement is actually initiated, by a mental event which we may call variously an "act of will", a "feeling of innervation" or a "sense of effort". Of these names I shall use the last. This term "sense of effort", or any synonym of it, does not appear in modern textbooks of physiology. Why not? It seems natural enough, if a conscious sensation is the mental index of the arrival of sensory impulses at the cortex, that some conscious feeling should accompany the departure from the cortex of voluntary motor impulses. But in making such an identification of the sense of effort there is a complication. In almost every instance the initiation of a voluntary movement is followed in a very few milliseconds by the arrival of sensory impulses set up by the moving part, in the skin, the joints and so on. How much of the sense of effort is a true index of motor efferent activity and how much is due to these sensory concomitants of the resultant muscular activity? In the middle of the eighteenth century the philosopher David Hume gave an answer to this question. He asserted that the sense of effort (he did not use this actual term) was *all* due to the sensory concomitants of muscular action. Hume's views were followed enthusiastically by William James in his textbook of psychology (1890), and it appears to have been by this route that they reached and convinced Sherrington. When Sherrington in 1894 made his great discovery of the sensory nature of the muscle spindles, he saw in them the principal sense organ for the "feeling of innervation". If the whole of the sense of effort were due to the signals of "muscular sense" it would be superfluous to have a special name for it, and, apparently as a result of

Sherrington's enormous influence, the term disappeared (Sherrington, 1900).

Was Sherrington's view correct? Helmholtz would have said that it was not, and I believe that Helmholtz was right. Hughlings Jackson, interestingly enough, also backed Helmholtz (Jackson and Paton, 1909). Helmholtz considered the one striking case in which the initiation of a voluntary movement does not set up conscious sensory messages from the part moved, namely the eyes when vision is excluded. Helmholtz's arguments, to be found in section 29 of the translation of his *Physiological Optics*, are powerful if somewhat indirect (Helmholtz, 1962). Having recently rehearsed them at length (Merton, 1964a, b) I shall be brief here. The main point is that, although we are normally aware how far we have moved our eyes when we voluntarily change the direction of gaze, this knowledge is not due to sensory messages from the eye muscles or other tissues around the eye, for, if for any reason (such as an ocular palsy of recent onset) the eye does not move, we are not aware of this and interpret our visual sensations as if it had moved in accordance with our intentions. Thus a patient with a palsy of the left external rectus muscle who attempts to look to the left has an irresistible illusion that objects seen with the left eye have moved to the left. That is to say he has an illusion which reconciles his belief that he has moved his fixation point to the left with the fact that objects previously at the fixation point are still at the fixation point after his effort to move. Conversely, if the eyeball is moved passively, for example by tugging at the outer canthus, the subject interprets what he sees as if the eyeball had stood still; that is to say, the external world appears to jump about. Brindley and Merton (1960) directly checked corollaries of both these points by anaesthetizing the conjunctiva and manipulating the eyeball with forceps. With vision excluded, passive movements of the eyeball are not appreciated by the subject, while during active voluntary movements he cannot tell whether he has been successful in moving his eye or whether the movement has been restrained by the experimenter.

The conclusion from all these observations is that we only know how far we have moved our eyes by judging the effort we put into moving them, and not because we get any sensory feedback from the eyeball or its surroundings. Hence, for the eyes, we must admit a "sense of effort".

The extra-ocular muscles are peculiar in many ways, both physiologically and neurologically, but as regards sense of effort there is no longer any real reason to doubt that the limb muscles behave in the same way as eye muscles when sensations from skin and joints are excluded; this is not, of course, an easy thing to do, but it can be done. If a joint and the skin around it are rendered insentient either by infiltration of local anaesthetic (see, for example, Browne, Lee and Ring, 1954; Provins, 1958) or by ischaemia from a pneumatic cuff above the joint (Chambers and Gilliatt, 1954; Merton, 1964b), passive movements of the joint are not perceived, or are only perceived at a much larger excursion than usual, but active movements can still be performed, almost as accurately as usual. The muscles moving the joint thus behave just like extra-ocular muscles. Their contraction too must be graded by the subject's sense of effort.

Another way of looking at the whole matter is to contend that muscles are insentient. Muscles are full of afferent end-organs but their afferent messages do not reach consciousness. (It appears very likely from the animal evidence, however, that these messages do reach the cerebral cortex [Albe-Fessard and Liebeskind, 1966; Swett and Bourassa, 1967] so we now have to entertain for the first time the possibility of afferent impulses arriving at the cortex without causing any subjective response.) Haller in the eighteenth century pulled on tendons exposed in wounds and found that the patient experienced no sensation other than pain. A century later Helmholtz, as we have already seen, brought forward the arguments to show that the extra-ocular muscles are insentient. Sherrington would have none of all this, and even those who felt the force of Helmholtz's case could argue that the eye muscles were only insentient because, in man, unlike all the limb muscles they contained no muscle spindles. In the limbs it was as Sherrington said. This position ceased to be tenable in 1949 when Cooper and Daniel published a convincing modern demonstration of typical muscle spindles in the human extra-ocular muscles (Sherrington had not seen muscle spindles).

Since the muscle receptors, which are extremely numerous, do not arouse conscious sensation we can surmise that their general function is to control, by feedback action, the activity of the motor system. They are presumably there to ensure that the muscles do what we ask of them either in conscious voluntary activity or in reflex or other automatic actions such as breathing. We do not, of course, know what we do ask of them. That is a problem in motor coding. On the sensory side we do not know, for example, the code for "triangle". Equally, on the motor side, we do not know the code for "bend the index finger" or for "take a breath". It used to be tacitly supposed that when the motor cortex called for some muscle to contract it merely demanded a certain rate of motor discharge from its motoneurones. Then came the idea that by feedback action the nervo-muscular machinery could be made to function as a "follow-up" length servo to which the input would be a coded demand for a change in length (Merton, 1953). Although this idea is almost certainly too unsophisticated it is not clear in what direction it needs modification. Before I read the book on *Breathlessness* edited by Howell and Campbell (1966) in preparation for this meeting I thought I might hazard a guess at what is demanded of the respiratory muscles when we take a breath, but now I shall not.

A more tractable problem might be the part played by the sense of effort in detecting added inspiratory loads. Is this done by detecting a mismatch between the effort made and the inspiratory volume achieved? Many experiments so far performed, perhaps all, would be consistent with the view that the effort made is not judged but merely assumed by the subject to be constant from breath to breath. This point could, no doubt, be easily dealt with, but it is relevant in another connexion. I used to think that experiments on subjects with respiratory muscles totally paralysed by disease or drugs and artificially ventilated, using a negative pressure respirator, could determine at once if sense of effort were involved in judging inspiratory loads. If inspiratory loads could be detected in these circumstances, this detection could clearly not be anything to do with a sense of effort. But, equally clearly, it is open to such subjects likewise to assume that the stroke of the bellows is constant from breath to breath and to judge accordingly, even if in ordinary circumstances they did make an actual estimate of the effort.

Such subjects might, however, give an answer to another important question, for if the essential sensory information for the task is the inspiratory volume achieved, then paralysed patients ought not to be able to distinguish an inspiratory load from a simple reduction in respiratory stroke, provided that no spurious clues were available, such as a change in the duration of the stroke, tactile clues from the air seal round the neck, or larger pressure differences between the airways and the outside of the neck and face when inspiring against an added load. For investigating the mechanism by which patients become aware of the increased inspiratory load caused by pathological processes in the thorax, the pressure alterations in the upper airways are merely an irrelevant complication of experiments with added external loads, and the aim must be to exclude them. They might not come into play in patients with a tracheostomy, or they might be obviated by enclosing the head and neck in a box sealed to the respirator, the subject breathing through the box with loads added to the inlet of the box. There would then be no change in the pressure difference across the tissues of the face and neck during an inspiration, after an inspiratory load had been added.

## SUMMARY

In certain situations it has been shown that voluntary movements can be made accurately without any conscious sensory information from the moving part, using what nineteenth century writers termed "the sense of effort"; but evidence concerning the part played by the sense of effort in breathing and breathlessness is more difficult to obtain.

## REFERENCES

ALBE-FESSARD, D., and LIEBESKIND, J. (1966). *Expl Brain Res.*, **1**, 127–146.
BRINDLEY, G. S., and MERTON, P. A. (1960). *J. Physiol., Lond.*, **153**, 127–130.
BROWNE, K., LEE, J., and RING, P. A. (1954). *J. Physiol., Lond.*, **126**, 448–458.
CHAMBERS, R. A., and GILLIATT, R. W. (1954). *J. Physiol., Lond.*, **123**, 42P.
COOPER, S., and DANIEL, P. M. (1949). *Brain*, **72**, 1–24.
HELMHOLTZ, H. VON (1962). *Physiological Optics*, vol. 3, sect. 29. Trans. Southall, J. P. C. New York: Dover.
HOWELL, J. B. L., and CAMPBELL, E. J. M. (eds). (1966). *Breathlessness*. Oxford: Blackwell.
JACKSON, J. H., and PATON, L. (1909). *Lancet*, **1**, 900–905.
JAMES, W. (1890). *The Principles of Psychology*, vol. 2, p. 507. London: MacMillan.
MERTON, P. A. (1953). *Ciba Fdn Symp. The Spinal Cord*, pp. 247–255. London: Churchill.
MERTON, P. A. (1964a). In *The Oculomotor System*, pp. 314–320, ed. Bender, M. B. New York: Hoeber, Harper and Row.
MERTON, P. A. (1964b). *Symp. Soc. exp. Biol.*, **18**, 387–400.
PROVINS, K. A. (1958). *J. Physiol., Lond.*, **143**, 55–67.
SHERRINGTON, C. S. (1894). *J. Physiol., Lond.*, **17**, 211–258.
SHERRINGTON, C. S. (1900). In *Textbook of Physiology*, vol. 2, pp. 1002–1013, ed. Schaefer, E. A. Edinburgh and London: Young J. Pentland.
SWETT, J. E., and BOURASSA, C. M. (1967). *J. Neurophysiol.*, **30**, 530–545.

## DISCUSSION

*Paintal:* Have you studied changes in the sense of effort before and after amputation? Does a patient with, say, a mid-calf amputation experience a sense of effort in the calf although he is receiving no messages from it and, if so, does this sensation change after amputation?

*Merton:* I do not know.

*Dornhorst:* Patients feel a sense of effort from a phantom limb for some time after amputation, and this feeling is associated with a vivid sensation of movement in the phantom under appropriate conditions. Angina pectoris, radiating to the phantom arm, with relief obtained by clenching the phantom fist, has been described (Harman, 1948).

*Fillenz:* The use of the phantom limb as a model for assessing the sense of effort may be dangerous; sensory impulses may travel up from the phantom or from the cut end of the nerve.

*Dornhorst:* I agree.

*Campbell:* I do not accept that this is dangerous. Do we know exactly where the sensory information about the phantom limb comes from?

*Dornhorst:* A neuroma is certainly one site that can provide sensory input.

*Campbell:* But how can the sensation of movement of the toe be generated from a neuroma? The point is not so much that the subject feels the presence of his limb after amputation as that he feels he can move it.

*Merton:* In acute experiments in cats, Granit, Leksell and Skoglund (1944) showed that "... nerve impulses, set up in a motor root, are transmitted to the sensory fibres in a cut region of the nerve and can be picked up in the sensory root of the same segment. The cut region thus serves as an 'artificial synapse'." Similar phenomena cannot be ruled out in a phantom limb. There are so many possibilities of this kind that the study of the sense of effort in phantom limbs should, in my view, be left to the neurophilosophers.

*Guz:* How accurately can the sense of effort you have described be measured?

*Merton:* After the blood supply to the limb has been cut off for 90 minutes the standard deviation of repeated attempted movements of the distal thumb joint over an excursion of 20° with the eyes shut is about 1·5°; this is an increase of only about 50 per cent and might be explained by the often considerable discomfort.

*Howell:* Milic-Emili and Tyler (1963) have shown that, for a given amount of ventilatory stimulus, the output of the respiratory centre is a constant work rate by the inspiratory muscles, regardless of the amount of external respiratory resistance. It should be possible to carry out similar studies to assess the rate of work done in moving the thumb when opposed by varying loads, and thus see if work rate is constant for a given amount of conscious effort.

*Merton:* Work rate might be a useful index. It has not been used, as far as I know.

*Dornhorst:* Surely the work demanded depends on the circumstances. Common experience shows that in some situations a major movement can be carried out in the face of variable loads without extra thought. Steering a car on an uneven road is a good illustration of this. On the other hand, it is also quite easy to arrange experimental situations where tension is demanded, as in an experiment when subjects lift up similar-looking weights, one heavy and the other made of cardboard, and there is an inappropriately strong response to the cardboard "weight". This is a different set-up from the example I gave of steering a car because the subject does not anticipate a variable load but rather pre-sets a range of tensions before he moves. In ordinary movements either set of conditions may be present and it is therefore dangerous to assume that only one or the other applies to respiration.

*Campbell:* I suspect that this inappropriate response reflects the nature of the proprioceptive information (for further discussions see Campbell, Bennett and Rubenstein, 1963).

*Wood:* Both these sorts of conditions occur in breathing. Taking a deeper breath does not improve the ability to detect a respiratory load, but reducing the load without previous warning will cause the subject to use an inappropriately large effort.

*Widdicombe:* Can we conclude from these observations that curarized subjects do not know when their respiratory centres are firing off. If they try to take a deep breath do they feel the sense of effort? Professor Campbell, when you were curarized did you know when your respiratory centres, which must have been firing away full blast, were trying to make your paralysed muscles contract?

*Campbell:* I did not know what my inspiratory centre was doing; I felt no rhythmic or continuous sensation of any sort in my chest or my head. The only sensation I experienced on attempting voluntary movements of the limbs was surprise that nothing happened.

*Merton:* Our use of the word "voluntary" may be too limited. Patients who have a sudden ocular palsy do not make conscious, voluntary efforts to move their eyes to the left—they try automatically to do this when they want to see something in the left visual field. But it is quite harmless to speak about a sense of effort with these automatic movements because they can also be made voluntarily and, as far as the illusion is concerned, the results appear to be the same whether the movement is strictly "voluntary" or "automatic", so presumably the same mechanisms are functioning in both situations. Similarly with breathing, one may be consciously gauging the effort for each breath in order to detect an added respiratory load, but even if one were breathing automatically one would still notice a sufficient added load.

*Campbell:* My experience in detecting mechanical loads added to breathing supports this interpretation. I do not consciously take a breath to see if I can detect the load but I know when it is added. Indeed, one signals detection almost unconsciously; one is even surprised to realize that one's thumb has pressed the buzzer to indicate detection.

*Guz:* The example you quoted in your presentation, Dr Merton, involves voluntary effort arising from the visual cortex of the cerebrum, or at least the midcollicular regions of the pons; but carbon dioxide affects the medullary centres only. We are tending to make confusing generalizations and comparisons.

*Merton:* It is certainly an interesting question how and by what pathways the cortex is kept informed of the difficulties the medulla has run up against. Perhaps the problem could be approached more easily if the centres in question were even farther away from the cortex. One possible way of tackling this problem would be to study the detection of added loads during micturition.

*Newsom Davis:* A consideration of the sense of effort in the context of breath-holding is also of interest. If, at the break-point, a maximum inspiratory effort is made against a closed glottis, there is an enormous sensation of effort but the distress of breath-holding diminishes to bearable levels for a period, suggesting that the sense of effort is in some way distinct from the feeling of distress.

*Dornhorst:* Have you done this experiment using a non-respiratory effort as a distracter? Most subjects make non-respiratory efforts to extend their breath-holding time; would something like a maximal gripping effort inhibit small respiratory efforts?

*Sears:* It is at the point of extreme discomfort, when breath-holding cannot be maintained, that voluntary activation of the respiratory muscles, resulting in a maximum increase in expiratory or inspiratory pressure, abolishes the discomfort and allows breath-holding to be prolonged further.

*Dornhorst:* Did adverse circulatory effects become prominent towards the end of breath-holding? I would have expected this.

*Sears:* Yes, in the form of a brief "grey-out".

*Viljanen:* We have studied the correlation between the electrical activity and the sensation of volume in man by asking the subject to inspire a certain volume and by recording at the same time the electrical activity from the respiratory muscles. We did two types of experiment. The subject either inspires the same volume of air several times or a sequence of different volumes of air. Our results are still only preliminary but my impression is that there is some sort of correlation between the number of impulses recorded from the inspiratory muscles and volume sensation. The correlation seems to depend on which type of experiment we are doing. Some other (also preliminary) results from experiments with the abductor muscle of the forefinger showed the same sort of correlation.

*Campbell:* We have discussed the sense of effort associated with movement of the finger and related this to sensations experienced when breathing against respiratory loads. When one works a syringe or stretches an elastic band one feels not effort but resistance. Dr Merton, how do we detect that one elastic band or syringe is stiffer than another?

*Merton:* We can assess the effort we put into stretching the elastic or moving the plunger of the syringe. We also receive sensory impressions from the elastic or syringe on the finger tips and, in addition, we can use our eyes to see how much the elastic extends or the plunger moves.

*Campbell:* Do proprioceptive impulses from the joints help us to assess how much the rubber band extends?

*Merton:* I imagine so.

*Fillenz:* Penfield and Rasmussen (1950) described stimulating the exposed motor cortex in man. During this procedure the subjects experienced a sense of movement, which is presumably analogous to the sense of effort.

*Merton:* Is it certain that Penfield did not ask his patients leading questions or otherwise suggest to them unconsciously what answer would be acceptable?

*Fillenz:* Possibly.

*Plum:* Short-latency sensory projections from both cutaneous and muscle receptors have recently been described in the motor cortex of the cat (Oscarsson, 1966; and others).

*Merton:* Yes, this is most interesting; and it has been shown that it is muscle receptors which project to these neurones (for references see Swett and Bourassa, 1967). An intriguing new idea arises from this discovery: that impulses arriving at the motor cortex may not result in conscious sensation. Thus Swett and Bourassa (1967) have shown in the cat that behaviour cannot be conditioned using group I volleys from nerves from muscle, whereas it can through afferent fibres from the skin. In other words, impulses from muscle spindle afferents in the limbs of the cat reach the motor cortex but cannot be used to condition behaviour, whereas afferent impulses from the skin can. Spindle afferents have also been shown to project to the precentral motor cortex of the monkey (Albe-Fessard and Liebeskind, 1966). There is no guarantee that spindle afferent signals reach the human motor cortex, but if (as seems likely) they do, they certainly do not arouse conscious sensations.

*Fillenz:* The importance of this work (Oscarsson and Rosén, 1966; Albe-Fessard, Liebeskind and Lamarre, 1965) is surely that the sensory impulses from muscle spindles end in the precentral not the postcentral gyrus, and must therefore be concerned with the regulation of voluntary movement rather than with sensation from the limb.

*Merton:* It is apparent that in the body there are two classes of afferent signals. Some are only needed to supply information for subconscious nervous mechanisms, whereas it is advantageous for others to enter into our conscious life. Thus, we are immediately conscious of the slightest obstruction to our respiratory activities but changes in blood pressure demanding an increase in the work of the heart are wholly unappreciated. In the limbs, receptors near the joints supply information on which our conscious knowledge of limb position is based, while receptors in the muscles, notably the muscle spindles, have no access to consciousness. In the case of muscle spindles one can see why there might be no advantage, and indeed a positive disadvantage, for us to be consciously aware of their signals. That is if we suppose that there is some truth in the idea that the muscle spindles in the stretch reflex arc function after the manner of misalignment detectors in a follow-up length servo-mechanism (Hammond, Merton and Sutton, 1956; Merton, 1953). Such a mechanism is analogous to the power-assisted steering on modern cars, the muscle spindle representing the sensing element which turns in the servo-motor when it detects a misalignment between the angle of the road, the position of the wheels demanded by the driver and their actual direction. We see at once that to display the signals from the sensing element to the driver could only make him drive less well, by distracting his attention from the road to no purpose—the inner workings of automatic mechanisms should not obtrude. When these rationalizations were first offered it was thought that the muscle-servo based on the stretch reflex was a low-level affair, and that spindle afferents did not project to the cortex. It has now been found that spindle afferents do project to cortex—to motor cortex. So there would seem to be, in the "voluntary" motor cortex itself, a mechanism using spindle feedback the workings of which, like the workings of a servo-steering gear, it pays us to keep out of sight. Is this (as suggested by Phillips, 1969) the same type of mechanism previously thought to be confined to lower levels, or is it something new and different?

REFERENCES

ALBE-FESSARD, D., and LIEBESKIND, J. (1966). *Expl Brain Res.*, **1**, 127–146.
ALBE-FESSARD, D., LIEBESKIND, J., and LAMARRE, Y. (1965). *C.r. hebd. Séanc. Acad. Sci., Paris*, **261**, 3891–3894.
CAMPBELL, E. J. M., BENNETT, E. D., and RUBENSTEIN, D. (1963). *Clin. Sci.*, **24**, 201–207.

GRANIT, R., LEKSELL, L., and SKOGLUND, C. R. (1944). *Brain*, **67**, 125–140.
HAMMOND, P. H., MERTON, P. A., and SUTTON, G. G. (1956). *Br. med Bull.* **12**, 214–218.
HARMAN, J. B. (1948). *Br. med. J.*, **1**, 188–192.
MERTON, P. A. (1953). *Ciba Fdn Symp. The Spinal Cord.* pp 247–255. London: Churchill.
MILIC-EMILI, J., and TYLER, J. M. (1963). *J. appl. Physiol.*, **18**, 497–504.
OSCARSSON, O. (1966). *Nobel Symposium I, Muscular Afferents and Motor Control*, pp. 307–316, ed. Granit, R. New York: Wiley-Interscience.
OSCARSSON, O., and ROSÉN, I. (1966). *J. Physiol., Lond.*, **182**, 164–184.
PENFIELD, W., and RASMUSSEN, T. (1950). *The Cerebral Cortex of Man: A Clinical Study of Localization of Function.* New York: MacMillan.
PHILLIPS, C. G. (1969). *Proc. R. Soc. B*, **173**, 141–174.
SWETT, J. E., and BOURASSA, C. M. (1967). *J. Neurophysiol.*, **30**, 530–545.

# THE ROLE OF AFFERENT IMPULSES FROM THE LUNG AND CHEST WALL IN RESPIRATORY CONTROL AND SENSATION

S. GODFREY AND E. J. M. CAMPBELL

*Institute of Diseases of the Chest, London, and Department of Medicine,
McMaster University, Hamilton, Ontario*

JUST over a hundred years ago Hering (1868) and Breuer (1868) showed that vagally mediated reflexes could be elicited by lung inflation and deflation. Adrian (1933) demonstrated that afferent traffic could be detected in the vagus of animals with respiratory rhythm which was modified by inflation and deflation of the lungs, and this has now also been demonstrated in man (Guz et al., 1966a). On evidence such as this a large literature has developed which invokes pulmonary afferent information as an important source of respiratory control and sensation.

We wish to present data which critically examine the role of information from the lungs, the chest wall and from chemical sources in the genesis of respiratory sensation. One of the most striking ways of generating severe and rapidly increasing respiratory sensation is by breath-holding and most of the work we describe concerns experiments of this sort.

What happens if the breath-hold is begun at resting lung volume? For the first 20 or 30 seconds nothing particular is experienced, but then spasmodic contractions of the diaphragm and respiratory muscles begin and breath-holding can only be continued if the airways close. This respiratory muscle contraction increases in violence and an unpleasant sensation builds up so that after a further 15 to 30 seconds the sensation has become so intolerable that the subject must break the breath-hold. The sensation is relieved, probably within the cycle of the first breath (see later).

Many of the pioneers of pulmonary physiology have investigated breath-holding and established the principal factors known to affect breath-holding time. The prevention of hypoxia lengthens breath-holding time (Hill and Flack, 1908; Douglas and Haldane, 1909), as does the lowering of $Pco_2$ (carbon dioxide partial pressure) by hyperventilation (Klocke and Rahn, 1959). Elevation of the initial $Pco_2$ shortens the breath-holding time (Godfrey and Campbell, 1969). A reciprocal relationship between oxygen and carbon dioxide was clearly shown in the papers of Douglas and Haldane (1909) and Otis, Rahn and Fenn (1948). Mechanical factors are also known to influence breath-holding time, particularly the lung volume at which the breath is held. Muxworthy (1951) showed that the larger the lung volume the longer the breath-holding time. All these experiments suggested to Mithoefer (1959) that $P_{CO_2}$, $P_{O_2}$ and lung volume interacted in some simple way that might be explained by equations such as those proposed by Gray (1946) for the stimuli to breathing.

However, one needs to return to the work of Hill and Flack (1908) who clearly demonstrated that there could be no simple explanation of the genesis of sensation in terms of static thresholds for $P_{O_2}$ or $P_{CO_2}$ modified by lung volume. They showed that their subjects could rebreathe a bag of

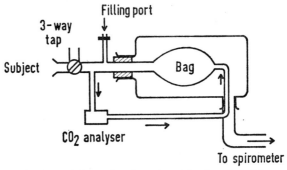

FIG. 1. Circuit used for performing rebreathing/breath-holding carbon dioxide response curves. The subject rebreathes a mixture of carbon dioxide 7 per cent in oxygen from the bag and the excursions of the bag are recorded by a spirometer attached to the bottle. End-tidal carbon dioxide is analysed with an infrared analyser (Godfrey and Campbell, 1969; reproduced by permission of *Q. Jl exp. Physiol.*).

expired air for far longer than they could hold their breath, despite the fact that, at the break-point of rebreathing, the $P_{CO_2}$ was far higher and the $P_{O_2}$ far lower than at the breaking point of a breath-hold. This point was driven home most eloquently by Fowler (1954), who showed that, at the break-point, a few breaths of gas which did not alter the blood gases allowed the breath-hold to be resumed, and that this process could be repeated three or four times consecutively. In other words, not only could rebreathing be continued, despite a greater degree of asphyxia, but further breath-holding was possible at a degree of asphyxia far worse than at the break-point of the previous breath-hold.

Many of the standard experiments on breath-holding suffer from the disadvantage that more than one factor is varied at a time, so that the interactions are very complicated. Moreover, the experiments themselves are tedious to perform and it is difficult to get standard conditions. This prompted us to develop a technique of rebreathing and breath-holding which is illustrated in Figs. 1 and 2. The subject rebreathes a mixture of carbon dioxide 7 per cent in oxygen from a 3–4-litre bag; this manoeuvre rapidly establishes equilibrium for $P_{CO_2}$ between the gas in the bag, the

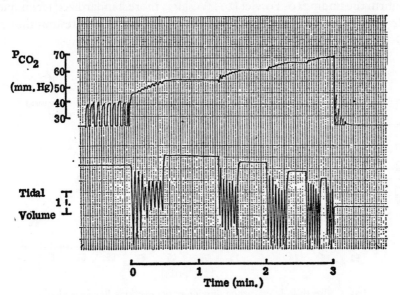

FIG. 2. Record obtained during performance of breath-holding carbon dioxide response curve. The subject commenced rebreathing, which is shown by the lower trace (inspiration downwards), and rapid mixing ensued so that the $P_{CO_2}$ shown in the upper trace began to rise at a steady rate. He then expired to residual volume and held his breath; no rise in $P_{CO_2}$ was recorded at the mouth during the breath-hold but the $P_{CO_2}$ continued to rise in the lungs and blood. At the break-point of breath-holding, rebreathing was resumed and the $P_{CO_2}$, recorded at the mouth, again rose. A series of breath-holds at progressively higher levels of $P_{CO_2}$ were performed. Note the shortening of breath-holding time as $P_{CO_2}$ rises. The shrinkage of the system due to oxygen consumption is clearly shown by the progressive elevation of the level of residual volume recorded by the spirometer (from Campbell and Godfrey, 1969).

subject's lungs and his mixed venous blood and, after recirculation, the $P_{CO_2}$ of the blood/lung/bag system rises at a uniform rate of about 6 mmHg/min. This rise occurs whether or not the subject breathes, though of course if one is recording end-tidal $P_{CO_2}$ at the mouth, the rise is not shown during the breath-hold. As soon as a subject commences rebreathing at the break-point of the breath-hold, the small difference in $P_{CO_2}$ between the bag and the blood/lung system is rapidly removed.

In all our experiments the subject breathed high concentrations of oxygen so that hypoxia was never a stimulus. Using this technique we found that the subjects could perform four, five or more serial breath-holds separated by rebreathing and that as the $P_{CO_2}$ rose so the breath-holding time fell. This relationship was linear, whether one considered the $P_{CO_2}$ at the beginning or at the end of the breath-holds (Fig. 3). We were thus able to confirm the findings of Fowler (1954) using a more standardized technique. We then examined the factors which would permit the resumption of

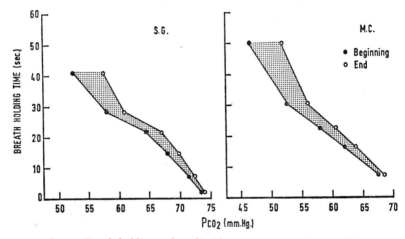

FIG. 3. Breath-holding carbon dioxide response curves in two subjects. The lines for each subject show the results of plotting breath-holding time against the $P_{CO_2}$ at the start or end of breath-holds. The two lines converge to a point at which breath-holding is impossible, and therefore the breath-holding time is zero. At this point the whole stimulus is of chemical origin (Godfrey and Campbell, 1969; reproduced by permission of Q. Jl exp. Physiol.).

breath-holding at break-point by looking at the duration of a second breath-hold after different numbers of breaths at the break-point of the first breath-hold. We found no difference between one or more breaths; indeed, we noticed that the sensation was apparently relieved during the course of the very first breath. This suggested to us that a stimulus built up during the breath-hold and that this stimulus was relieved by the act of breathing even though this did not change any of the known chemical drives. A rather similar suggestion was made by Fowler (1954) and by Dornhorst (1963), who suggested that there was an accumulation of a central excitatory state in a pool of respiratory neurones which was discharged by each breathing cycle.

Although we can adequately explain the chemical stimulus in terms of $P_{CO_2}$ (or its effect on the cerebrospinal fluid) and in terms of hypoxia, there is still no adequate explanation of the non-chemical stimulus which must summate with the chemical stimulus to produce the sensation at the break-point. Obviously if no such summation occurred then the rebreathing/breath-holding experiment in the presence of a worsening degree of hypercapnia would be impossible.

Because of the prominent effect of lung volume it would seem, at first sight, that the Hering-Breuer reflexes could provide the non-chemical stimulus. In order to test this hypothesis, experiments were undertaken to investigate the effect of lung volume and the rate of lung shrinkage during breath-holding by performing breath-holds at normal and reduced atmospheric pressure. Under conditions of breath-holding the lungs shrink because oxygen is consumed while carbon dioxide excretion is blocked by the high $P_{CO_2}$ which exists in the lungs. If the barometric pressure is reduced, gas density is reduced and therefore, for any given number of molecules of oxygen consumed, lung shrinkage is increased. We found that not only did the increased rate of shrinkage fail to effect the relationship between breath-holding time and $P_{CO_2}$ (Fig. 4) but also that there was no correlation whatsoever between either $P_{CO_2}$ or lung volume at break-point. It was quite possible to begin a breath-hold at a smaller lung volume and a higher $P_{CO_2}$ than existed at the break-point of the previous breath-hold, and we showed that previous experiments suggesting such a fixed relationship between $P_{CO_2}$ at break-point and lung volume were based on a fortuitous coincidence. Although absolute lung volume affects breath-holding time, it cannot be the whole source of the non-chemical stimulus; and nor can the magnitude or rate of lung shrinkage.

In order to seek the non-chemical stimulus we have investigated situations in which it might be altered. It has been shown that patients who are artificially hyperventilated tend to adopt the pattern of imposed respiration, suggesting that a mechanical effect on the lungs (because $P_{CO_2}$ was held constant) could alter the setting of the control system (Smith, Spalding and Watson, 1962). We therefore performed breath-holding carbon dioxide response curves in normal subjects before and after prolonged isocapnic hyperventilation and found that the curves were not shifted (Godfrey and Campbell, 1969). In the presence of airways obstruction the ventilatory response to carbon dioxide is grossly reduced (Milic-Emili and Tyler, 1963) and it was therefore interesting to observe the effect of an airways obstruction on the ventilatory and breath-holding responses to carbon dioxide in normal subjects (Fig. 5). It was found that whereas the ventilatory curve

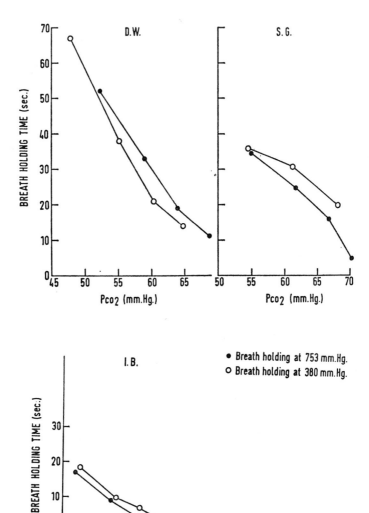

FIG. 4. Breath-holding carbon dioxide response curves performed at normal atmospheric pressure and reduced atmospheric pressure in order to increase lung shrinkage. There is no significant difference between the curves obtained at the different barometric pressures in any of the three subjects (Godfrey, Edwards and Warrell, 1969; reproduced by permission of Q. Jl exp. Physiol.).

was grossly flattened there was no change in the breath-holding curve (Clark and Godfrey, 1969). During muscular exercise there are generally assumed to be non-chemical factors present which account for the increased ventilation because little change in blood gases and acid-base status occurs, at least at moderate levels of physical exertion. We performed breath-holding and ventilatory carbon dioxide response curves in subjects exercising at different work loads, and found that there was a small shift to the left of a ventilatory response curve to carbon dioxide but a marked flattening of the breath-holding response curve (Fig. 6). When these data were

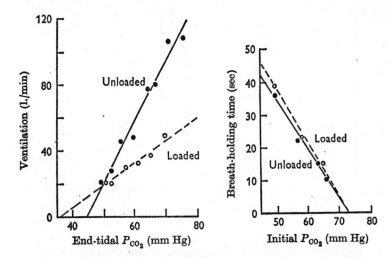

FIG. 5. The effect of an added resistive load on the ventilatory and breath-holding responses to carbon dioxide. The graph on the left shows that the ventilatory response was grossly flattened; the graph on the right showed no alteration in the breath-holding response curve (Clark and Godfrey, 1969; reproduced by permission of *J. Physiol., Lond.*).

analysed in terms of the model described, there appeared to have been an increase in rate of rise of non-chemical sensation (Clark and Godfrey, 1969).

The break-point of breath-holding is reached as a result of the summation of a chemical stimulus, which can be regarded as $P_{CO_2}$ for practical purposes, and a non-chemical stimulus which is not lung shrinkage, is not changed by isocapnic hyperventilation or the addition of a resistance to breathing but which is apparently increased during exercise. This non-chemical stimulus is abolished by a single breath thus permitting the resumption of breath-holding.

Guz and co-workers (1966b) have clearly shown that breath-holding time can be prolonged by blocking both vagal nerves in the neck. All the evidence we have presented suggests that the known types of reflex which travel up the vagus from the lungs are most unlikely to be the source of a stimulus which shortens breath-holding time. Therefore, superficially, these two sets of findings are contradictory. But if the information carried by the vagus were to be about the pattern or frequency of lung movement, it is quite conceivable that the loss of information about lung immobility caused by blocking the vagus would prolong breath-holding time.

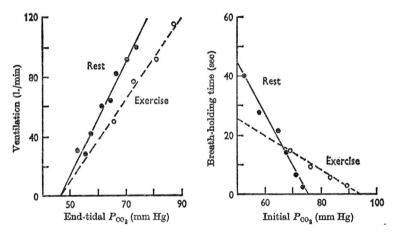

FIG. 6. The effect of exercise on the ventilatory and breath-holding responses to carbon dioxide. The graph on the left shows a small change in the ventilatory response to carbon dioxide during muscular exercise while the breath-holding curve on the right was markedly flattened. This was due to an increased rate of rise of non-chemical stimulus (see text) (Clark and Godfrey, 1969; reproduced by permission of *J. Physiol., Lond.*).

*The sensation at breaking point*

One of the striking features of breath-holding described earlier is the muscular contractions which occur as the breath-hold proceeds. This was quantitated by Agostoni (1963) who recorded the diaphragmatic electro-myograph and showed that the onset of diaphragmatic activity was related to $P_{CO_2}$ but (rather surprisingly) not to lung volume.

The fact that these muscular contractions are such a prominent part of the breath-holding story and that the associated sensation seems to develop *pari passu* with the contractions prompted us to consider the effect of the abolition of muscular contraction by total paralysis with curare. One can envisage three possible effects of total paralysis. (*a*) If a sensation arises from the lungs and/or from chemical sensation directly via the vagus and chemo-receptors, total paralysis should have no effect on breath-holding time. (b) Since voluntary swallowing movements and expiratory efforts against the closed glottis partially relieve the sensation during a breath-hold, it is possible that total paralysis would shorten the breath-holding time by making these movements impossible. (c) If sensation arises not directly, as described above, but indirectly through muscular contraction, total paralysis should prolong breath-holding time.

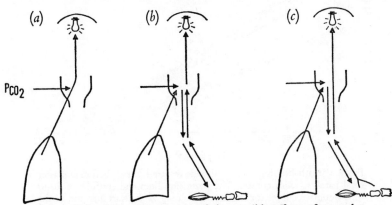

FIG. 7. Schematic representation of the possible effects of muscular paralysis on breath-holding and sensation. If chemical and mechanical sensation reaches consciousness directly via the respiratory centres then muscular paralysis will not affect breath-holding time (Fig. 7 a). If the voluntary muscular contractions so common in breath-holding contribute towards the increase of the unpleasant sensation then muscular paralysis will shorten breath-holding time (Fig. 7 b). If the development of muscular tension during the breath-hold is an essential part of the genesis of sensation then muscular paralysis will abolish this sensation (Fig. 7 c).

These three possibilities are illustrated schematically in Fig. 7. We found that total paralysis by curare not only grossly prolonged the breath-holding time (that is, the time which the observers were prepared to allow the subject to remain apnoeic) but totally abolished any sensation whatever in the subjects although they were fully conscious (Campbell et al., 1967). This was even true at such grossly elevated $Pco_2$ concentrations that the subject would have been totally unable to hold his breath under control conditions (Campbell et al., 1969). These latter results are shown in Fig. 8.

*A model of the control system*

We have tried to explain our observations in terms of a simple model (Godfrey and Campbell, 1968) such as a systems analyst or engineer might

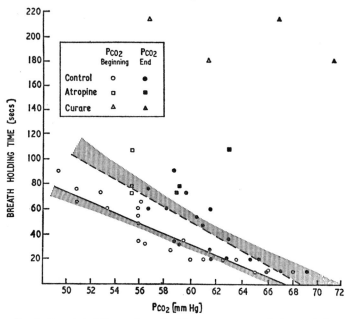

FIG. 8. Breath-holding carbon dioxide response curves before and after total paralysis with curare. The regression lines and confidence limits of the control curves for the breath-holding at the start and end of the breath-holds are shown in the figure. The squares represent breath-holds performed after atropine and the triangles represent breath-holds performed after total paralysis with curare. Note the enormous prolongation of breath-holding time after curarization compared with all the other points. In fact, the breath-holds were stopped by the observers at the times shown after the curarization and not by the request of the subject, who felt no unpleasant sensation (Campbell *et al.*, 1969; reproduced by permission of *Clin. Sci.*).

use (Fig. 9). Each square represents a function generator, that is, it receives one or more input signals, modifies them in some way and provides an output. Following the model from left to right, during breath-holding the increased chemical drive ($P_{CO_2}$ in this simplification) together with the non-chemical drive (which may be a self-cycling loop) summate to produce a central, driving-stimulus build-up. This produces a demand for ventilation which is transmitted to the motor pathways of the brain and spinal cord and drives the lower motor neurones governing the respiratory muscles. These muscles in turn contract but, because the lung volume is prevented from getting smaller by the voluntary act of breath-holding, there is a disproportion between the tension developed in these muscles and the motor effect produced. This discrepancy between tension and motor effect is in some way transmitted to sensation by afferent impulses from the muscles and chest wall. We originally thought that static lung volume might operate reflexly by modifying the output of the motor pathways (that is, upstream from the respiratory muscles) but as Agostoni (1963 and personal communications) has shown the efferent discharge is the same whatever the lung volume, which implies that the effect of lung volume is downstream from the respiratory muscles. We believe that lung volume acts at the level of the setting of muscle-joint receptors in the chest wall. The sensory endings serving the sensation and the nature of the sensation

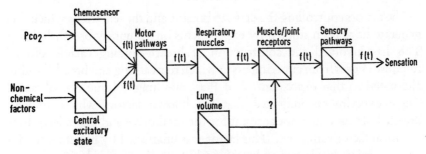

FIG. 9. Model of the control of breath-holding and origin of sensation. In the model shown, chemical sensation (simplified as $Pco_2$) and non-chemical sensation of uncertain origin provide stimuli which summate and result in an efferent discharge down the motor pathways. This causes contraction of the respiratory muscles. During a breath-hold these muscles are voluntarily prevented from shortening and this results in a discrepancy between the length and tension of the muscles which is sensed by receptors in the muscles or chest wall. This sensory information travels up the sensory pathways and eventually reaches consciousness as the unpleasant sensation. Static lung volume is thought to affect the sensation by acting at the level of the muscle or chest wall, downstream from the motor pathways. The implications of this model are discussed in the text (from Godfrey and Campbell, 1968).

of breath-holding remain obscure but we do not think there has been any reason to modify the description of it as inappropriateness or mismatching of tension and length (Campbell, 1966).

## Implications for respiratory control

Our experiments have all been concerned with the drive to breathe. We have shown that when all the known chemical or mechanical factors are considered there still remains a large non-chemical factor which can be abolished by lung or chest wall movement. We believe that this factor is probably an inherent build-up of central excitation within the central nervous system and that it is abolished during each respiratory cycle by information carried by the vagus but not by the Hering-Breuer reflexes.

Moreover, we found that the genesis of the sensation itself seems far from a simple appreciation of chemical and non-chemical stimuli, and involves contraction of the respiratory muscles and sensory mechanisms in the chest wall. It is a sobering thought that in this centenary plus one year of Hering and Breuer we still do not fully understand the role of the vagus in the control of breathing.

## SUMMARY

The factors controlling the drive to breathe and the sensations which they generate have been studied by experiments on voluntary breath-holding. This has involved the construction of breath-holding carbon dioxide response curves from experiments in which rebreathing and breath-holding alternated so that exact control of $P_{CO_2}$ and lung volume was obtained. These experiments indicated that the known factors which influence breath-holding could not account for the total drive and that a large non-chemical factor remained. This factor was unaffected by hyperventilation or mechanical hindrance to breathing but was increased during exercise. It is postulated that information travelling in the vagus may be important for the genesis of this stimulus, but that the Hering-Breuer reflexes are unlikely to be involved since a gross increase in the rate of lung shrinkage did not affect breath-holding. As far as the genesis of sensation is concerned, our experiments in the curarized subject suggest that both chemical and non-chemical sensation during breath-holding arise indirectly via mechanisms involving the muscles of breathing. The implications of these experiments are discussed.

## REFERENCES

ADRIAN, E. D. (1933). *J. Physiol., Lond.,* **79,** 332–358.
AGOSTONI, E. (1963). *J. appl. Physiol.,* **18,** 30–36.
BREUER, J. (1868). *Sber. Akad. Wiss. Wien,* **58,** part 2, 909–937.
CAMPBELL, E. J. M. (1966). In *Breathlessness,* pp. 55–64, ed. Howell, J. B. L., and Campbell, E. J. M. Oxford: Blackwell.
CAMPBELL, E. J. M., FREEDMAN, S., CLARK, T. J. H., ROBSON, J. G., and NORMAN, J. (1967). *Clin. Sci.,* **32,** 425–432.
CAMPBELL, E. J. M., and GODFREY, S. (1969). *J. Physiol., Lond.,* **202,** 5–7P.
CAMPBELL, E. J. M., GODFREY, S., CLARK, T. J. H., FREEDMAN, S., and NORMAN, J. (1969). *Clin. Sci.,* **36,** 323–328.
CLARK, T. J. H., and GODFREY, S. (1969). *J. Physiol., Lond.,* **201,** 551–566.
DORNHORST, A. C. (1963). *Br. med. Bull.,* **19,** 4–6.
DOUGLAS, C. G., and HALDANE, J. S. (1909). *J. Physiol., Lond.,* **38,** 420–440.
FOWLER, W. S. (1954). *J. appl. Physiol.,* **6,** 539–545.
GODFREY, S., and CAMPBELL, E. J. M. (1968). *Resp. Physiol.,* **5,** 385–400.

GODFREY, S., and CAMPBELL, E. J. M. (1969). *Q. Jl exp. Physiol.*, **54**,117–128.
GODFREY, S., EDWARDS, R. H. T., and WARRELL, D. A. (1969). *Q. Jl exp. Physiol.*, **54**, 129–140.
GRAY, J. S. (1946). *Science*, **103**, 739–744.
GUZ, A., NOBLE, M. I. M., TRENCHARD, D., SMITH, A. J., and MAKEY, A. R. (1966a). *Resp. Physiol*, **1**, 382–389.
GUZ, A., NOBLE, M. I. M., WIDDDICOMBE, J. G., TRENCHARD, D., MUSHIN, W. W., and MAKEY, A. R. (1966b). *Clin. Sci.*, **30**, 161–170.
HERING, E. (1868). *Sber. Akad. Wiss. Wien*, **57**, part, 2, 672–677.
HILL, L., and FLACK, M. (1908). *J. Physiol., Lond.*, **37**, 77–111.
KLOCKE, F. J., and RAHN, H. (1959). *J. appl. Physiol.*, **14**, 689–693.
MILIC-EMILI, J., and TYLER, J. M. (1963). *J. appl. Physiol.*, **18**, 497–504.
MITHOEFER, J. C. (1959). *J. appl. Physiol.*, **14**, 701–705.
MUXWORTHY, J. F. (1951). *Breath-Holding Studies: Relationship to Lung Volume.* Air Force Technical Report 6528, pp. 452–456. Ohio: Wright-Patterson Air Force Base.
OTIS, A. B., RAHN, H., and FENN, W. O. (1948). *Am. J. Physiol.*, **152**, 674–686.
SMITH, A. C., SPALDING, J. M. K., and WATSON, W. E. (1962). *J. Physiol., Lond.*, **160**, 22–31.

# DISCUSSION

*Dornhorst:* Were all your experiments done at high oxygen tensions?

*Godfrey:* Yes. The $Po_2$ was always above 150 mmHg.

*Guz:* You suggested that all the mechanical and chemical sensations connected with the drive to breathe arise from the respiratory muscles and are therefore abolished when these muscles are paralysed. This is a sweeping claim to make from these experiments which were done only during breath-holding.

*Godfrey:* It is only during breath-holding that one can actually study the drive to breathe and the sensations which accompany it.

*Guz:* Were there any controls for your $Pco_2$-response curve experiments? Was air administered to the conscious, paralysed subject without his realizing it, and his sensations assessed in these circumstances? I am asking these questions simply to limit your claims.

*Godfrey:* The subject was relaxed and comfortable, during ventilation with an oxygen-nitrogen mixture, before the rebreathing experiments were started. In the second curare experiment, the subject rebreathed carbon dioxide to high $Pco_2$ levels before we began the breath-hold. So we have some information about sensation in the chest as $Pco_2$ rose. Professor Campbell, as you were the subject in these experiments, can you tell us what you felt?

*Campbell:* I experienced no abnormal sensations in the chest when my $Pco_2$ was high provided I was unable to breath. The experiment Dr Godfrey described had to be stopped after about 280 seconds because, without any sensation in my chest, I was losing consciousness—I was being anaesthetized.

*Howell:* If you started a voluntary breath-hold under curare did you feel any tendency to rhythmic breathing?

*Campbell:* There was no sensation of any kind in the chest.

*Howell:* In an anaesthetized curarized cat, Joels and Samueloff (1956) showed a continuing rhythmic discharge from the phrenic nerve. Presumably, therefore, you had a similar rhythmic phrenic discharge when you were paralysed and not breath-holding. How can you be sure that you were not inhibiting your breathing consciously?

*Campbell:* I may inhibit discharges from the respiratory centre when I am paralysed, but this seems unlikely as I cannot do this when I am not paralysed. My respiratory muscles contract during breath-holding.*

*For further discussion of this paper, see p. 246.

REFERENCES

JOELS, N., and SAMUELOFF, M. (1956). *J. Physiol., Lond.,* **133**, 360–372.

# EFFECT OF SELECTIVE PERIPHERAL NERVE BLOCKS ON RESPIRATORY SENSATIONS

M. I. M. Noble, J. H. Eisele, Diana Trenchard and A. Guz

*Department of Medicine, Charing Cross Hospital Medical School, London*

There has been much interest in recent years in the neurophysiological mechanisms concerned with the sensation of breathlessness (Comroe, 1956; Campbell and Howell, 1963; Howell and Campbell, 1966). The considerable difficulties involved in the analysis of such sensation in patients has led to the study of reproducible respiratory sensations in normal man or in patients who are normal apart from a specific neurological lesion.

The sensations to be discussed are: (1) The sensation arising when one breathes through a resistance or from a closed drum; these sensations can be quantified to a certain extent by estimating the subjects' ability to detect such added loads to breathing (Bennett *et al.*, 1962; Campbell *et al.*, 1961). (2) The sensation arising during breath-holding; this is variously described as a bursting sensation or a pressure in the lower chest and is relieved during the first breath after the break-point, even if the inspired gas mixture does not improve the blood gas tensions (Fowler, 1954). A change in the maximum breath-holding time is an objective indication of a change in this sensation. (3) The sensation arising during rebreathing of carbon dioxide; this is accompanied by hyperpnoea and a feeling of inability to get enough air into the chest. The response of minute ventilation, tidal volume and respiratory frequency to the rising partial pressure of carbon dioxide ($Pco_2$) are objective accompaniments of reported sensations. (4) The sensation associated with the presence of a catheter in the tracheobronchial tree in patients with tracheostomy. In patients without neurological lesions this produces cough, lacrimation and a feeling of irritation.

## SUBJECTS AND PATIENTS

A problem of experimental design arises over the choice of subjects. We have preferred to use trained subjects, such as ourselves, because we believe that the only way to understand what a sensation is like is to experience it oneself. This choice is open to the scientific objection that it is undesirable to use subjects with knowledge of the research. We have therefore repeated the experiments in untrained subjects unfamiliar with the design of these experiments.

## Vagal block

The vagus was blocked at the base of the skull as previously described (Mushin, 1945). In addition to the two normal subjects (M.N. and J.W.) previously reported (Guz et al., 1966a) we have now blocked the vagus in the same way in a normal subject (C.W., female, aged 21 years) unacquainted with the research. This procedure involves block of the glossopharyngeal nerve as well as the vagus, and for this reason we have done most of our studies with oxygen 100 per cent as the inspired gas; this produces a functional denervation of the peripheral chemoreceptors (Bouverot et al., 1965; Bernards, Dejours and Lacaisse, 1966). Vagal block alone (in the neck) has only been carried out in patients with lung disease (see Guz et al., 1970b). Atropine was given before each study to block vagal efferent fibres.

## Chest wall block

These studies were performed on four patients with normal lungs undergoing genito-urinary investigations and surgery. One of these (C.W.) also had a vagal block on a separate occasion (see above). Spinal anaesthesia was induced and raised to include the motor pathways at the level of the first thoracic segment (T1) of the spinal cord; the sensory level extended to the seventh to eighth cervical segment (C7-8) (Eisele et al., 1968). The intercostal muscles were paralysed but diaphragmatic contractions were not impaired. This procedure also blocks sympathetic afferent fibres from the thoracolumbar chain.

## Phrenic block

Bilateral phrenic block was carried out in two of the authors (M.N. and J.E.) and in one normal volunteer (S.B.). The method we used has been described by Sarnoff and Sarnoff (1951). A needle, which was insulated electrically except at its tip, was introduced behind the lower end of the sternomastoid and anterior to the scalenus anterior muscle. The position of the needle was adjusted until stimuli passed through the tip produced a powerful diaphragmatic jerk. Local anaesthetic was then injected until stimuli had no effect. The block was never absolutely complete as judged by fluoroscopy. There was a 20-30 per cent decrease in inspiratory capacity. The same procedure was attempted without success in a further eight subjects; there was either failure to block the phrenic nerve and/or block of the vagus nerve.

## Cervical cord transection

We have studied three patients with spinal injuries.* (a) A man (T.M., aged 23 years) with a complete lesion at the level of C7. His accident occurred one year before the study, at which time he was well. Breathing was entirely diaphragmatic (vital capacity: 3·2 litre). (b) A man (T.S., aged 21 years) with a complete lesion at the level of C6. He had not been treated with intermittent positive-pressure respiration for two and a half years, but had had many febrile episodes associated with patchy pulmonary collapse. Breathing was entirely diaphragmatic (vital capacity: 820 ml). (c) A man (R.A., aged 24 years) in whom the motor lesion was complete at the level of C3 but there was some patchy sensory sparing on the abdomen. No diaphragmatic movement was seen on fluoroscopy. The patient breathed spontaneously using his hypertrophied accessory muscles of respiration which were innervated by the spinal accessory nerve. By this means he achieved a vital capacity of 820 ml and an end-tidal $Pco_2$ of 34 mmHg. All these patients had permanent tracheostomies.

## Muscular paralysis

One female (I.H., aged 55 years) with old poliomyelitis (nine years) was studied.† Her vital capacity was 20 ml (produced by contraction of the sternomastoids). She had had a right vagophrenic anastomosis eight years previously but this had failed to restore any movement to the diaphragm. She had a permanent tracheostomy and was maintained on intermittent positive-pressure respiration.

### THE SENSATION OF ADDED RESISTIVE AND ELASTIC LOADS TO BREATHING

When resistive and elastic loads are added to the mouthpiece in a normal subject, there are greater changes in pressure within the subject's airways (including the mouth, nose, pharynx and larynx) than before the addition of the load. Are these pressure changes in upper airway pressure responsible for the ability to detect the load or is the participation of the lungs, chest wall and diaphragm necessary? This problem has been approached in a patient (A.N., male, aged 63 years) with chronic obstructive airways disease, whose ability to detect added resistive loads when breathing

---

* In collaboration with Dr H. L. Frankel, Stoke Mandeville Hospital, Aylesbury.
† In collaboration with Dr G. T. Spencer and Professor S. J. G. Semple, St. Thomas' Hospital, London.

through an air-tight cuffed tracheostomy tube was markedly depressed (Fig. 1). When the cuffed tube was replaced by one without a cuff, we were able to allow the pressure changes within the trachea to be transmitted to the upper airways (the mouth was kept shut and the nose occluded). In these circumstances, the patient's ability to detect added loads was almost normal (Fig. 1).

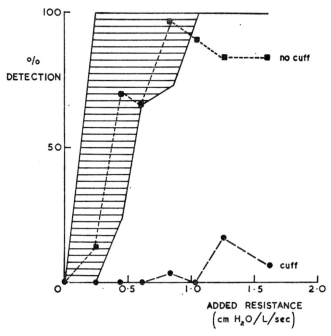

FIG. 1. The ability to detect (per cent detection: ordinate) different resistances added to the airway (abscissa) in a patient with chronic obstructive airways disease breathing through a cuffed tracheostomy tube (closed circles) and through a non-cuffed tube (closed squares) with the mouth and nose closed. Hatched area indicates the range of results obtained in normal mouth-breathing subjects.

This experiment suggests that the upper airways are very sensitive detectors of added respiratory loads and can restore the overall detection ability to normal, even in the presence of a grossly depressed ability to detect loads with the thorax. In these circumstances, one would not expect the peripheral nerve blocks described above to have any effect in normal subjects breathing through their mouths. We have found that the ability to detect elastic loads and the associated sensation is completely unaffected by bilateral vagal block (Guz et al., 1966a) and by chest wall block using spinal anaesthesia up to the level of T1 (Eisele et al., 1968). The ability to detect resistive loads is completely unaffected by bilateral phrenic block. Newsom Davis (1967), from studies of subjects with high spinal cord lesions, concluded that chest wall receptors (probably joint receptors) mediate the sensation experienced with added loads to breathing. In other studies (Wiley and Zechman, 1966; Zechman, O'Neill and Shannon, 1967) it was concluded that such patients show a normal ability to detect loads.

In order to study thoracic mechanisms of load detection the upper airways must, therefore, be excluded by using an air-tight tracheostomy

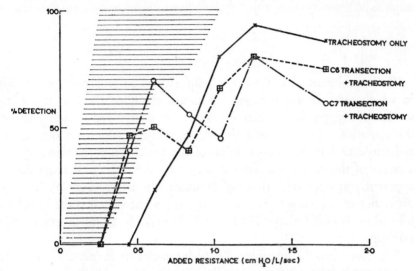

FIG. 2. The ability to detect (per cent detection: ordinate) different resistances added to the airway (abscissa) in three patients with air-tight tracheostomy tubes, one following a laryngectomy (tracheostomy only), one with a cord transection at C6 and the third with a cord transection at C7. Hatched area indicates the range of results obtained in normal mouth-breathing subjects.

tube. We have found that a patient (W.S., male, aged 55 years, with no airways disease) with a tracheostomy following laryngectomy was able to detect resistive loads although not quite so efficiently as normal subjects can (Fig. 2). The ability to detect added resistive loads in the patients with C6 and C7 cord transections (also with tracheostomies) was very similar to that in the patient who had had a laryngectomy (Fig. 2). This suggests that intercostal muscle and other chest wall receptors are not involved.

The patient with a C3 transection had the same detection ability as the control subject (W.S.) at the lowest and highest resistance; the intermediate resistances were not tested.*

* Note added in proof: these intermediate loads have now been tested and the ability to detect them has been found to be within the normal range.

These added resistances and elastances are small threshold loads, and the sensation they produced may not be comparable to that of the high airway resistances found in disease. Dr J. M. Petit, an asthmatic subject, has undergone vagal block at the base of the skull following intravenous atropine. He was tested with a histamine aerosol which produced broncho-constriction of comparable severity before and during vagal block; this was accompanied by tachypnoea, hyperventilation and breathlessness before and not during the vagal block. Vagal block also abolished the unpleasant sensation this subject feels during intermittent airways occlusion.

BREATH-HOLDING

The experiments described by Campbell and co-workers (1967, 1969), in which total muscle paralysis by curare abolished the breath-holding sensation, suggest that muscular contraction is involved in the genesis of this sensation. The sensation was also markedly reduced in our case of poliomyelitis but the interpretation of this finding is complicated by the absence of the vagus and phrenic nerves on the right. These results are apparently at odds with those of Patterson and co-workers (1962). The difference may be due to the fact that our patient switched the ventilator off and on herself (using a head switch) in order to simulate true breath-holding.

We have asked the question: "Which muscles are involved?" The first step towards answering this was the experiment in which the chest wall was blocked. No change in maximum breath-holding time or sensation was produced by this block (Fig. 3). These results, therefore, excluded the intercostal muscles and sympathetic afferent endings as a source for this sensation. Support for this conclusion is given by the fact that breath-holding time and sensation were normal in the patient with a C7 transection

TABLE I

BREATH-HOLDING TIMES IN NORMAL SUBJECTS AND PATIENTS AT FUNCTIONAL RESIDUAL CAPACITY

| Subjects | Number | Breath-holding time (s) | Diaphragmatic contraction | End-tidal $P_{CO_2}$ (mmHg) | Sensation |
|---|---|---|---|---|---|
| Normal | (10) | 41 (21–76) | + | 28–39 | + |
| C7 transection | (1) | 69 | + | 35 | + |
| C6 transection | (1) | 19 | + | 24 | + |
| C3 transection | (1) | 205 | − | 32 | − |
| Poliomyelitis | (1) | 240 | − | 21 | − |

and the breath-holding time was short in the patient with a C6 transection (Table I). These results are similar to those obtained in three similar cases by Silver (quoted by Guz, 1966).

The next step was to test whether the diaphragm was involved in this sensation. Phrenic block prolonged breath-holding time (Fig. 3) and greatly alleviated the sensation. This suggests that diaphragmatic contraction is involved. The fact that the sensation was not abolished is understandable in view of the sub-total nature of the block. Circumstantial

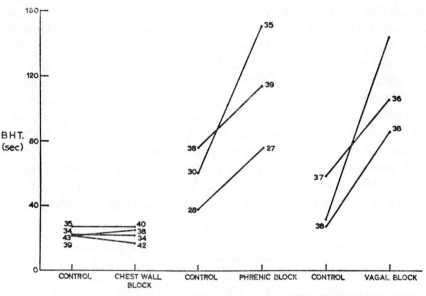

FIG. 3. Breath-holding times (BHT) in normal subjects before and during chest wall block, bilateral phrenic nerve block and bilateral vagus and glossopharyngeal block. The numbers indicate the end-tidal $P_{CO_2}$ (mmHg) at the start of breath-holding. Breath-holding was done at the end of a normal expiration at functional residual capacity.

evidence in support of the diaphragm as the seat of the sensation is given by the fact that the onset of the sensation during a breath-hold coincides with the onset of diaphragmatic contractions (Agostoni, 1963) before and during chest wall block (Eisele et al., 1968) and that most subjects feel the sensation in the lower chest in the area of diaphragmatic attachment.

The very unlikely possibility that the accessory muscles of respiration are involved in the genesis of the breath-holding sensation is excluded by the fact that the patient with a C3 transection had a prolonged breath-holding time. This patient held his breath until "things started to go black"; there was no other sensation. Since this patient's main difference from the patients with C6 and C7 transections was that his diaphragm was separated from his brain, the absence of the usual breath-holding sensation again points to the diaphragm as the source of the sensation. We presume that frustrated contractions of the diaphragm stimulate diaphragmatic receptors and that this can be consciously appreciated.

The next question to be considered is: "What is the stimulus for these diaphragmatic contractions?" We have found that the breath-holding sensation is abolished and breath-holding time prolonged by bilateral vagal block (Fig. 3). One of us (M.N.) has had his vagi blocked and also been curarized (Campbell et al., 1967); the abolition of the sensation (Howell and Campbell, 1966) was comparable in the two states. We have also recorded prolongation of breath-holding time in patients whose vagi were anaesthetized in the neck following surgical exposure (that is, no concomitant glossopharyngeal block was present). Another patient studied by the same technique showed abolition of the usual breath-holding sensation but his breath-holding time was not tested. Vagal block abolishes the diaphragmatic contractions that accompany breath-holding.

It thus appears that the build-up of the stimulus to diaphragmatic contractions during breath-holding is dependent on vagal afferent information. We would welcome suggestions as to the precise nature of this afferent

TABLE II

MAXIMUM BREATH-HOLDING TIMES IN SECONDS IN PATIENTS WITH
PAINLESS PNEUMOTHORAX

| Subjects | Functional residual capacity (FRC) | | Residual volume (RV) | |
|---|---|---|---|---|
| | Control | Deflated | Control | Deflated |
| A.T. | 50 (35) | 25 (31) | 25 (35) | 15 (31) |
| S.W. | 45 | 13 | 40 | 7 |
| M.F. | 57 (38) | — | 44 (38) | 30 (30) |
| M.C. | 41 | 15 | 36 | 12 |
| U.C. | 58 (33) | 16 (28) | — | — |

Numbers in parentheses: $Pa_{CO_2}$ (mmHg) at the beginning of breath-holding; FRC: breath-holding at the end of normal expiration; RV: breath-holding at the end of a maximum expiration; control: breath-holding with the lung inflated by intercostal drainage; deflated: breath-holding with the lung deflated. Hyperoxia was maintained throughout by preliminary breathing of oxygen 100 per cent for at least two minutes.

mechanism. A clue may be provided by some studies on breath-holding in five patients with painless pneumothorax (Table II). In this condition, one lung is deflated (but not necessarily collapsed, as judged radiographically) and separated from the chest wall, so that the effect of lung deflation per se can be studied. Hyperoxia was maintained throughout each study.

Breath-holding time was consistently decreased by lung deflation and the unpleasant sensation was intensified even though the $P_{CO_2}$ was lower. These results would be consistent with the hypothesis that during breath-holding some terminal ventilatory units tend to collapse while others enlarge in compensation. This pattern of change may give rise to an "inspiratory augmenting reflex" (Reynolds and Flom, 1968). The tendency for some units to collapse would be enhanced if the lung were deflated before the breath-hold.

### REBREATHING CARBON DIOXIDE

Our interest in the sensation of "inability to get enough air" which occurs during the rebreathing manoeuvre arose from our almost accidental finding that this sensation was abolished by bilateral vagal block at the base of the skull (Guz *et al.*, 1966*b*). The change in the carbon dioxide response curve produced by vagal block and lung deflation (particularly the effect on respiratory frequency) has been described in another contribution to this symposium (Guz *et al.*, 1970*a*). This sensation is completely different in quality to the breath-holding sensation.

Chest wall block had no effect on either the sensation or the ventilatory response to carbon dioxide (Eisele *et al.*, 1968). Phrenic block had no effect on the carbon dioxide response curve in one subect (J.E.) and in the other two the curve was shifted to the left; the usual sensation was present in full intensity in all three subjects. We were therefore tempted at this stage to conclude that the major muscles of respiration are not involved but that this sensation is produced by a purely vagal mechanism, for example by hyperpnoea stimulating stretch receptors or irritant receptors (Mills, Sellick and Widdicombe, 1970).

Contradictory evidence comes from Patterson and co-workers (1962) who gave carbon dioxide to a patient with poliomyelitis and fixed ventilation (thus hyperpnoea could not occur) and claimed that she experienced dyspnoea. However, the descriptions given by their patient (for example, "things were beginning to die away with me") are not like those given by normal subjects. We repeated this experiment in the patient with poliomyelitis (*v.s.*). She tolerated a rise of $P_{CO_2}$ from 36 mmHg to 64 mmHg (she normally sets her ventilator to give a $P_{CO_2}$ of 14 mmHg). She said that this manoeuvre was not unpleasant and she never felt that she was not getting enough air. She felt she was being anaesthetized and said, "I do not think it affected anything except my brain". The interpretation in this case is complicated by the presence of a right vagotomy but the results are nevertheless suggestive that this sensation does not occur with muscular paralysis. The results of Campbell and co-workers (1969) suggest the same thing.

We therefore compared the effect of spontaneous rebreathing of carbon dioxide with the effect of adding carbon dioxide to the intermittent positive-pressure respirator in the patient with the C3 transection. When the patient was rebreathing spontaneously, using his accessory muscles, he developed tachypnoea (Fig. 4) and stopped at a $Pco_2$ of 49 mmHg, complaining that he felt short of breath and could not breathe enough. When he

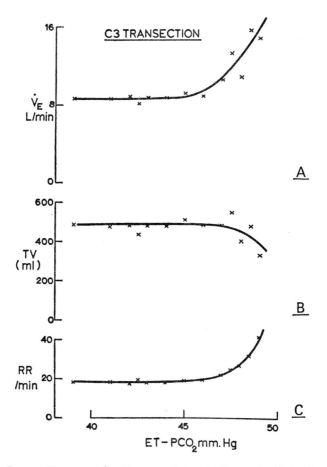

FIG. 4. Response of minute ventilation (ordinate, *a*) tidal volume (ordinate, *b*) and respiratory rate (ordinate, *c*) to end-tidal $Pco_2$ (common abscissa) during spontaneous rebreathing in the patient with a cord transection at C3. Tidal volume was always below the vital capacity of 820 ml.

was put on the ventilator at a fixed ventilation ($P_{CO_2} = 29$ mmHg) slightly greater than that maintained by his spontaneous efforts ($P_{CO_2} = 34$ mmHg), he was able to tolerate an increase of $P_{CO_2}$ to 64 mmHg without discomfort. A patient with a C2 transection, on intermittent positive-pressure respiration (Prys-Roberts and Spalding, 1968), was able to detect an increase in $P_{CO_2}$.

The striking contrast in our patient between the effects on sensation of carbon dioxide when rebreathed spontaneously and when on a ventilator is susceptible to three possible interpretations: (a) The sensation was generated in the accessory muscles themselves which were inadequate to achieve the ventilation demanded. (b) A sense of effort was generated centrally as a result of activation of motoneurones unaccompanied by the corresponding response. (c) Stimulation of pulmonary receptors by the hyperpnoea gave rise to the sensation. The fact that the patient did not have the usual increase in tidal volume (Fig. 4) suggests that the third explanation is unlikely although, as respiratory frequency increased, the total stimulus per minute would also have increased.

At this time it is not possible to decide which is the correct interpretation for the findings in this particular patient, but in the other subjects the third hypothesis has the attraction that it can explain the effects of vagal block and muscular paralysis and the lack of effect of chest wall and phrenic block. Inflation of the lungs with the chest open is the only physiological stimulus to the ventilatory system which we know produces evoked potentials in the cerebral cortex (Kazakov, 1966).

### THE SENSE OF TRACHEOBRONCHIAL IRRITATION

It is well-established (Widdicombe, 1964) that the afferent limb of the cough reflex is in the vagus nerve. This has been confirmed in man by Klassen, Morton and Curtis (1951) who also showed that (a) the afferent limb of the cough reflex of each lung was transmitted in the vagus on the same side; (b) electrical stimulation of the bronchial mucosa produced "aching pain"; (c) patients could localize the site of such electrical stimulation quite accurately (Morton, Klassen and Curtis, 1950); and (d) the "pain" produced by electrical stimulation was abolished by vagal section on the same side (Morton, Klassen and Curtis, 1951). The irritation and cough produced by oral inhalation of ammonia vapour is abolished by bilateral vagal block (Guz et al., 1966a).

The sensation which can be observed in any patient with a tracheostomy (for example, in the patient with a laryngectomy already described) when a catheter is inserted into the trachea (before applying suction for the removal of secretions) is usually described as an intense irritation rather than a pain. The difference in the description given by Morton, Klassen and Curtis' patients (*loc. cit*) may be due to the use of electrical stimulation.

We have asked the question "Does the sensation of irritation persist when the efferent limb of the cough reflex cannot produce a motor response because of a neurological lesion or muscular paralysis ?" All the patients with tracheostomies (described above) had this typical sense of irritation when a catheter was passed into the trachea even though they could not cough. Other aspects of the reflex, for example lacrimation, were usually present. The patient with poliomyelitis was of particular interest in this study because she had a right vagotomy. When questioned about this irritant sensation she said, "the tube in the trachea causes irritation and tickle. Years ago it was much worse but now I am hardened. I feel as if I am sneezing and others say my nose moves as if it is sneezing. My eyes stream. This happens when the tube is in the trachea or on the left side but not on the right side. There is no satisfaction of sucking out the right side whereas on the left there is great satisfaction. I can direct the operator of the tube to get it into the left side since I know where the tip of the tube is."

The only possible interpretation of these findings is that cough receptors are involved, that the afferent fibres pass up the vagus nerve on the same side and that the afferent discharge can be appreciated by consciousness and interpreted as a sense of irritation in the absence of any efferent response.

SUMMARY

Respiratory sensations, namely (1) added respiratory loads, (2) breath-holding, (3) rebreathing carbon dioxide and (4) tracheobronchial irritation have been studied in normal subjects before and during (a) vagal block, (b) chest wall block and (c) phrenic block, and in patients with (i) transections of the spinal cord at the levels of the sixth to seventh cervical segment, (ii) transection at the third cervical segment, and (iii) poliomyelitis with respiratory muscles paralysed. In all the patients tracheostomies were present.

Added respiratory loads were detected normally, before and during all the blocking procedures, by the normal subjects (probably using the upper airways). The ability to detect loads in the patients with the lower transections and tracheostomy was normal.

The sensation of breath-holding was alleviated by vagal block, phrenic block, transection at the third cervical segment and poliomyelitis. The sensation arises from frustrated contractions of the diaphragm stimulated by a reflex with its afferent limb in the vagus.

The sensation of rebreathing carbon dioxide was abolished by vagal block. The patient with the transection at the third cervical segment became breathless when rebreathing carbon dioxide spontaneously using his accessory muscles of respiration, and he had to stop at a $P_{CO_2}$ of 49 mmHg. This patient, and the patient with poliomyelitis, tolerated a rise of $P_{CO_2}$ to 64 mmHg when on an intermitent positive-pressure respirator without the appearance of the usual sensation. This sensation depends on the development of hyperpnoea and on the integrity of vagal afferent fibres.

The sensation of tracheobronchial irritation was only affected by vagal block or section.

## REFERENCES

AGOSTONI, E. (1963). *J. appl. Physiol.*, **18**, 30–36.
BENNETT, E. D., JAYSON, M. I. V., RUBINSTEIN, D., and CAMPBELL, E. J. M. (1962). *Clin. Sci.*, **23**, 155–162.
BERNARDS, J. A., DEJOURS, P., and LACAISSE, A. (1966). *Resp. Physiol.*, **1**, 390–397.
BOUVEROT, P., FLANDROIS, R., PUCCINELLI, R., and DEJOURS, P. (1965). *Archs int. Pharmacodyn. Thér.*, **157**, 253–271.
CAMPBELL, E. J. M., FREEDMAN, S., CLARK, T. J. H., ROBSON, J. G., and NORMAN, J. (1967). *Clin. Sci.*, **32**, 425–433.
CAMPBELL, E. J. M., FREEDMAN, S., SMITH, P. S., and TAYLOR, M. E. (1961). *Clin. Sci.*, **20**, 223–231.
CAMPBELL, E. J. M., GODFREY, S., CLARK, T. J. H., FREEDMAN, S., and NORMAN, J. (1969). *Clin. Sci.*, **36**, 323–328.
CAMPBELL, E. J. M., and HOWELL, J. B. L. (1963). *Br. med. Bull.*, **19**, 36–40.
COMROE, J. H., JR. (1956). *Mod. Concepts cardiovasc. Dis.*, **25**, 347.
EISELE, J., TRENCHARD, D., BURKI, N., and GUZ, A. (1968). *Clin. Sci.*, **35**, 23–33.
FOWLER, W. S. (1954). *J. appl. Physiol.*, **6**, 539–545.
GUZ, A. (1966). Doctoral thesis, University of London, Faculty of Medicine.
GUZ, A., NOBLE, M. I. M., EISELE, J. H., and TRENCHARD, D. (1970a and b). This volume, pp. 17–39 and 315–319
GUZ, A., NOBLE, M. I. M., WIDDICOMBE, J. G., TRENCHARD, D., MUSHIN, W. W., and MAKEY, A. R. (1966a). *Clin. Sci.* **30**, 161–170.
GUZ, A., NOBLE, M. I. M., WIDDICOMBE, J. G., TRENCHARD, D., and MUSHIN, W. W. (1966b). *Resp. Physiol.*, **1**, 206–210.
HOWELL, J. B. L., and CAMPBELL, E. J. M. (eds). (1966). *Breathlessness*. Oxford: Blackwell.
KAZAKOV, V. N. (1966). *Fiziol. Zh. SSSR*, **52**, 847–854. (*Neurosci. Translat.* [1967–68], **3**, 291–298.)
KLASSEN, K. P., MORTON, D. R., and CURTIS, G. M. (1951). *Surgery, St Louis*, **29**, 483–490.
MILLS, J. E., SELLICK, H., and WIDDICOMBE, J. G. (1970). This volume, pp. 77–92.
MORTON, D. R., KLASSEN, K. P., and CURTIS, G. M. (1950). *Surgery, St Louis*, **28**, 699–704.
MORTON, D. R., KLASSEN, K. P., and CURTIS, G. M. (1951). *Surgery, St Louis*, **30**, 800–809.
MUSHIN, W. W. (1945). *Proc. R. Soc. Med.*, **38**, 308.
NEWSOM DAVIS, J. (1967). *Clin. Sci.*, **33**, 249–260.

PATTERSON, J. L., MULLINAX, P. R., BAIN, T., KREUGER, J. R., and RICHARDSON, D. W. (1962). *Am. J. Med.*, **32**, 811–816.
PRYS-ROBERTS, C., and SPALDING, J. M. K. (1968). Communication to the Medical Research Society, London. Unpublished.
REYNOLDS, L. B., and FLOM, M. H. (1968). *J. appl. Physiol.*, **25**, 238–243.
SARNOFF, S. J., and SARNOFF, L. C. (1951). *Anesthesiology*, **12**, 270–275.
WIDDICOMBE, J. G. (1964). In *Handbook of Physiology*, sect. III, vol. 1, pp. 585–630, ed. Fenn, W. O., and Rahn. H. American Physiological Society. Baltimore: Williams and Wilkins.
WILEY, R. L., and ZECHMAN, F. W., JR. (1966). *Resp. Physiol.*, **2**, 73–87.
ZECHMAN, F. W., JR., O'NEILL, R., and SHANNON, R. (1967). *Physiologist, Wash.*, **10**, 356

# DISCUSSION

*Cross:* Duchenne de Boulogne (1851–73) first described how to define the phrenic nerve point over one hundred years ago.

*Widdicombe:* How could you be sure that spread of anaesthetic had not induced vagal block in the experiments in which you anaesthetized the phrenic nerve?

*Noble:* We assumed that the vagus had not been infiltrated if heart rate (when atropine was not given) and voice were unaffected and the carbon dioxide response curve was not flattened.

*Newsom Davis:* I was intrigued by the huge vital capacity of the subject who was breathing with the sternomastoid muscles alone. Was there any activity in the scaleni?

*Noble:* This patient was using all the muscles supplied by the spinal accessory nerve, including the scaleni.

*Newsom Davis:* The scalene muscles are innervated by the third to seventh cervical nerves (C3–C7), which suggests that there might have been some preservation of motor function at this level.

*Guz:* This man had been a patient in the Stoke Mandeville Hospital for Spinal Injuries for two years and the level of the lesion (C2) was diagnosed there.

*Noble:* What was important for these particular experiments was the absence of movement in the diaphragm and intercostal muscles in this patient, and there is no doubt about that.

*Petit:* From my own experience of vagal block I do not agree with two of your comments, Dr Noble. First, vagal block delays but does not abolish diaphragmatic contractions during breath-holding; and second, my sensation at the end of a breath-hold is the same whether the vagi are blocked or intact.

*Widdicombe:* During vagal block, in my experience, the break-point is not associated with any sudden intensification of sensation and the feeling is only mildly unpleasant. Provided my vagal conduction is intact, the break-point is sharp and the breath-holding time reproducible for any given lung volume.

*Noble:* In all our normal subjects the break-point of breath-holding was clear-cut in the control state but vague during vagal block.

*Cohen:* Is diaphragmatic activity during breath-holding greater than any residual diaphragmatic activity that is present during the expiratory phase of normal breathing? The diaphragmatic bursts during breath-holding are obviously smaller than during a normal inspiration.

*Noble:* These points are best illustrated by showing Agostoni's record (1963) (Fig. 1) of the diaphragmatic electromyogram (EMG) during breath-holding in a normal subject; there are bursts of discharges increasing in frequency and intensity up to the break-point. Fig. 2 shows an EMG of a mildly asthmatic subject. Normal intercostal activity is present during breath-holding (between the arrows) but the diaphragm is silent.

*Guz:* Unfortunately, we have no control studies for the asthmatic subject (J.P.) in Noble and co-workers' series (this volume, p. 238). Dr Petit has himself recorded his capacity for breath-holding on other occasions, monitoring diaphragmatic contraction with a pneumogram and inspiratory intercostal activity by electromyography. The diaphragmatic contractions during breath-holding occurred simultaneously with inspiratory intercostal contractions. We have also found this in other subjects.

*Cohen:* Where in the nervous system does the control of breath-holding take place? The subject shown in Fig. 1 (Noble p. 236) is unable to inhibit phrenic discharge completely since some diaphragmatic contraction occurs, but he is still able to keep his glottis closed.

*Dornhorst:* That is an oversimplification. The impulses that get down to the diaphragm during breath-holding are quite different—shorter and weaker—from the impulses reaching the diaphragm at the break-point, when enormous swings occur. During breath-holding the output of the phrenic neurones is inhibited. To what extent can the relief from breathing gases which do not change the chemical state be attributed to the respiratory movement achieved, or is this relief due to recurrent inhibition of the respiratory centre by phrenic impulses? Even in a curarized subject the phrenics fire as the $Pco_2$ builds up, and this phrenic discharge may continuously inhibit the respiratory centre.

*Campbell:* I was not aware that phrenic activity just before the end of breath-holding is less than phrenic activity during the released breath.

*Dornhorst:* The *pattern* of phrenic activity is different in these two situations. There may be a build-up of impulses. But the small inspiratory bursts that occur during breath-holding are much less strong than the inspiratory activity immediately following a breath-hold.

*Campbell:* I am not sure that I agree. There is a great deal of muscular activity towards the end of a long breath-hold, and it is difficult to compare this disorganized quasi-isometric activity with the rhythmic activity that occurs during the breaths following the break-point.

*Zechman:* The detection of added air-flow resistance in patients with tracheostomies may depend on the initial air-flow resistance. Dr Noble, Figs. 1 and 2 in your paper (pp. 236, 237) showed the ability of tracheostomized subjects to detect changes in resistance, but the scores were plotted against the added resistance without reference to the level of resistance at the start of the experiment. This is important because threshold for detection is related to a proportional rather than to absolute changes of air-flow resistance (Wiley and Zechman, 1966); if the initial resistance is high, a higher absolute load will be needed to reach threshold.

*Noble:* This is a valid criticism of our data. We could not plot the initial resistance in these experiments because we did not measure it. I can only say that the asthmatic subject in Fig. 1 (p. 236) had clinically obvious airways obstruction, and the other subjects (Fig. 2, p. 237) did not.

*Zechman:* If the initial resistance of a patient breathing through a tracheostomy tube is high, he would need a greater absolute resistance load for detection even though his threshold for detection were unchanged. The proportional change needed for detection must be determined before one can say whether or not the ability to detect resistance has changed.

*Guz:* We accept this criticism. Fortunately we also studied the patient with a tracheostomy and a high airways resistance and found that he could not detect a series of resistances presented to the tracheostomy. But when the upper airways were involved in the pressure changes (by letting the cuff down), his ability to detect resistances was normal. If we had done this experiment at the mouth only we would not have discovered this abnormality.

*Petit:* Dr Noble, the sensation of dyspnoea in your patient with a $C_3$ transection of the spinal cord depended on the development of hyperpnoea with carbon dioxide stimulation. Is this because of the altered lung mechanics, especially the increase in frequency-dependent compliance, in hyperpnoea rather than because of the hypernoea itself?

*Noble:* We have no data on the lung mechanics in the patient; he was too ill to investigate in this way.

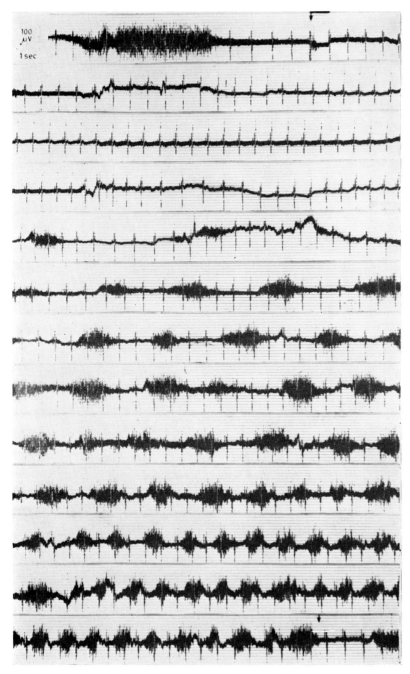

FIG. 1 (*Noble*). Electrical activity of the diaphragm during breath-holding at 80 per cent vital capacity, patient breathing oxygen; beginning and ending of apnoea are indicated by arrows. Before apnoea the subject made a full inspiration followed by an expiration to 80 per cent vital capacity. At the break-point the subject made a quick expiration for an analysis of alveolar carbon dioxide (Agostoni, 1963; reproduced by permission of *J. appl. Physiol.*).

[*To face page 248*

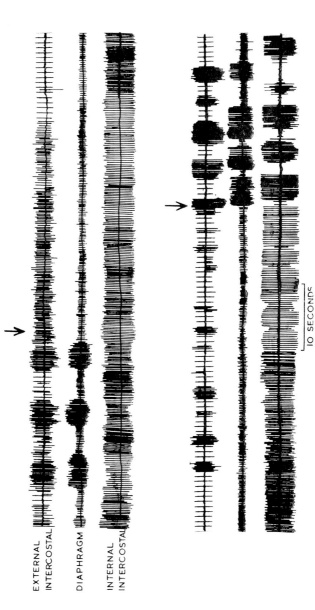

Fig. 2 (*Noble*). EMG from intercostal muscles and diaphragm in a mildly asthmatic subject during breath-holding (between the arrows). (For full explanation see text.)

*Prys-Roberts:* Some of our results in six paralysed, tracheostomized patients (Prys-Roberts and Spalding, unpublished observations) are at variance with some of Dr Noble's findings. One patient was exactly comparable since he had a complete C2 spinal cord transection. A second patient was paralysed below C3 following poliomyelitis. Three patients were studied at the stage of maximal paralysis resulting from polyneuritis and a sixth patient was studied during complete curarization for tetanus. The last five patients, all of whom had paralysed diaphragms but unimpaired chest wall sensation, were able to detect passive lung inflation and changes in the carbon dioxide concentration of the inspired gas mixture. Within one minute of raising $Pa_{CO_2}$ from $2 \cdot 7 - 3 \cdot 3$ kN m$^{-2}$ to $5 \cdot 3 - 6 \cdot 0$ kN m$^{-2}$ (20–25 to 40–50 torr), they all experienced tightness within the chest or complained of "shortness of breath", a quite different and temporally separate sensation from the throbbing headache and general discomfort induced by maintaining the elevated $Pa_{CO_2}$.

Our patient with a complete C2 spinal cord transection (subsequently proven at autopsy) had no diaphragmatic activity and no chest wall sensation. He was able to detect tracheal irritation from suction catheters but could not detect passive lung inflation. He could detect an increase in $Pa_{CO_2}$ from $2 \cdot 7 - 5 \cdot 3$ kN m$^{-2}$ (20–40 torr) induced by adding carbon dioxide to the inspired gas mixture, and he associated this with a sensation of "shortness of breath". An identical sensation was perceived during episodes of left ventricular failure secondary to a myocardial infarct which had probably occurred at the time of the operation which caused his transection. During episodes of left ventricular failure, his $Pa_{CO_2}$ rose from $2 \cdot 7 - 3 \cdot 7$ kN m$^{-2}$ (20–30 torr), but at other times this degree of $Pa_{CO_2}$ elevation was not perceived. We believe that the sensations that he experienced could only have been conducted through the vagus nerves, as there were no other sensory connexions. It is tempting to speculate that Professor Paintal's J receptors are involved in the detection of both pulmonary capillary distension during left ventricular failure and increased carbon dioxide concentrations in the alveolar gas.

*Newsom Davis:* I have studied, with Drs S. J. G. Semple and G. T. Spencer (unpublished), a man with clinical signs of total spinal cord transection at C3, in whom at autopsy the cord was almost totally "destroyed" at this level. This patient was unable to detect movements of the chest wall and indeed could not tell whether he was being ventilated or not. However, like the patients with poliomyelitis studied by Opie, Smith and Spalding (1959), a greater rise of $Pco_2$ could be tolerated when this was produced by adding carbon dioxide to the inspired air rather than by reducing ventilation. This suggests that although vagal afferents did not provide information about ventilatory movements, they were able in some way to alter the subjective effects of a raised $Pco_2$.

*Guz:* This particular patient could not feel a catheter being passed into his trachea. Nor did he have the usual response of paralysed subjects to tracheal irritation: streaming eyes instead of coughing. And yet this man had otherwise normal facial sensation. Are you sure that the afferent vagal pathways were intact in this patient, Dr Newsom Davis? It is difficult to explain these conflicting findings on an anatomical basis.

*Newsom Davis:* I agree. We did not study the lacrimal response in this patient. Other vagal functions appeared normal. He could swallow, elevate the soft palate, and phonate when given a column of air through his larynx; pharyngeal stimulation and, early in his illness, tracheal stimulation were felt as unpleasant. Atropine caused a tachycardia. The anaesthetist reported that the patient did not know when secretions accumulated in his bronchi, however. Whether this represented a selective impairment of vagal function is not certain.

*Dornhorst:* How long had he had his tracheostomy before you studied him?

*Newsom Davis:* About three months.

*Dornhorst:* Could metaplasia of the epithelium explain the patient's tracheal insensitivity?

*Newsom Davis:* Probably.

*Godfrey:* If the afferent traffic up the vagus stimulates the diaphragm to contract reflexly, why isn't this traffic greatly increased with lung shrinkage?

*Noble:* I do not know. The study in the patients with painless pneumothorax had the advantage that the lung was deflated but the chest was not. Breath-holding time is much reduced in these circumstances. However, this is not the same as your experiment, Dr Godfrey because we started with a deflated lung and did not influence the *rate* of deflation. Deflation of certain units or areas of the lung, not the whole lung, may be what is important. Reynolds and Flom (1968) showed that even during tidal breathing some ventilatory units decreased and some increased in size. These possible excitatory effects will be even more pronounced when there is no ventilation, as during breath-holding.

The size of the lung does affect sensation during breath-holding after vagal block, however. Breath-holding *time* is longer after maximal inspiration than at residual volume, both in normal conditions and after vagal block. After maximal inspiration, of course, the $Pco_2$ rises and the $Po_2$ falls more slowly, because there is more gas in the lungs. During vagal block, the usual *sensation* is abolished at all lung volumes. At residual volume the diaphragm is domed upwards. This stretching may produce more tension on the tendon receptors. The muscle fibres of the diaphragm will be longer and (because of the length-tension diagram) may develop more force. These factors might contribute to intensify the sensation of breath-holding at residual volume compared with higher volumes in the normal state.

*Widdicombe:* It seems that the sensation associated with breath-holding during vagal block differs in different individuals.

## REFERENCES

AGOSTONI, E. (1963). *J. appl. Physiol.*, **18**, 30–36.
DUCHENNE DE BOULOGNE, G. B. A. (1851–73). *Contributions à l'Étude du Système Nerveux et du Système Musculaire.* (Series of Lectures) Paris: Ballière.
OPIE, L. H., SMITH, A. C., and SPALDING, J. M. K. (1959). *J. Physiol., Lond.*, **149**, 494–499.
REYNOLDS, L. B., and FLOM, M. H. (1968). *J. appl. Physiol.*, **25**, 238–243.
WILEY, R. L., and ZECHMAN, F. W., JR. (1966). *Resp. Physiol.*, **2**, 73–87.

# SOME PSYCHOLOGICAL AND PHYSIOLOGICAL CONSIDERATIONS OF BREATHLESSNESS

R. C. B. AITKEN, A. K. ZEALLEY AND S. V. ROSENTHAL

*Department of Psychiatry, University of Edinburgh*

BREATHING has been identified with man's feelings since time immemorial. The agony of breathlessness is taken almost for granted, yet the emotional consequences of the symptom have attracted remarkably little scientific examination.

In a psychiatric study of the dying, Hinton (1963) observed that only one-fifth of patients with dyspnoea were relieved by treatment, in contrast to those suffering pain of whom four-fifths were relieved of their distress. There was clear evidence of anxiety in twice as many dying patients who were breathless as compared with those who had pain, nausea and vomiting or malaise.

Campbell and Howell (1963) put forward an attractive theory to account for the neural basis of the sensation of breathlessness: that it reflected an appreciation of length-tension inappropriateness. They remarked how the symptom could arise in anxious patients but they did not refer to activity in neural structures consequent to the unaccustomed afferent signals and appreciation of their unpleasantness. At a symposium on *Breathlessness* in 1965 (Howell and Campbell, 1966) there was almost no mention of the emotional response, at either psychological or physiological levels, which accompanies hindrance to breathing.

Moruzzi and Magoun (1949) discovered that the reticular formation in the brainstem is responsible for the state of wakefulness. Since then neural pathways have been identified whereby signals from the peripheral nervous system are relayed to structures in the limbic system, where the emotional state is modulated (Smythies, 1967). Such structures can be influenced by signals which fail to reach consciousness and also by activity primarily in the cerebral cortex. Thus, information regarding pulmonary length-tension relationships, when inconsistent with the physiological requirements for alveolar ventilation, can not only reach consciousness but can also excite psychological responses, with associated psychophysiological activity. Severinghaus (1966) pointed out that increased wakefulness from feedback of information on inadequate respiration can benefit associated dyspnoea.

The gamma motor system projects diffusely and, unlike with alpha motor neurone activity, is incapable of precise control. If additional gamma activity causes increased alveolar ventilation, it will simultaneously spread to accessory muscles of respiration and often beyond, causing generalized muscle tenseness. Involuntary increase in muscle activity also develops in hypocapnia, and indeed such change can be detected by electromyography long before the development of clinical tetany.

Emotional arousal probably produces increased gamma activity in respiratory muscles involuntarily, just as it does elsewhere; change in respiration can then occur, with similar consequences to those associated with deliberate overbreathing. Kerr, Dalton and Gliebe (1937) showed that hyperventilation produced tetany easily in patients with anxiety neurosis. Frequently it is impossible to decide in a particular patient whether overbreathing occurred deliberately or otherwise, especially if there is slight pulmonary or cardiac pathology, as well as neurotic disorder. The distinction of malingering from anxiety or hysteria is often involved and, whereas recognition of the aetiology as psychogenic is usually sufficient for appropriate management, psychiatric exploration for the underlying cause, or at least for one contributing to the distress, can be rewarding (for example, Burns and Howell, 1969).

As well as the direct neural activity that results from emotional arousal, ACTH will be released through hypothalamic connexions, thus increasing circulating steroid levels. Associated sympathetic stimulation will cause the release of adrenaline and noradrenaline, both of which produce hyperventilation by a direct effect on the brain (Whelan and Young, 1953; Young, 1957). In this way, a complex servosystem operates, involving muscle, neurotransmitters and endocrine metabolism, and through which the response to a threatening situation—such as dyspnoea—may feed back on respiration and cardiac action, as well as on the feeling state. Some of these aspects of the psychophysiology of breathlessness are illustrated in Fig. 1.

The sensation of breathlessness can accompany increased respiratory frequency or volume, both of which can be measured precisely. This sensation can also be due to mechanical hindrance of the act of breathing, the perception of which cannot be measured directly. The degree of asphyxia experienced is a subjective phenomenon, and the observer has to rely on communication from the patient; usually this has to be in a language with few suitable quantitative terms, such as mild, moderate or severe. Measurement is made easier if the subject is presented with an analogue scale on which he can indicate his feelings (Aitken, 1969).

Comroe (1966) emphasized that dyspnoea "is subjective . . . it involves both perception of the sensation by the patient and his reaction to the sensation." Unlike many measures related to metabolism, there is wide variation between persons, and between occasions in the same individual, with regard to response to a threatening situation. The nature and degree

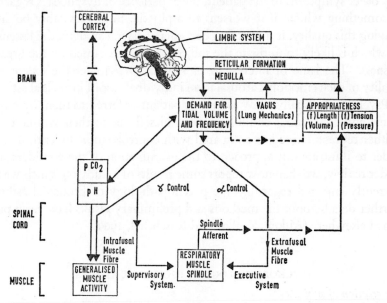

FIG. 1. Some aspects of the psychophysiology of breathlessness.

of the response, both psychic and physical, are dependent upon personality traits and are influenced by previous experience often far remote in time.

Christie (1935) gave detailed accounts of different types of respiration in neurotic patients. Feleky (1916) drew attention to the way in which different emotions influenced the pattern of respiration, and Finesinger (1944) to the effect of thoughts with different emotional implications on this pattern. Mezey and Coppen (1961) showed that anxious patients hyperventilate for unit oxygen extraction and have a raised oxygen consumption, particularly during and after exercise. After studying hyperventilation in normal subjects, Fink (1961) concluded that cerebral activity associated with wakefulness is the main determinant of respiratory drive, and that the partial pressure of carbon dioxide in arterial blood

($Pa_{CO_2}$) merely augments the effect of this activity. These studies emphasize that in the investigation of breathlessness results can be misleading unless attention is paid to the emotional state of the subject.

Psychiatrists have made intensive studies of selected patients with bronchial asthma and seldom of those with other pulmonary disorders. Like allergists, they have stalked the aetiology of bronchospasm, only to conclude that multiple factors seem probable in most cases (Rees, 1956). Dyspnoea may be felt as endangering life to a greater extent than almost any other symptom: to the patient, the experience of dyspnoea is regarded as something which, if it worsens to asphyxia, must inevitably be fatal. Having this quality, it must often be associated with anxiety, the lessening of which is likely to mitigate the subjective distress caused by the breathlessness. The issue of interest to us is what determines the extent and quality of such emotional arousal in an individual case of bronchial asthma.

Psychiatrists usually study asthmatic patients referred to them by physicians; and conclusions could have been biased due to their sample being neither representative nor compared with controls studied identically. In order to illustrate our approach to the examination of the considerations under review, we shall now report some results of a study on which we are currently engaged regarding the psychopathology of bronchial asthma. Further details about the methods and preliminary results have been published elsewhere (Aitken, Zealley and Rosenthal, 1969).

### PSYCHOPATHOLOGY OF BRONCHIAL ASTHMA

*Description of subjects*

Twenty-four patients with bronchial asthma were selected at *random* from a register of patients attending a local Asthma Clinic. Sixteen were female, eight were male and their mean age was 40 years (range: 20–56) They had had their first attack of asthma an average of 18 years previously (range: 1–47).

Seventeen patients (71 per cent) had noted precipitation of certain attacks by upper respiratory tract infection, and ten (42 per cent) by contact with some kind of animal or vegetable matter. Twelve (50 per cent) acknowledged that disturbance of emotion precipitated at least some of the attacks.

Each patient was matched for sex, age ($\pm 8$ years) and social class with either a healthy normal or an anxiety neurotic subject. These two control groups provided bipolarity of neurotic response, with which the asthmatics could be compared.

The asthmatics had a reduced mean forced expiratory volume in the first second ($FEV_1$) compared with the normals and neurotics. There were no significant differences between the groups either in forced vital capacity (FVC) recorded at the time of testing or in FVC predicted from age and height nomograms (Needham, Rogan and McDonald, 1954). The means and ranges of these measurements are shown in Table I.

TABLE I

LUNG FUNCTION TESTS

| Lung volumes | | Asthmatics (N=24) | Normals (N=12) | Neurotics (N=12) | F | P< |
|---|---|---|---|---|---|---|
| | | | *Controls* | | *Analysis of variance between groups* | |
| $FEV_1$: | mean | 2353 | 3339 | 2802 | | |
| (ml) | range | 570–4050 | 1850–4530 | 1400–3680 | 6·3 | 0·01 |
| FVC: | mean | 3486 | 4254 | 3663 | | |
| (ml) | range | 900–6000 | 2600–5550 | 2200–5600 | 0·9 | N.S. |
| Predicted | | | | | | |
| FVC:* | mean | 3396 | 3476 | 3180 | | |
| (ml) | range | 2431–4968 | 2531–5250 | 2461–4610 | 0·4 | N.S. |

* From nomogram by Needham, Rogan and McDonald (1954); in this and subsequent Tables (II–VII) N=number of subjects in each group; N.S.=not significant.

*Assessment of personality traits at interview*

Two psychiatrists recorded independently the presence of a selection of traits. The proportions of subjects with those traits which discriminated significantly between the groups are shown in Table II. It can be seen that asthmatics were characterized by each trait more often than the normal

TABLE II

A SELECTION OF THE PERSONALITY TRAITS ASSESSED AT INTERVIEW BY TWO RATERS

| Personality traits | Asthmatics (N=24) (Percentage) | Normals (N=12) (Percentage) | Neurotics (N=12) (Percentage) | $\chi^2$ | P< |
|---|---|---|---|---|---|
| | | *Controls* | | | |
| Obsessional | 54 | 0 | 58 | 11·5 | 0·01 |
| Lack of confidence | 54 | 8 | 83 | 13·8 | 0·001 |
| Sensitive | 58 | 33 | 92 | 8·6 | 0·02 |
| Anxious | 54 | 33 | 100 | 11·9 | 0·01 |
| Dependent | 29 | 16 | 83 | 12·3 | 0·01 |
| Unstable mood | 4 | 0 | 50 | 16·2 | (0·001)* |

Table II shows the percentage of subjects in each diagnostic group who were assigned the traits listed: a trait was assigned if one or other rater felt it was markedly present, or if both raters considered it was present to a moderate extent.

The following traits were found no more commonly in one group than in another: irritable, solitary, hysterical, schizoid, submissive, timid, paranoid, cyclothymic, hostile-aggressive, competitive-aggressive, "bottled-up-feelings".

* This P value is in parentheses because, in calculating $\chi^2$, the "expected" value in three of the six cells was less than five.

controls but less often than the neurotics. Nearly as many asthmatics as neurotics were obsessional while, in contrast, only one was considered unstable in mood. Rees (1956) found these same traits in asthmatics more commonly than in controls after detailed study of over 400 cases.

*Psychometric tests of personality*

The Taylor Manifest Anxiety Scale (TMAS) (Taylor, 1953), Foulds' Hostility Questionnaire (HDHQ) (Caine, Foulds and Hope, 1967) and the Eysenck Personality Inventory (EPI) (Eysenck and Eysenck, 1964) discriminated significantly between the groups of subjects (Table III). The

TABLE III

PSYCHOMETRIC TESTS OF PERSONALITY

| | | Controls | | Analysis of variance between groups | |
| Personality tests | Asthmatics (N=24) | Normals (N=12) | Neurotics (N=12) | F | P< |
|---|---|---|---|---|---|
| Eysenck Personality Inventory: | | | | | |
| Neuroticism score | 10·3 | 4·2 | 15·8 | 18·2 | 0·001 |
| Extraversion score | 9·6 | 9·5 | 10·0 | 0·1 | N.S. |
| Lie score | 3·8 | 4·8 | 3·9 | 1·4 | N.S. |
| Taylor Manifest Anxiety Scale: | | | | | |
| Total score | 14·1 | 5·8 | 29·0 | 27·5 | 0·001 |
| Foulds' Hostility Questionnaire: | | | | | |
| Total score | 14·7 | 8·8 | 22·5 | 15·0 | 0·001 |
| Direction score | +3·8 | +0·3 | +7·3 | 3·6 | N.S. |

Each value is the mean score of the group. Where the F value is significant, t tests were done between pairs of groups and each was found to differ significantly at least at P < 0·01.

asthmatics reported more anxiety, neuroticism and hostility than the normal controls, but less than the neurotic controls. As these results were comparable with the observations made at psychiatric interview, we deduce that both assessment techniques are valid for these subjects. On no test did the asthmatics' scores differ significantly from published data on normal people.

*Feeling of resistance to breathing*

Campbell and his group found that in normal subjects the threshold for detection of resistance to breathing was at an added elastance load of 2·47 $cmH_2O/l/s$ (Campbell et al., 1961 b) and a resistance load of 0·59 $cmH_2O/l/s$ (Bennett et al., 1962). Aitken (1969) examined the relationship between subjective experience of resistance to breathing and pressure loading of expiration. He found that the relationship was curvilinear, obeying the Weber-Fechner Law as described with other sensory modalities.

We were interested in the question: What degree of asphyxia do our groups of subjects perceive, or communicate that they perceive, when exposed to pressure loading in an external airway?

Subjects exhaled against a selection of pressure loadings between two and 8 cmH$_2$O in a balanced design. They wore a face-mask (RAF type P) and helmet in which were microphone and earphones. A solenoid-operated open/shut valve was attached to the exhalation tube from the

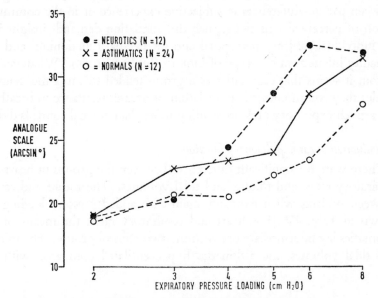

FIG. 2. Feeling of resistance to exhalation at different pressure loadings. The points represent the means obtained on two occasions from each subject in the groups. Measurements in mm from the threshold end were transformed to the *arcsin* to achieve normality of distribution before calculation (Snedecor and Cochran, 1967).

mask: when mask pressure exceeded the selected value, the valve opened so that expiration could proceed unimpeded. Subjects communicated their perception of the degree of asphyxia by marking a 10-cm line, the two ends of which were defined as representing "no resistance to breathing" and "impossible to exhale" respectively (Aitken, 1969).

For the different pressure loadings used, the mean scores on the analogue scale for each group are shown on Fig. 2. There were no differences between groups at the lowest value but, as the pressure loading was raised, the neurotics indicated that they experienced a greater degree of asphyxia than the other two groups. Unfortunately the differences on raising the pressure loading did not become significant even between neurotics and normals ($F=2 \cdot 53$, $P<0 \cdot 15$; for $P<0 \cdot 05$, $F=4 \cdot 38$). Nevertheless, the consistency of the response pattern is striking and, as in the examination of personality traits, the asthmatics usually lay intermediate between the two control groups. The probability that such an order between the groups could have occurred by chance on the six occasions is $0 \cdot 03$ (Kendall's coefficient of concordance $= 0 \cdot 58$).

Clearly the method used to look at this question cannot distinguish between patient-differences in subjective experience or in the communication of perceived sensations; such differentiation demands insight into the individual subject's perceptual and intellectual functioning, and is a difficulty inherent in this type of inquiry (Ingham, 1969). Whatever the reason, it seems that asthmatics as a group tended towards the neurotic mode; they communicated appreciation of greater resistance to breathing for a given expiratory pressure loading more than normal controls did.

*Examination of cardiopulmonary function*

There were no significant differences between the groups in heart and respiratory rates, and minute and tidal volumes. The means and ranges between subjects when exhaling against no added pressure loading are shown in Table IV. For heart and respiratory rates, the means of the asthmatics lay intermediate between the two control groups. For minute and tidal volumes, the asthmatics hyperventilated compared with the

TABLE IV

MEASUREMENTS OF CARDIOPULMONARY FUNCTION AT REST

| | | | Controls | | Analysis of variance between groups | |
| | | Asthmatics ($N=24$) | Normals ($N=12$) | Neurotics ($N=12$) | | |
| Cardiopulmonary measures | | | | | $F$ | $P<$ |
|---|---|---|---|---|---|---|
| Heart rate: | mean | 76·2 | 70·3 | 77·0 | 1·31 | N.S. |
| (beats/min) subject range | | 57–101 | 52–92 | 66–97 | | |
| Respiration rate: | mean | 14·6 | 12·6 | 15·5 | 1·24 | N.S. |
| (breaths/min) subject range | | 6–27 | 9–16 | 9–22 | | |
| Minute volume: | mean | 7·9 | 6·6 | 7·3 | 1·77 | N.S. |
| (l/min) subject range | | 4·4–13·0 | 4·1–8·8 | 4·8–11·0 | | |
| Tidal volume: | mean | 0·59 | 0·54 | 0·50 | 0·77 | N.S. |
| (l/breath) subject range | | 0·36–1·32 | 0·42–0·75 | 0·30–1·09 | | |

The values are based on the means of seven readings in each subject taken at 30-s intervals during the first 3 min of recording. Heart rate was read from an instantaneous ratemeter, using a suitable lead of a standard electrocardiogram as input. Respiration rate was read from another ratemeter; the input signal to this was taken through a zero switch from a Greer Manometer (type A10 capsule) on a pneumotachograph attached to the mask inhalation tube. The inhalation signal was also integrated, and displayed on a pen-recorder for measurement of ventilation volume. (This system had been calibrated for sine wave flow and found to have 95 per cent confidence limits ± 0·6 l/min.)

healthy controls. The ranges between subjects were large, inviting speculation on the contributory factors.

When exhaling against pressure loading there were significant changes in heart and respiratory rates, but there was no consistent trend in the changes which were observed (Table V). Tidal and minute volumes increased considerably, by an amount that was a function of the pressure loading but not of subject group (Fig. 3).

Campbell and co-workers (1961a) have reported a similar increase in

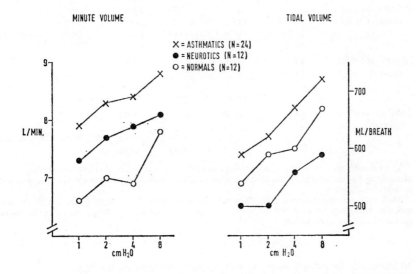

FIG. 3. Ventilation response to pressure loading: (a) minute volume; (b) tidal volume.
No additional loading was applied for the scores at 10 mm water, this being the pressure needed to operate the internal mask-valve itself.

tidal volume on threshold loading of breathing in conscious healthy subjects; they noted that on expiratory loading there was an increase in end-inspiratory lung volume. Breathing against resistance increases pressure in bronchial airways and this in turn can dilate bronchioles. A central integrative mechanism must be involved to account for the increase in inspiratory volume as a tactic to overcome expiratory pressure loading. In our subjects, such a mechanism seemed to operate in a similar way irrespective of whether they were asthmatics, normals or neurotics.

TABLE V

MEASUREMENTS OF CARDIOPULMONARY FUNCTION WHILE EXHALING
AGAINST PRESSURE LOADING

| Cardiopulmonary measures | Pressure loading (mm water) | Asthmatics (N=24) | Controls Normals (N=12) | Controls Neurotics (N=12) | Analysis of variance Between groups F | Analysis of variance Between groups P< | Analysis of variance Between pressures F | Analysis of variance Between pressures P< |
|---|---|---|---|---|---|---|---|---|
| Heart rate: | 10 | 76·2 | 70·3 | 77·0 | | | | |
| (beats/min) | 20 | 74·9 | 68·9 | 76·8 | | | | |
| | 40 | 74·7 | 69·9 | 77·0 | 1·5 | N.S. | 3·6 | 0·05 |
| | 80 | 75·9 | 71·4 | 78·8 | | | | |
| Respiration rate: | 10 | 14·6 | 12·6 | 15·5 | | | | |
| (breaths/min) | 20 | 15·4 | 12·7 | 16·3 | | | | |
| | 40 | 15·1 | 12·1 | 15·0 | 1·4 | N.S. | 3·1 | 0·05 |
| | 80 | 14·2 | 12·3 | 14·4 | | | | |
| Minute volume: | 10 | 7·9 | 6·6 | 7·3 | | | | |
| (l/min) | 20 | 8·3 | 7·0 | 7·7 | | | | |
| | 40 | 8·4 | 6·9 | 7·9 | 1·5 | N.S. | 7·2 | 0·001 |
| | 80 | 8·8 | 7·8 | 8·1 | | | | |
| Tidal volume: | 10 | 0·59 | 0·54 | 0·50 | | | | |
| (l/breath) | 20 | 0·62 | 0·59 | 0·50 | | | | |
| | 40 | 0·67 | 0·60 | 0·56 | 0·7 | N.S. | 8·4 | 0·001 |
| | 80 | 0·72 | 0·67 | 0·59 | | | | |

These figures are the means of six readings in each subject taken at 30-s intervals during 3 min exhaling against the stated pressure loading. Preceding each period subjects breathed for 3 min against no additional loading.

Mask pressure was measured with a Greer manometer (type A300 capsule); the instrument was modified with limit detectors and relays so it could open the solenoid-operated valve when a selected pressure loading was exceeded.

*Relationship between severity of asthma and psychometric test scores*

There does not seem to be a universal index for severity of the asthmatic diathesis. Only one patient (the only chronic bronchitic in the asthma sample) was dyspnoeic during investigation, though ten (43 per cent) had an $FEV_1$ less than 70 per cent of their FVC. Fourteen of the patients (58 per cent) had been in hospital for the treatment of asthma, and fourteen were also taking prednisolone regularly with a mean daily dose of 6·7 mg.

The asthmatic patients were divided into sub-groups by these criteria, and the psychometric test scores examined. The only significant difference was in the TMAS, where the mean score was lower for those taking prednisolone (11·1) than for those not on this treatment (18·2) ($P< 0·05$); this implied less proneness to anxiety in those patients on a regular steroid regime, which supports observations by Baraff and Cunningham (1966).

*Relationship between measurement of cardiopulmonary function and Taylor Manifest Anxiety Scale scores*

The index of psychopathology which discriminated best between the groups was the TMAS score. In order to look at any association between psychopathology and cardiopulmonary function, correlation coefficients were calculated between the TMAS scores and the physiological measurements recorded when breathing at rest (Table VI).

TABLE VI

CORRELATION COEFFICIENTS BETWEEN TMAS SCORES AND
MEASUREMENTS OF CARDIOPULMONARY FUNCTION

| Cardiopulmonary measures | Asthmatics (N=24) | Physically healthy subjects (N=24) | All subjects (N=48) |
|---|---|---|---|
| Heart rate | 0·22 | 0·42* | 0·32* |
| Respiration rate | 0·02 | 0·49* | 0·24 |
| Minute volume | 0·04 | 0·06 | 0·00 |
| Tidal volume | 0·02 | −0·34 | −0·19 |

* $P < 0.05$.
The values constituting Table IV were taken as the measures of cardiopulmonary function.

In the non-asthmatic subjects, there were associations between TMAS scores and both heart and respiration rates: for heart rates, this remained significant when calculated for all subjects together. The inverse relationship between TMAS scores and tidal volumes nearly reached significance for physically healthy subjects. There appeared to be no association between TMAS scores and minute volumes.

*Relationship between tidal volume and other variables*

There was no evidence that patients with severer asthma (as assessed by taking prednisolone or having a $FEV_1$ of less than 70 per cent of their FVC) had higher heart or respiration rates or minute or tidal volumes. Thus these criteria of severity did not appear to account for the large variation observed in the measures of cardiopulmonary function.

We have just described how some of the variation in heart and respiration rates, at least in non-asthmatic subjects, could be attributed to varying proneness to anxiety (*viz* TMAS scores); but this index of psychopathology did not account for the variation in ventilation volume, particularly in the asthmatics who hyperventilated in comparison with both control groups. The asthmatics therefore lie orthogonal to the neurotic dimension, and their hyperventilation cannot be a function solely of this type of psychopathology.

We then looked for an association between tidal volumes and standard measures of lung volume (Table VII). For the asthmatics we found that tidal volume was a function of lung capacity; but this was *not* the case in the non-asthmatics. We also found that the more recent the onset of asthma, the greater was the tidal volume.

TABLE VII

CORRELATION COEFFICIENTS BETWEEN TIDAL VOLUMES AND OTHER VARIABLES

| Variables | Asthmatics (N=24) | Physically healthy subjects (N=24) | All subjects (N=48) |
|---|---|---|---|
| Duration of asthma | −0·54* | — | — |
| Age | −0·38 | 0·19 | −0·08 |
| Height | 0·41† | 0·03 | 0·20 |
| Predicted FVC | 0·54* | −0·09 | 0·27 |
| Actual FEV$_1$ | 0·46† | −0·13 | 0·15 |
| Actual FVC | 0·43† | 0·04 | 0·25 |
| $\dfrac{\text{Actual FVC}}{\text{Predicted FVC}}$ | 0·12 | 0·19 | 0·06 |
| $\dfrac{\text{Actual FEV}_1}{\text{Actual FVC}}$ | 0·00 | −0·37 | −0·22 |

* $P < 0·01$; † $P < 0·05$.
All figures in the last three columns are correlation coefficients between tidal volume and the variables in the first column.

## DISCUSSION

In these results we have reported examination of the psychopathology of bronchial asthma from four quite distinct viewpoints—personality traits revealed at interview, psychometric tests, feelings about breathing against resistance, and cardiopulmonary function; and in identical fashion we have examined matched control groups, bipolar for the dimension of neuroticism under study.

The physiological data were recorded with considerable precision and were direct measures of the activity concerned. On the other hand, the psychological data were only indicants of the psychopathology—feelings of anxiety and of asphyxia are not amenable to measurement, scores only reflecting quite crudely the psychological dimension. (The TMAS consists of only fifty questions and cannot be expected to embrace the many manifestations of proneness to anxiety. The psychometric tests used are sufficiently reliable to discriminate groups and thus have validity in this sense; but they are inadequate for drawing conclusions about individuals.)

Though tachycardia, tachypnoea and hyperpnoea are signs of disorder in cardiopulmonary function, they can also be determined by neuro-humoral activity related to emotion. By multivariate analysis it should be quite feasible to calculate how much any psychopathology (at least an imprecise measure of it) and how much any pulmonary pathology contributed to the between-subject variance of these measures. Our preliminary results suggest that heart and breathing rates may be influenced more by an emotional factor than a pulmonary one; and ventilation volume more by a pulmonary factor than an emotional one. It seems to be an open question why asthmatics hyperventilate even when free from bronchospasm, but we do not concede that the cause will be found only in the lung; the relationship between tidal volume and duration—rather than severity—of the disease makes us still speculate about the influence of higher nervous centres.

Our randomly selected sample of asthmatics did not differ from the healthy population in amount of neurotic disorder. However, more of them seemed to have obsessional, underconfident and sensitive traits in their personalities than the normal and neurotic controls, even though their mood stability was within normal limits. The significance of obsessional symptoms is far from clear; this character trait was assigned to those who paid excessive attention to tidiness and orderliness and were pedantic and overconscientious with inconclusive and inflexible ways of thinking and acting (Lewis, 1936). As such people tend to feel insecure, it is easy to surmise the effect of bronchospasm, with the uncertain duration and severity of a developing attack, on their mood. They may well tend to ruminate about the condition, be oversensitive to the onset of minimal dyspnoea, and fail to habituate to the initial emotional excitation which accompanies this onset. These reasons may account for the recurrent declaration of symptoms in some patients, just as Robinson and Wood (1968) showed that neuroticism played a large part in the declaration of anaemia.

If anxiety can be reduced and confidence gained by mastery of distress, the patient should be less disabled by his intermittent dyspnoea even if the aetiology of the bronchospasm is elsewhere. Behaviour therapy by systematic desensitization aims to do just that (Dudley, Martin and Holmes, 1968). Should our reasoning be logical, then a formulation of the psychopathology in terms of a specific phobia is appropriate. Phobic-obsessional psychiatric patients often experience more distress anticipating a feared situation in fantasy than in reality. Gelder, Marks and Wolff (1967) showed that, if the personality is otherwise stable and the phobia does not spread to other situations, systematic desensitization is superior to other forms of psychotherapy. Moore (1966) has reported promising results treating asthmatics by this method. In one case currently under treatment by us we have reason to hope we have induced improvement, since there has been a gradual rise in $FEV_1$ accompanied by increased subjective well-being over the period of treatment. We are currently working on this development from phenomenology to therapy.

### SUMMARY

The psychophysiology of breathlessness is reviewed. The neural basis for Campbell and Howell's (1963) theory on the appreciation of length-tension inappropriateness is extended to include emotional factors as contributing to the sensation of breathlessness and subsequent change in cardiopulmonary function.

A study on the psychopathology of bronchial asthma is reported. A representative sample, with matched normal and neurotic controls, was examined from four distinct viewpoints—personality traits revealed at interview, psychometric tests, feelings about breathing against resistance, and cardiopulmonary function. More of the asthmatics had obsessional, underconfident and sensitive traits, but there was no greater prevalence of overt neurotic disorder. Neurotics and asthmatics tended to communicate more feeling of resistance when exhaling against pressure loading than normals; and they also had a relative tachycardia and tachypnoea. Asthmatics tended to hyperventilate compared with the controls, and in all groups ventilation volume increased on pressure loading. Rates of breathing and heartbeat were related to proneness to anxiety, while volume of breathing was related to lung capacity.

Comroe has emphasized that dyspnoea "involves both perception of the sensation by the patient and his reaction to the sensation." (Comroe, 1966). Distress from dyspnoea will be enhanced by the prevailing psychopathology but should be amenable to treatment aimed at the reduction of anxiety, without the psychopathology being asserted as the cause of bronchospasm.

ACKNOWLEDGEMENTS

We would like to thank Dr I. W. B. Grant of the Northern General Hospital, Edinburgh for permission to study patients who have attended the Asthma Clinic. We would also like to thank Professor G. M. Carstairs for his encouragement and the provision of laboratory facilities. This work is supported by grants from the Medical Research Council and Mental Health Research Fund, to whom we are indebted.

## REFERENCES

AITKEN, R. C. B. (1969). *Proc. R. Soc. Med.*, **62**, 989–993.
AITKEN, R. C. B., ZEALLEY, A. K., and ROSENTHAL, S. V. (1969). *J. psychosom. Res.*, **13**, 289–297.
BARAFF, A. J., and CUNNINGHAM, A. P. (1966). *J. psychosom. Res.*, **10**, 291–295.
BENNETT, E. D., JAYSON, M. I. V., RUBINSTEIN, D., and CAMPBELL, E. J. M. (1962). *Clin. Sci.*, **23**, 155–162.
BURNS, B. H., and HOWELL, J. B. L. (1969). *Q. Jl Med.*, **38**, 277–294.
CAINE, T. M., FOULDS, G. A., and HOPE, K. (1967). *Manual of the Hostility and Direction of Hostility Questionnaire (HDHQ)*. London: University of London Press.
CAMPBELL, E. J. M., DICKINSON, C. J., DINNICK, O. P., and HOWELL, J. B. L. (1961a). *Clin. Sci.*, **21**, 309–320.
CAMPBELL, E. J. M., FREEDMAN, S., SMITH, P. S., and TAYLOR, M. E. (1961b). *Clin. Sci.*, **20**, 223–231.
CAMPBELL, E. J. M., and HOWELL, J. B. L. (1963). *Br. med. Bull.*, **19**, 36–40.
CHRISTIE, R. V. (1935). *Q. Jl Med.*, **4**, 427–432.
COMROE, J. H., JR. (1966). In *Breathlessness*. pp. 1–7, ed. Howell, J. B. L., and Campbell, E. J. M. Oxford: Blackwell.
DUDLEY, D. L., MARTIN, C. J., and HOLMES, T. H. (1968). *J. psychosom. Res.*, **11**, 325–339.
EYSENCK, H. J., and EYSENCK, SYBIL B. G. (1964). *Manual of the Eysenck Personality Inventory*. London: University of London Press.
FELEKY, A. M. (1916). *J. exp. Psychol.*, **1**, 218–241.
FINESINGER, J. E. (1944). *Am. J. Psychiat.*, **100**, 659–667.
FINK, R. (1961). *J. appl. Physiol.*, **16**, 15–20.
GELDER, M. G., MARKS, I. M., and WOLFF, H. H. (1967). *Br. J. Psychiat.*, **113**, 53–73.
HINTON, J. M. (1963). *Q. Jl Med.*, **32**, 1–21.
HOWELL, J. B. L., and CAMPBELL, E. J. M. (eds). (1966). *Breathlessness*. Oxford: Blackwell.
INGHAM, J. G. (1969). *Proc. R. Soc. Med.*, **62**, 492–494.
KERR, W. J., DALTON, J. W., and GLIEBE, P. A. (1937). *Ann. intern. Med.*, **11**, 961–992.
LEWIS, A. J. (1936). *Proc. R. Soc. Med.*, **29**, 325–326.
MEZEY, A. G., and COPPEN, A. J. (1961). *Clin. Sci.*, **20**, 171–175.
MOORE, N. (1966). *J. psychosom. Res.*, **9**, 257–276.
MORUZZI, G., and MAGOUN, W. H. (1949). *Electroenceph. clin. Neurophysiol.*, **1**, 455–473.
NEEDHAM, C. D., ROGAN, M. N., and McDONALD, I. (1954). *Thorax*, **9**, 313–325.
REES, L. (1956). *J. psychosom. Res.*, **1**, 98–114.
ROBINSON, J. O., and WOOD, W. M. (1968). *Br. J. prev. soc. Med.*, **22**, 23–26.
SEVERINGHAUS, J. W. (1966). In *Breathlessness*, pp. 85–92, ed. Howell, J. B. L., and Campbell, E. J. M. Oxford: Blackwell.
SMYTHIES, J. R. (1967). *Brain*, **90**, 697–706.
SNEDECOR, G. W., and COCHRAN, W. G. (1967). *Statistical Methods*, 6th edn. Iowa: State University Press.
TAYLOR, A. J. (1953). *J. abnorm. soc. Psychol.*, **48**, 285–290.
WHELAN, R. F., and YOUNG, I. M. (1953). *Br. J. Pharmac. Chemother.*, **8**, 98–102.
YOUNG, I. M. (1957). *J. Physiol., Lond.*, **137**, 374–395.

## DISCUSSION

*Dornhorst:* The use of analogue scoring for measuring such subjective parameters as dyspnoea is a considerable advance and certainly more reliable than asking the subject to describe what he feels in words.

*Wood:* I suggest that your results, Dr Aitken, do not confirm the Weber–Fechner Psychophysical Laws (Fechner, 1965) but actually refute them. Weber's Law states that the increase in intensity that must be added to a stimulus to produce a "just noticeable difference" is relative to the initial intensity of the stimulus. Fechner extended this law to include the subjective rating of the intensity of an above-threshold stimulus. He suggested that the magnitude of the sensation produced by such a stimulus could be predicted in terms of units of "just noticeable differences". This is sometimes called the Weber–Fechner Law.

*Aitken:* I apologize for referring colloquially to the Weber and Fechner Laws, but this was a convenient shorthand way of drawing attention to the curvilinear relationship between threshold and increase in sensation with stimulus magnitude. In 1962, I conducted a small experiment with air crew who exhaled against a series of spring-loaded valves and communicated their feelings on a simple analogue scale (Aitken, 1969). There was a rectilinear relationship between the mean sensation scores and the logarithm of pressure load. Extrapolation of the regression to the point meaning "no detection of resistance" gave, very easily, an estimate of threshold. An analogue scale score is not a measure of perception, but only of the subject's communication about the sensation; the score is produced by components from both parts. Such compounding, of course, applies to measurement of all feelings.

*Wood:* Treisman (1964) claimed that the extrapolation of such a regression line to zero stimulus intensity showed a curvilinear relationship, and the point at 0·25 cmH$_2$O on your line supports this claim, although one should not really generalize from a single point on such a variable.

My results (unpublished) showing that severity of breathlessness using an analogue scale is a good predictor of internal airways resistance, support yours, Dr Aitken. May I make two points about the results of these studies in relation to the Weber–Fechner Law? Patients with high internal airways resistances have a higher threshold for stimulus detection (greater just noticeable differences) than normal subjects do (Bennett *et al.*, 1962; Wiley and Zechman, 1966). Asthmatics also have high internal resistances. Therefore the magnitude of one particular high external respiratory load will be equivalent to a smaller number of just noticeable differences for the patients (asthmatics) than for the normal subjects. The Weber–Fechner Law would predict from this that the patients should rate this added load as less severe than the normal subjects would. Dr Aitken's results, and my own findings, show the converse. This may be because *patients* have a tendency to exaggerate their symptoms. However, ratings of a high respiratory load by normal subjects, before and during the elevation of their internal airways resistances by cotton dust inhalation, show the same tendencies: when the internal resistance is high the external load is rated as more difficult.

*Dornhorst:* These findings are not relevant to the situation in asthma because the asthmatic's effort is in inspiration; expiration in asthmatics usually remains passive.

*Wood:* My studies have so far only been concerned with the inspiratory phase of respiration.

*Petit:* It is misleading to compare the behaviour of asthmatics and normal subjects exhaling against external resistances because there are many differences between the two groups even before one starts the experiment. The asthmatic is anxious during any test of respiratory function simply because he is an asthmatic. A chronic asthmatic, also, has long experience in observing his respiratory sensations whereas the normal subject has not. And the asthmatic at rest may already have a tachycardia if he is taking bronchodilator drugs. I do not entirely agree with Comroe's (1966) comment (quoted by Dr Aitken) that dyspnoea "involves both perception of the sensation by the patient and his reaction to the sensation", although of course we must try to distinguish between the asthmatic's sensation of dyspnoea and his distressed reaction to it.

*Aitken:* It is true that we should make this distinction but it is quite acceptable to describe observed phenomenology, certainly in asthma where there have been so few controlled studies. Caution is always necessary in suggesting explanations for noted differences, so we must be clear what the term *normal* means. Physiologists often use it to mean "without pathology" thus denoting "basal", and we have used it in this sense. In contrast, psychologists often use "normal" to refer to a random sample of the general population, where the distribution of scores may be far from basal. In order to establish where the asthmatic group was situated we needed two control samples, bipolar toward the extremities of the neurotic dimension.

*Dornhorst:* You indicated your appreciation of problems connected with these two different meanings of normal when you showed that the asthmatics were on the population norm for neuroticism and the normal controls were "supernormal". A possible trap would be to have deduced from this that the asthmatics were abnormal in this respect. It is certainly misleading to identify the sensation of dyspnoea with what can be observed by measurement; these two parameters are important but separate. Deformation of the chest wall, for example, is the same whether it is produced as a response to an external resistance or to an equivalent internal resistance caused by airways obstruction, but the associated sensation will be different in each case.

*Wood:* I have found (unpublished data) that patients can usefully communicate as separate entities the difficulty and the anxiety experienced when inspiring against a high resistance (Comroe's [1966] "perception of and reaction to" sensation). The anxiety is highly correlated with neuroticism, as measured by the Maudsley Personality Inventory.

*Campbell:* Will you describe this work in some more detail?

*Wood:* I used a detection technique based on one described by Bennett and co-workers (1962). Normal subjects and patients with chronic airways obstruction were included. Using techniques discovered recently in psychophysics, a measure of a subject's ability to detect respiratory loads of low intensity was obtained (Swets, Tanner and Birdsall, 1961), uncontaminated by either the type of instructions or the motivation of the subject. A measure of the motivation in terms of response bias was also derived. The classical threshold is a combination of these two measures in unknown proportions. My results for detection simply confirmed previous workers' findings that normal subjects can detect lower respiratory loads ($0.24$ cm$H_2O$/l/s) than patients ($0.86$ cm$H_2O$/l/s). However, the results also clearly showed that motivation in patients and normal subjects was different; the former were significantly more willing to admit the presence of the stimulus.

*Dornhorst:* How do these results fit in with the findings in Dr Guz's tracheostomized patient who could appreciate levels of external resistances when he was breathing through his upper airways but not when he breathed through the tracheostomy tube? This patient must have detected resistances by means of sensation in his upper airways. There seems to be some discrepancy between these results and yours, Mr Wood, although one might have expected that, whatever is happening below the tube, patients could detect changes in load through their mouth and pharynx.

*Wood:* Some of our preliminary results do suggest that intra-oral pressure is an important determinant in the detection of external respiratory loads. But resistance, which is intra-oral pressure corrected for flow rate (in my experiment), is a better indication of what the subject is detecting. Flow rate is not so important but not entirely dispensable. Dr Guz's results require that flow is detected somewhere in the pharynx which contradicts some work of Professor Campbell's group (Bennett *et al.*, 1962).

*Campbell:* The question is whether patients with chronic airways obstruction can detect external ventilatory loads more or less easily than normal subjects. Dr Zechman, didn't you show (Wiley and Zechman, 1966) that patients with chronic bronchitis were less good at detecting external loads than normal subjects?

*Zechman:* No. We studied one bronchitic subject in detail for comparison with our normal subjects. The bronchitic patient had a pulmonary resistance of $4\cdot8$ $cmH_2O/l/s$ and required the addition of a resistance of $1\cdot3$ $cmH_2O/l/s$ for detection. The average pulmonary resistance of the normal subjects was $1\cdot9$ $cmH_2O/l/s$ and they, on the average, detected an increase of resistance of $0\cdot5$ $cmH_2O/l/s$. The proportional change, $\Delta R/R_{total}$ (where $\Delta R$ is the change of resistance added externally and $R_{total}$ is the initial pulmonary resistance plus the minimum resistance of the breathing circuit) is about $0\cdot25$ in each case. The same relationship was obtained when we experimentally increased the pulmonary resistance of our control subjects by various techniques (for example placing them in a five degree, head-down position). We therefore concluded that a certain proportional change rather than the absolute change is used in the detection process. On this basis, the patient with chronic bronchitis has a threshold for detection which is identical with that of our normal subjects.

*Dornhorst:* Do you mean by proportional that the absolute level of detection was increased in the patients? You would have to make allowance for their higher internal resistance, of course.

*Zechman:* That is so.

*Dornhorst:* So these results support what you found, Dr Guz. Could your patient have been abnormal because his upper airways were usually excluded from his effective respiratory passages?

*Guz:* I doubt it. Dr Newsom Davis was the first person to show the importance of the upper airways in detecting external loads (Newsom Davis, 1967).

*Newsom Davis:* I studied a group of patients with incomplete lesions of the cervical cord, predominantly involving the posterior columns, with loss of postural sense in the limbs. These patients had difficulty in detecting inspiratory loads when compared to a group of control subjects. When oral sensation was reduced by an amethocaine lozenge, further impairment of detection occurred in the patients with cord lesions but not in the control subjects. This indicated that the patients, deprived of somatic afferent information from the chest wall, were relying upon oral sensation to detect the inspiratory load, through the transient change in intra-oral pressure which is produced by inspiring against the load.

*Guz:* All these results show is that loading experiments should not be done at the mouth!

*Merton:* Could this difficulty be avoided if the subject were put in a skin diving-suit and resistances added to the face-piece outside the suit so that changing the resistances would not give rise to pressure changes on the face? Has the same sort of mouth-piece been used in all these experiments? Another discrepancy might be introduced if a face mask were used in some cases and a mouth-piece in others.

*Campbell:* Certainly mouth-pieces of different sizes may have been used, and the head held in different positions and so on. But I doubt if your solution would work because clues arise from all sorts of sources as well as the upper airways; for example, the mask may fit badly and move during the experiment. It is difficult to devise a technique with external loading in which clues from all other sources are eliminated, because one is detecting such a small load.

*Dejours:* A certain type of breathing pattern exists for every individual, practically specific for life (like a finger-print) and not related to compliance or airways resistance or anything else that I know of. Any individual can be recognized by a graph of his breathing pattern. This has nothing to do with the fit of the mask or other external conditions: it depends on the individual personality. I suggest that exercise is not a particularly useful tool for assessing pulmonary function in respiratory disease because of this. The variation in, say, respiratory frequency among even normal subjects on exercise is so wide—from five to twenty-five breaths per minute at least (Dejours, 1961), so one has difficulty in establishing what is normal.

*Cotes:* Dr Aitken, your asthmatic patients had increased ventilation minute volumes and tidal volumes, but the relationship of ventilation minute volume to tidal volume was the same as in the normal subjects. This is also our experience (Cotes, Johnson and McDonald, this volume, p. 297). By contrast, your neurotically anxious patients with moderately increased ventilation had reduced tidal volumes so were genuinely tachypnoeic; that is, their increase in respiratory rate was out of proportion to the increase in ventilation minute volume. Could you expand your comments on the respiratory sensations experienced by these patients?

*Aitken:* We have few observations other than the measurements I have already described. The neurotics did not complain of breathlessness or distress when breathing against the high expiratory load, nor did the asthmatics or the normal subjects. Occasionally a subject would describe his sensation after the test, but our experience has been that their remarks did not help us to understand why the neurotics communicated feelings of more load.

## REFERENCES

AITKEN, R. C. B. (1969). *Proc. R. Soc. Med.*, **62,** 989–993.
BENNETT, E. D., JAYSON, M. I. V., RUBINSTEIN, D., and CAMPBELL, E. J. M. (1962). *Clin. Sci.*, **23,** 155–162.
COMROE, J. H. (1966). In *Breathlessness*, pp. 1–7, ed. HOWELL, J. B. L., and CAMPBELL, E. J. M. Oxford: Blackwell.
DEJOURS, P. (1961). *J. Physiol., Paris*, **53,** 320.
FECHNER, G. (1965). *Elements of Psychophysics*, vol. 1, trans. Adler, H., ed. Boring, E. G., and Howes, D. H. New York: Holt, Rinehart and Winston.
NEWSOM DAVIS, J. (1967). *Clin. Sci.*, **33,** 249–260.
SWETS, J. A., TANNER, W. P., JR., and BIRDSALL, T. G. (1961). *Psychol. Rev.*, **68,** 301–340.
TREISMAN, M. (1964). *Psychol. Rev.*, **71,** 314–330.
WILEY, R. L., and ZECHMAN, F. W., JR. (1966). *Resp. Physiol.*, **2,** 73–87.

# GENERAL DISCUSSION III

*Dornhorst:* In our discussions on respiratory sensation we have talked about the sense of effort, the sensation of distress associated with breath-holding, and the effects of various interferences—experimental and clinical—on respiratory sensations in different situations; and finally we considered some possible pyschological aspects of the sensation of breathlessness. Professor Campbell, could you try to put all these ideas together into some general statement about respiratory sensations?

*Campbell:* I am now much better informed about the peripheral anatomy of breathlessness but I retain most of my uncertainty about its physiology. The work of Dr Guz and his colleagues over the past few years has made a great contribution to working out the wiring diagrams for the act of breathing in man. But we still have not grasped the nature of the sensation or sensations of breathlessness. Exercise, chemical and mechanical loading and various other procedures have been used to mimic situations in which breathlessness occurs, and we are getting nearer to defining the sensation. We should go on trying to distinguish between the different sorts of sensations that are called at one time or another "breathlessness", even though we cannot be entirely objective in making these distinctions. The sensations in the head when the $Pco_2$ is raised, and in the chest when breathing is made difficult by external or internal resistances or when parts of the lung are collapsed through breathing pure oxygen, seem to be different and all need further study. Although we try to avoid subjective matters in scientific research we have to recognize that sensation is subjective, and breathlessness, therefore, must be considered subjectively. Dr Merton, from your unorthodox, uncommitted and iconoclastic Cambridge stance, would you be prepared to say what you now think about the nature of breathlessness?

*Merton:* It is many years since I even saw a dyspnoeic patient and I have never taken part in any investigations on respiratory disease. A better adjective for my stance might therefore be "untutored". As an outsider, however, it seems to me an attractive idea that some of the simpler kinds of breathlessness may result from a mismatch between the effort made and the depth of inspiration achieved, or some elaboration of this idea such as length-tension inappropriateness. Would it be possible to assess simple breathlessness quantitatively by using a triggered positive-pressure respirator and measuring how much positive assistance is needed to abolish the patient's unpleasant sensation?

*Dornhorst:* Patients with severe respiratory distress may continue to breathe at a rate far too high for efficient oxygenation during triggered respiration, and thus remain uncomfortable.

*Sears:* Jere Mead at Harvard (unpublished results) has worked with a servo-controlled respirator—the Elephant—in this sort of way. This machine is a pump generating pressures that are proportional to two signals, air flow and lung volume. It can be set up so that a normal subject can breathe on the pump so that the work of breathing is halved. On the first assisted breath, breathing becomes easier. If after some minutes the pressure-assistance is suddenly removed, breathing immediately becomes more difficult; the extra load is experienced, with no time-lag, in the next breath. These results suggest the presence of a dynamic interaction between respiratory movement and sensation; but habituation eventually occurs. So Dr Merton's suggestion of experiments using triggered respiration is a good one.

*Campbell:* The experience of a medical student I met in Melbourne supports what you have said. This young man had had a cyst in one lung since childhood, but he did not realize that he had previously been breathless until after the cyst was removed. The point I am trying to make through this illustration is that breathlessness of this sort, unlike (for example) pain, is quantitatively but not qualitatively different from a normal sensation.

*Dornhorst:* This is only one part of the problem. The increased breathing effort of exercise is subjectively different from the dyspnoea associated with acetylcholine-induced bronchoconstriction.

*Petit:* In my experience at least three different kinds of breathless feelings exist. First, a pain in the chest which arises from the lungs and seems similar to the pain felt in the nose and pharynx during acute inflammation. Second, the sensation that occurs with increased internal or external resistances. This is similar to the unpleasant sensation experienced during breath-holding and can be distinguished from, third, the "tightness" felt in the chest during an attack of asthma when the vagi have been blocked or local anaesthetic inhaled. This third sensation may be associated with the detection of pressure in the upper airways. All three sensations can occur separately or together and all three can induce distress.

*Aitken:* Qualitative changes in sensation can only be described with words. But I have indicated how the measurement of feelings resulting from a quantitative change—an extension in the range of a normal sensation—has poor resolution with only words. A question at issue is whether a change in these measurements might be attributed to specific qualitative change only because of the inadequacy of our vocabulary to describe it.

*Plum:* Dr Guz, have you or Dr Noble identified receptors in the intercostal muscles and chest wall that, when blocked, eliminate the sensation of breathlessness?

*Noble:* No. We showed in our paper (this volume) that blocking the afferents from the chest wall (excluding the diaphragm) had no effect on the four standard respiratory sensory inputs. But these standard inputs may not have much connexion with dyspnoea. Gold and Nadel (1966) have shown that dyspnoea was relieved by blocking afferents from the chest wall in one case of pleural thickening.

*Guz:* We have studied a patient with a paralysis and sensory denervation of the chest wall, due to a physiologically complete transection of the spinal cord at the level of the sixth cervical (C6) segment. This patient had repeated episodes of pulmonary collapse, always associated with a sense of discomfort felt in the chest and called (by the patient) "breathlessness".

*Plum:* My question has not been exactly answered by these comments. Our discussion seems to be directed towards finding a single receptor system to explain the mechanism producing dyspnoea, whereas several different types of dyspnoea, with different causes and neurological pathways, must exist. Do somatic afferents from the chest wall, for example, contribute at all to the sense of breathlessness?

*Dornhorst:* In some circumstances, pleurisy for example, they do.

*Plum:* Dr Guz, you have described impulses arising from the lung, mediated through vagal afferents, that evoke dyspnoea. Is that right?

*Guz:* That statement needs qualification. The only unpleasant sensation from the lung that we know, unequivocally, to be mediated through vagal afferents is the sense of irritation when the airways are touched. We also know that it is difficult to dissociate a barrage of afferent vagal impulses from the motor response to them; one may be feeling the motor response rather than the afferent stimulus. To sort out these problems about sensation we need to find out what a paralysed apnoeic human subject feels when graded electrical stimulation is applied to his exposed vagi. We have not done this experiment for obvious reasons.

*Newsom Davis:* Some further observations we made in the patient with complete transection of the spinal cord at C3 (see p. 250) who had unequivocal signs of complete somatic deafferentation of the chest wall may be relevant here, although results in a single subject are never altogether satisfactory. After ventilation with 100 per cent oxygen this patient was disconnected from the respirator (so that lung volume was at functional residual capacity) and a volume of 500 ml of air was then withdrawn from the lungs by means of a bellows. Every time this was done the patient immediately complained of tightness in the chest. In contrast, when the same volume was expelled by pressure on the chest and abdomen, he was unaware of any sensation at all. This distortion of the airways caused by the negative pressure may have stimulated vagal receptors and induced the feeling of tightness.

*Campbell:* There is good evidence of sensation arising in the upper airways, but what about the lungs? I would like "subjectively" to describe my sensations in response to various respiratory stresses, including severe exercise, the detection of loads, breath-holding and respiratory paralysis. I am unaware of any differences in the sensation in the chest between breath-holding, the addition of a very severe load during quiet breathing, breathing against a modest load during moderate exercise and the feeling during supramaximal exercise when my breathing approaches my maximum breathing capacity. The discomfort in my chest in these four situations seems to me the same. On the other hand, when paralysed and hypercapnic I have no sensation in the chest.

*Dornhorst:* Is the sensation you experience with breath-holding similar to what you feel when you are breathing against a maximal expiratory load?

*Campbell:* Against a very high load, yes.

*Guz:* I do not agree that the sensations associated with different respiratory stresses cannot be differentiated. The four sensations that Dr Noble described in his paper are certainly distinguishable. Rebreathing carbon dioxide is described as "not having breathed enough" and breath-holding is usually described as a squeeze around the sites of origin of the diaphragm. The sensation associated with detecting loads is less well defined, but everyone can recognize the feeling of irritation from stimulation of the tracheobronchial tree.

*Godfrey:* The only unpleasant sensation that I feel on rebreathing carbon dioxide is in my head and not in my chest. Provided ventilation can keep pace with the rising carbon dioxide, sensation in the chest is similar to and no more unpleasant than the sensation of exertional dyspnoea; it does not become unpleasant until ventilation can no longer keep up with respiratory drive; and it is presumably this unpleasant sensation that disappears when chest wall afferents are blocked by curare.

*Noble:* These differences confirm that the sensations associated with a raised $Pco_2$ are felt differently by different subjects. Some people complain of a sense of suffocation, others, like Professor Campbell and Dr Godfrey, of cerebral effects.

*Dornhorst:* The experimental set-up that most closely resembles a naturally occurring disease process is assessment of the ventilatory response to carbon dioxide in the presence of an external resistance load. This mimics what happens in a patient with any type of airways disease who still has good respiratory drive. Dyspnoea in this situation is surely quite different from the sensation during breath-holding—a highly artificial manoeuvre in which there is this awful struggle with oneself.

*Noble:* The sensations when I rebreathe carbon dioxide with and without an external resistance are not the same. And vagal block abolishes the unpleasant sensation in uncomplicated rebreathing experiments but has no effect when a subject rebreathes carbon dioxide in the presence of an external resistance.

*Widdicombe:* I have breathed 7 per cent carbon dioxide when my vagi were blocked, both with and without an external resistance of about 31 $cmH_2O/l/s$. I could only continue rebreathing carbon dioxide with this resistance for two minutes because of intolerable respiratory distress. The sensation and tolerable duration of breathing through the resistance were the same whether the vagi were blocked or intact, but when the resistance was removed my symptoms completely disappeared.

*Dornhorst:* Did your ventilatory response decrease when the resistance was removed.

*Widdicombe:* Yes.

*Campbell:* In my experience, discomfort in the chest during quiet or moderately increased breathing occurs only when a mechanical load is added. Breathing or rebreathing fairly high concentrations of carbon dioxide or moderate exercise when the breathing is unhindered do not give rise to any discomfort in the chest in me. On the other hand, breathing against a resistance of 30 $cmH_2O/l/s$ or an elastance of 100 $cmH_2O/l$ for one to two minutes feels the same as breath-holding.

*Paintal:* Is the sensation during an acute attack of left ventricular failure similar to the sensation during breath-holding or the rebreathing of carbon dioxide?

*Dornhorst:* There is a striking dissociation between the length of time that a patient with left ventricular failure can hold his breath in expiration and his dyspnoea during spontaneous respiration. A man who is dyspnoeic at rest may have a breath-holding time as long as 15 seconds.

*Guz:* But this is the *maximum*. In patients with severe left ventricular failure the maximum breath-holding time at functional residual capacity may be as short as ten seconds; thus sensation begins to be uncomfortable two or three seconds after the start of expiration; if the patient breathes at a normal rate he will feel discomfort during every expiration. This might explain the increased respiratory rate in patients with pulmonary oedema.

*Paintal:* Is the sensation of breathlessness different with different lung pathologies?

*Howell:* Patients with pulmonary disease make a clear distinction between the sensation of a viscous resistance and that of an elastic load.

*Campbell:* Another problem about these experimental studies in naive patients (in contrast to respiratory physiologists) is that their only experience of increased ventilation is exertional breathlessness. It is not surprising, therefore, that they call whatever unexpected sensations they feel in response to our manoeuvres "breathlessness", and cannot differentiate more specifically between the different types.

*Dornhorst:* Breathing through an external resistance on the one hand, and bronchoconstriction caused by the inhalation of various chemicals on the other, inevitably produce different sensations. Bronchoconstriction gives rise to a sensation which comes from the middle of the chest and is presumably due to a pressure gradient across the airways; with an external resistance there is no gradient. Discharge from the stretch receptors, and possibly from superficial irritant receptors also, is increased during bronchoconstriction (Widdicombe, 1961) which must add a different flavour to the extra respiratory work. Dr Widdicombe, what do you think about these differences?

*Widdicombe:* I suspect that the two sensations are different because, as you say, different parts of the respiratory tract and different systems of afferent nerves are affected. In my own experience the sensations during hypercapnia, breathing through resistance, breath-holding and histamine bronchoconstriction have quite different features provided the distress is not too intense. Distinctions between different sorts of very severe dyspnoea, however, are very difficult to make. At the break-point of any of these experimental manoeuvres subtle differentiations are impossible. Even the cooperative respiratory physiologist is at the limit of toleration. In these circumstances I am no longer interested in analysing my sensations, I just want to stop!

*Cohen:* Dyspnoea may be perceived through information transmitted within the brain. In paralysed animals under certain conditions cortical bursts occur in synchrony with phrenic discharge; thus information must be transmitted from the respiratory centres to higher levels of the neuraxis (Kumagai *et al.*, 1966). Could the following experiment be done in man? Phrenic activity is monitored in a curarized, conscious respiratory physiologist, who would signal in some way (perhaps by blinking) when he thought a central inspiratory discharge was taking place. Would this be practicable?

*Widdicombe:* No!

*Cohen:* The point I am getting at is that dyspnoea could be perceived centrally by sensing either the gradually growing hypercapnia and hypoxia or the increasing brainstem respiratory discharge evoked by asphyxia. A contributing factor to the feeling of breathlessness would be the disparity between the increased central activity and the decreased peripheral motor responses, which are being inhibited in breath-holding. In the experiments in which you breathed 7 per cent carbon dioxide with and without added external loads, did you reach a higher level of carbon dioxide at the break-point when you were breathing without the load, Dr Widdicombe?

*Widdicombe:* No. The $P_{CO_2}$ was similar at the break-point when I was breathing carbon dioxide against resistance and after a corresponding interval when I was rebreathing carbon dioxide without the resistance. But because I could only continue to breathe for a much shorter time in the presence of the resistance, the $P_{CO_2}$ at the break-point was less with than without the resistance.

*Cohen:* The perception of what happens peripherally must be an important element in the computation of the respiratory behaviour needed to restore normocapnia.

*Dejours:* We have talked a great deal about sensations arising from the chest but less about sensations arising elsewhere, and it is certainly an oversimplification to think that the feeling of breathlessness originates in one place. In 1952, Dr W. O. Fenn and I held our breaths after a single breath of 15 per cent carbon dioxide (Fenn and Dejours, 1954). There were no abnormal sensations for about ten seconds and then, like a sudden explosion, we felt awful. This feeling has nothing to do with receptors in the lung or chest wall but is probably due to a direct effect on the chemoreceptors.

*Campbell:* I suggest that this feeling may be an indirect effect of the greatly increased drive to breathe to which the respiratory muscles respond involuntarily, within a fraction of a second.

*Widdicombe:* This may be analogous to the immediate relief by the inhalation of a single breath of oxygen of the unpleasant dyspnoea occurring during or after exercise. This relief occurs within a few seconds; I do not know if it occurs more quickly than the associated inhibition of the respiratory muscles.

*Plum:* Is this relief total or just an improvement?

*Guz:* The relief is total; it was well described by Wright and Branscombe (1954).

*Widdicombe:* The distress of breath-holding must be determined by many factors, just as is the control of breathing.

*Dornhorst:* Muscle fatigue is one of these factors. Part of the unbearableness of breath-holding may be due to one's knowledge that one is losing in the fight to achieve a steady state. But the sensation after rebreathing carbon dioxide is presumably due to its stimulation of chemoreceptors.

*Paintal:* The injection of lobeline into the left ventricle and the pulmonary artery produces two different sensations (Stern, Bruderman and Braun, 1966).

*Cotes:* Even in multifactorial processes it is worth investigating single factors, as Dr Noble did when he tried to isolate his four standard respiratory sensations. When a conscious human subject rebreathes carbon dioxide while his vagi are blocked, ventilation is decreased and there is no discomfort. Thus the subject has adopted a new pattern of breathing which is appropriate for the circumstances. When an external resistance is added, the relationship of ventilatory response to effort of breathing is disturbed so the subject experiences discomfort. I suggest that, during vagal block, the level of responsiveness of the whole respiratory system may be reduced. Thus differences in sensation when breathing carbon dioxide, during breath-holding and so on may be apparent rather than real: the responses may all be of similar type. If this is so then our discussion about the nature of sensation arising from the diaphragm should be re-evaluated.

*Widdicombe:* I doubt the validity of this hypothesis. My own sensations when I breathe carbon dioxide, or breath-hold with and without vagal block, do seem qualitatively different. When my vagi are intact I experience a progressive increase in unpleasant sensation, starting quite early and becoming intolerable far sooner than when my vagi are blocked.

*Noble:* The crucial observation, on which I based my suggestion that the sensations during breath-holding and breathing carbon dioxide are separate, is the difference between the effect of phrenic block on the two sensations.

*Cross:* Diaphragmatic sensation, as distinct from sensation caused by high levels of $P_{CO_2}$, undoubtedly exists. Stimulation of the diaphragm with a phrenic-nerve stimulator gives rise to clear-cut unpleasant tugging sensations low down inside the chest. I know of no other way of producing such sensations. The diaphragm (on one side only of course) can be contracted far more strongly by this method than by voluntary efforts.

*Dornhorst:* The central tendon will be pulled across, a highly unnatural occurrence.

*Cross:* I agree.

*Widdicombe:* This technique will stimulate the phrenic afferents, both by diaphragmatic contraction and by electrical stimulation of the fibres in the phrenic nerves on their way to the spinal cord.

*Cotes:* The sensory innervation of the diaphragm seems to be closely related to sensation during breath-holding and mediated mainly through the phrenic but also through the intercostal nerves. What are the relative contributions of these two sets of nerves to diaphragmatic innervation, and are these contributions changed by cord transection? A related question is this: how constant is the relationship between diaphragmatic contractions occurring during breath-holding and the unpleasant sensation of the breath-hold? Has any dissociation been observed that is due, for example, to any one group of fibres in the phrenic nerve being particularly sensitive to, or recovering especially rapidly after, local anaesthesia?

*Noble:* I would like to know in this context if fibres from the tendon receptors in the diaphragm travel in the intercostal nerves?

*von Euler:* No. The intercostal nerves do not contribute significantly to the innervation of the diaphragm, although phrenic contractions inevitably pull on the ribs and give rise to afferent impulses from the intercostal receptors. Spinal anaesthesia in the thoracic region does not alter dyspnoeic sensation (Noble *et al.*, this volume, p. 236) which suggests that the most significant contributions to the sensation of breathlessness come via the phrenic nerve. The evidence suggests that afferent traffic involved in this type of dyspnoea is not likely to be found among group IA or IB fibres—both groups are rather small (Corda, Euler von and Lennerstrand, 1965; Yaşargil, 1962)—but may be present in group III fibres, the thin muscle afferents. I see no contradiction in this.

*Fillenz:* Are there many group III fibres in the phrenic nerve?

*von Euler:* Yes. There do not seem to be fewer group III fibres in the phrenic nerve than in most other nerves to limb muscle (Landau, Akert and Roberts, 1962).

*Campbell:* It would be most valuable if we knew definitively whether

10*

sensory information from the chest arises in diaphragmatic or intercostal receptors.

*Cohen:* There is evidence that part of the sensation is mediated by vagal afferents, and also that diaphragmatic contractions occur during the breath-hold (Noble, p. 248, this volume). When the phrenic nerve is blocked, the efferent discharge causing these contractions is stopped and therefore the vagal afferent input is also changed. Could not the effect of phrenic block on breath-holding be due to this change in afferent input?

*Guz:* The experiments with curarization are highly significant (Campbell *et al.*, 1967) in this context. The problem is whether one feels the respiratory drive itself or its effect on the inspiratory musculature.

*Godfrey:* I agree. In some experiments in curarized human subjects which I did with Professor Campbell (unpublished observations), pressure changes in the airways did not occur because there were no diaphragmatic contractions and, therefore, no phrenic discharge. Or, to put it the other way round, when the diaphragm contracts and the glottis is closed, pressure fluctuations occurring in the airways may stimulate vagal as well as phrenic afferents.

*Campbell:* It is difficult to believe that afferent stimulation of intrapulmonary receptors can occur unless transpulmonary conditions are altered.

*Godfrey:* The stimuli may arise from extrapulmonary receptors in the upper airways, which are deformed by these pressure fluctuations.

*von Euler:* The "vagal drive" is supposed to act reflexly by causing increased inspiratory activity in the diaphragm. A similar increase in diaphragmatic contraction can be produced by other reflexes and by carbon dioxide. I suggest that these two causes of increased activity in the diaphragm cannot be differentiated from each other.

*Guz:* These two groups of drive have been clearly differentiated in some of our experiments with pneumothoraces (Noble *et al.*, this volume, p. 240, Table II). Arterial $P_{CO_2}$ is low and hyperoxia is ensured by breathing 100 per cent oxygen. The chemical drive to breath is thus at a minimum, but the breath-holding time is reduced and the sensation exaggerated with the lung deflated compared with the lung inflated. These patients may reach the break-point with $Pa_{CO_2}$ below 40 mmHg and without any hypoxia.

*Widdicombe:* This is unlikely to be due to any reflex mediated through the slowly adapting pulmonary stretch receptors. You have shown (Guz *et al.*, 1966), in healthy subjects when all discharge from the stretch receptors is blocked, that the pattern of breathing does not change and unpleasant respiratory sensation is alleviated rather than increased. The pulmonary stretch receptors can hardly be expected to cause the changes in sensation you have just described when discharge from them has been decreased but not completely blocked because of deflation of the lung. Some other type of receptor must be invoked.

*Noble:* Is there a difference between no discharge at all and a discharge of low frequency?

*Widdicombe:* Obviously, but a qualitative reversal of central nervous response seems implausible when decreased discharge is compared with abolition of discharge.

*von Euler:* Since it is difficult to conceive that a "vagal drive" can have a more specific reflex effect on the diaphragm than any other influence that increases its inspiratory activity, I see no other way of bringing together the data from vagal block, spinal anaesthesia and curarization experiments than by assuming that the type of dyspnoeic sensation under discussion must depend on a specific central convergence of some vagal and some phrenic afferents. (If afferent impulse traffic along one or other of these two sets of fibres is in some way diminished or abolished, dyspnoea does not seem to occur.) Such a hypothesis does not appear unlikely from a neurophysiological point of view and is accessible to experimental testing.

*Aitken:* It should be acknowledged that healthy people are reluctant to reveal feelings, perhaps from fear of an unwelcome response should they admit to alterations in their psychic state. It cannot be assumed that cooperation is only dependent on motivation, particularly at the extremes of discomfort experienced during breath-holding or exercising to the limit, when the additional hazard of cerebral dysfunction due to changes in $Pco_2$ or $Po_2$ may be present. In my opinion such alterations in psychic state were to be expected in many of the experiments on breathing described in the literature and in this volume and could account for the disparity in some of the results.

*Guz:* How can we help our patients to tell us what they feel?

*Wood:* As part of a project to evaluate methods of communicating symptoms, we have been using analogue rating scales to find out which symptoms are most closely associated with exposure to cotton fibres. Facilities were provided by Dr M. McDermott at the Pneumoconiosis Research Unit, Glamorgan. Our results (unpublished) suggest that specific symptoms, such as difficulty in breathing, and coughing and tightness in the chest, are closely related to changes in internal airways resistance. On the other hand, less specific symptoms, such as irritability and feeling unwell, are more closely associated with the dramatic rise in body temperature that occurs about five hours after inhalation of the dust. This pyrexial condition is sometimes called "mill fever".

*Dornhorst:* We have left many questions unanswered, but what has emerged from this part of our discussion is that we agree that a complex interaction exists between ventilatory drive, traffic up the vagus and events at the diaphragm, both normally and in the different states of respiratory distress. We shall no doubt return to these interactions in our discussion of clinical problems.

## REFERENCES

CAMPBELL, E. J. M., FREEDMAN, S., CLARK, T. J. H., ROBSON, J. G., and NORMAN, J. (1967). *Clin. Sci.*, **32**, 425–432.
CORDA, M., EULER, C. VON, and LENNERSTRAND, G. (1965). *J. Physiol., Lond.* **178**, 161–177.
FENN, W. O., and DEJOURS, P. (1954). *J. appl. Physiol.*, **7**, 313–319.
GOLD, W. M., and NADEL, J. A. (1966). In *Breathlessness*, p. 223, ed. HOWELL, J. B. L., and CAMPBELL, E. J. M. Oxford: Blackwell.
GUZ, A., NOBLE, M. I. M., WIDDICOMBE, J. G., TRENCHARD, D., MUSHIN, W. W., and MAKEY, A. R. (1966). *Clin. Sci.*, **30**, 161–170.
KUMAGAI, H., SAKAI, F., SAKUMA, A., and HUKUHARA, T. (1966). *Prog. Brain Res.*, **21**, 98–111.
LANDAU, B. R., AKERT, K., and ROBERTS, T. S. (1962). *J. comp. Neurol.*, **119**, 1–10.
STERN, S., BRUDERMAN, I., and BRAUN, K. (1966). *Am. Heart J.*, **71**, 651–655.
WIDDICOMBE, J. G. (1961). *J. Physiol., Lond.*, **159**, 436–450.
WRIGHT, G. W., and BRANSCOMBE, B. V. (1954). *Trans. Am. clin. clim. Ass.*, **66**, 116–125.
YAŞARGIL, G. M. (1962). *Helv. physiol. pharmac. Acta*, **20**, 39–58.

# RESPIRATORY SENSATION IN PULMONARY DISEASE

## J. B. L. HOWELL*

*Department of Medicine, University of Manchester*

PATIENTS with pulmonary disease experience a number of sensations which they relate to breathing, or to a disturbance of breathing. They tend to describe all of them as breathlessness, probably because of the way in which the inquiry is made by their doctors. But when asked to describe in detail what they feel, two things become apparent: first, patients experience great difficulty in describing their sensations and, second, there is more than one sensation which may be experienced.

There are no absolute qualities to a sensation that we can describe in words; we describe them by referring to known situations in which similar sensations have been experienced—for example, stabbing pain—or alternatively by emphasizing a prominent accompaniment—for example, the throbbing pain of a migraine headache. However, in considering the sensation of breathlessness, there is only one circumstance in which everyone has experienced breathlessness and that is on appropriately severe exertion. We can therefore distinguish with some confidence between respiratory sensations which resemble, and those which do not resemble, exertional breathlessness. Whether exertional breathlessness is to be regarded as abnormal or not depends upon the circumstances in which it occurs, that is, whether the severity of the sensation is appropriate to the severity of the exertion. Any other type of respiratory sensation is, therefore, abnormal regardless of the circumstances.

Respiratory sensations, either abnormal or normal, but occurring inappropriately, usually arise when disease causes a disturbance of pulmonary function. These disorders may be classified into two types: restrictive disorders of the lungs, such as may be present, for example, with pulmonary fibrosis or infiltrations, and obstructive lung disorders, such as the chronic airways obstruction which often occurs in association with chronic bronchitis or the intermittent airways obstruction associated with allergic disorders of the bronchial tree (asthma).

* Present address: Department of Medicine, University of Southampton.

Using the relatively crude techniques of clinical interrogation, the sensation of breathlessness on exertion in either type of disorder may be indistinguishable from the exertional breathlessness of health, or that occurring with other disorders especially those associated with disturbances of the circulation. However, the sensation may possess additional features, such as difficulty with breathing, gasping or exhaustion, which suggest that some extra factors are operating, such as, for example, coexisting hindrance to breathing or hypoxaemia. In my experience, the extent to which hypoxaemia may modify respiratory sensation is readily demonstrated by comparing the experience of increased ventilation induced by rebreathing oxygen from a bag with that induced by rebreathing air; the latter is a most unpleasant experience compared with the former.

The symptom of exertional breathlessness, simple or complicated, merely indicates that one or more of a variety of abnormalities may be present: it does not indicate their nature. By contrast, there is one respiratory sensation which, in my experience, does indicate a particular type of disorder. The sensation is usually described as a sensation of tightness and is very suggestive of the presence of airway disease.

## THE SENSATION OF TIGHTNESS AND AIRWAY DISEASE

Most patients with airways obstruction experience a feeling of tightness which is present on rising in the morning. Sometimes it is not present on waking but occurs promptly when the subject sits up. It is usually associated with shortness of breath on exertion. In patients with chronic bronchitis without evidence of allergic disease the sensation usually passes off in about half an hour, expecially after coughing up the night's accumulation of sputum; the tightness does not recur until the next morning, unless the subjects are exposed to inhaled irritants, and then the tightness may again be experienced in association with cough and breathlessness. This last symptom of "bronchial irritability" seems to be correlated with bronchial hyperreactivity to inhaled histamine and other irritants (de Vries et al., 1967).

A similar tightness on waking occurs in patients with allergic disorders of the bronchial tree. However, it may last longer and tends to recur for no apparent reason during the day, and especially at night, characteristically waking the patient between 2 and 4 a.m.

The mechanism for the production of this tightness is not established. During studies of the effects of added elastic loads on the ventilatory response of patients with airways obstruction (Howell, 1966), many patients commented that the sensation of breathing against the elastic load was similar to the feeling of tightness which they experienced in the morning, and which disappeared after they had coughed and produced sputum. This suggests that morning tightness in these patients may be due to accumulated sputum and to inactivity during the night altering the elastic properties of the lungs, perhaps by causing small areas of atelectasis which are gradually re-opened by the activity and bronchial toilet of the morning's productive coughing. However, some patients with allergic disease of the airways commented that their sensation of morning tightness and recurring tightness during the day was different from that induced by the elastic loads, suggesting that there are at least two types of sensation of tightness.

Further light was shed on this symptom during a study of pulmonary function in cotton workers with byssinosis, carried out in conjunction with A. A. E. Massoud, T. B. Stretton and C. B. McKerrow (Massoud, 1964). Byssinosis is a condition which occurs in cotton workers after many years of exposure to the dust of the cotton plant. It is characterized by the development of a sensation of tightness in the chest, beginning some hours after entering the cotton mill; it is worse on the first day of the working week and may not occur at all on other days. It has therefore become known as "Monday tightness". The sensation of Monday tightness has been correlated with the development of bronchospasm (McKerrow *et al.*, 1958). However, we observed many patients with this symptom in whom pulmonary function tests were the same at the end of the day as they had been in the morning, before the patients entered the mill. These tests included spirometry, estimations of lung volume, airways resistance and lung compliance, and the single-breath oxygen test of intrapulmonary distribution and $Pco_2$. These results suggested that the tightness was not secondary to mechanical changes in the lungs, and that nervous impulses arising in the bronchi might be responsible for the sensation. Further evidence that the sensation was not due to changes causing increased loading of the respiratory muscles was obtained when we studied the sensations induced by the addition of external elastic loads to these same subjects (J. B. L. Howell and W. R. Lee, unpublished results). None of the patients with pure byssinosis (that is, without associated chronic bronchitis) was able to identify his Monday tightness with the sensation induced by the added elastic load. By contrast, those patients who had chronic bronchitis and airways obstruction in addition to symptoms of byssinosis identified their sensation of tightness with that of the elastic load.

The fact that sensations may arise from stimulation of the bronchial tree is well known from the everyday experience of the effects of inhaled irritants, cold air, tracheitis and so on. Widdicombe (1964) has reviewed the receptors and afferent pathways involved in the objective effects of such irritants.

While it is possible that the afferent pathway involving respiratory sensation might be in the sympathetic nervous system, it seems much more likely that the vagus nerve is involved, for the following reasons:

(1) *Spinal cord transection*

Some years ago I had the opportunity to study a patient who had received a stab wound which almost completely transected the spinal cord at the level of the third cervical segment (C3). There was total sensory loss below C3 and he was breathing largely by using his accessory muscles although a few fibres of the diaphragm might also have been contracting. When this patient was given an added threshold expiratory load he was able to detect that load, because he experienced a sensation of tightness in the chest. Because of the possible incompleteness of the transection, the sensation may have been mediated via the vagi or through afferent fibres in the phrenic nerves.

More recently, Newsom Davis, Semple and Spencer (1968) reported their studies on a man with a similar lesion, but one that had caused complete transection at the level of C3 and complete denervation below this level. These three authors noted that when suction was applied to the trachea the subject experienced a sensation of tightness in the chest. The only nervous communication between the thorax and the central nervous system was via the vagi, so the sensation of tightness could only have been mediated via this nerve.

(2) *Vagal block*

In a study of the effect of vagal blockade on the bronchoconstrictor response to histamine in one asthmatic subject, Petit (1969, personal communication) observed that while the objective changes still occurred the sensation of tightness was modified after vagal block. This is convincing evidence that the sensation of tightness is not a single sensation, and that one of its components can arise from stimulation of receptors in the bronchial tree and be conveyed to the central nervous system by the vagi. The other component is presumably caused by changes in pulmonary mechanics and can be detected by somatic mechanisms.

SUMMARY

A variety of sensations related to breathing may arise in different forms of pulmonary disease. These sensations are related to increased ventilation, increased hindrance to breathing, and hypoxaemia and seem to be related to the act of breathing itself and not to any known specific receptor. By contrast, in some patients with airways obstruction, the sensation of tightness appears to be a simpler type of sensation involving a specific receptor and a single afferent pathway. Although at present little additional information of clinical significance can be elicited from a detailed analysis of the sensation of exertional breathlessness, the presence of the sensation of tightness, especially in the morning, is very suggestive of airways obstruction, and the tendency for this sensation to recur during the day and at night suggests that there is an allergic component to the bronchial disease that is present.

## REFERENCES

HOWELL, J. B. L. (1966). In *Breathlessness*, pp. 55–64, ed. Howell, J. B. L., and Campbell, E. J. M. Oxford: Blackwell.

McKERROW, C. B., ROACH, S. A., GILSON, J. C., and SCHILLING, R. S. F. (1958). *Br. J. ind. Med.*, **15**, 75.

MASSOUD, A. A. E. (1964). *Pulmonary Function in Workers in the Cotton Spinning Industry.* Ph.D. thesis, University of Manchester, Faculty of Medicine.

NEWSOM DAVIS, J., SEMPLE, S. J. G., and SPENCER, G. T. (1968). Communication to the Medical Research Society, London. Unpublished.

VRIES, K. DE, BOOIJ-NOORD, H., GOEI, J. T., GROBLER, N. J., and ORIE, N. G. M. (1967). *Acta allerg.*, **22**, suppl. 8, 131–137.

WIDDICOMBE, J. G. (1964). In *Handbook of Physiology*, sect. III, vol. 1, pp. 585–630, ed. Fenn, W. O., and Rahn, H. American Physiological Society. Baltimore: Williams and Wilkins.

## DISCUSSION

*Dornhorst:* How accurate were your measurements of airways resistance in the field work in the mill? Could you have obtained additional evidence if you had used a body plethysmograph?

*Howell:* Airways resistance was measured using the Clements multiple interruptor technique. Intra-oral pressure was recorded continuously during expiration from total lung capacity, the volume expired being continuously recorded as the rise in pressure in a large rigid container into which the subject breathed. This technique gave reproducible plots of airways resistance against changes in lung volume, and we would have detected changes in airways resistance of the order of 15–20 per cent if they had occurred. Body plethysmography would have been easier but not much more sensitive.

*Cotes:* Did you measure the concentration of respirable dust (that is, particles of diameter 1–7 μm), in the mill? When dust concentration is above about 1 mg (1 × 10$^8$ particles)/m$^3$ a rise in airways resistance occurs in many normal subjects (McDermott, M., personal communication).

*Howell:* The dust concentration was 5·8 mg/m$^3$. This level was high enough to produce bronchoconstriction and the sensation of tightness in the chest in patients with hyperirritable bronchi and chronic bronchitis associated with their byssinosis, but not in subjects with no bronchitic symptoms.

*Dornhorst:* Did the investigators complain of symptoms?

*Howell:* No; our laboratory was not in the card room but in an empty part of the mill.

*Zechmann:* What is known about the distribution of dust in the lung in relation to particle size? Marked local changes in resistance or compliance may occur (because of unequal distribution of the dusts) which might not be detectable by the usual measures of pulmonary mechanics.

*Howell:* We did not measure frequency-dependent compliance changes; in cooperation with Dr C. B. McKerrow we measured static lung compliance.

*Zechman:* I doubt if abnormalities in a few units could be detected by this technique. Many units in the parallel circuit are needed before changes in overall static lung compliance show up.

*Howell:* I agree. Unfortunately we did not measure arterial oxygen tensions either, as these might have revealed a distribution defect. The only evidence about this that we do have is that single-breath oxygen did not change in the patients in whom symptoms of byssinosis were not accompanied by any measured changes.

*Cotes:* Could your patients differentiate between breathlessness in the sense of panting and in the sense of an increase in effort being needed to satisfy the ventilatory requirements?

*Howell:* Sometimes they could, but their ability to communicate these differences depended on how articulate they were.

*Guz:* I agree with your differentiation of breathlessness into two sensations: (*a*) the equivalent (roughly) of exertional breathlessness and (*b*) a feeling of tightness associated with breathing against an expiratory load. The latter sensation could be detected by our patient who had a spinal cord transection at the third cervical (C3) segment. Was there a relationship between the sensation of tightness and tachypnoea at rest in your patients?

*Howell:* There was no gross tachypnoea but we did not study this relationship in detail.

*Guz:* Tachypnoea seems to be the one objective measurement that correlates with the sensation of breathlessness. Tachypnoea may be part of the respiratory drive or an attempt to relieve the sensation of dyspnoea by taking another breath as soon as possible.

*Flenley:* Respiratory sensation and hypoxia are certainly related, but in a very complicated manner. When I breathe carbon dioxide at different levels of $Pa_{O_2}$ (Flenley and Millar, 1967) I become particularly irritable when I am hypoxic with a high ventilatory drive due to carbon dioxide; my only other sensation is an appreciation of the need for greater respiratory effort. But patients in status asthmaticus can sometimes remain hypoxic with $Pa_{O_2}$ levels of 50 mmHg for up to five days following the acute attack (Rees, Millar and Donald, 1968; McFadden and Lyons, 1968) and at a time when they are clinically much better. Similarly, Tai and Read (1967) and others (Rees, Millar and Donald, 1967; Rees *et al.*, 1967; Palmer and Diament, 1967) have shown that improvement in the forced expiratory volume in the first second ($FEV_1$) after sympathomimetic drugs in the asthmatic, although usually associated with subjective relief of symptoms, may in fact be associated with a fall in $Pa_{O_2}$.

*Dornhorst:* The range of $Pa_{O_2}$ levels is surely too high to induce any abnormal sensations.

*Flenley:* Not at all. Rees, Millar and Donald (1968) described an asthmatic whose $Pa_{O_2}$ more than one week after recovery from status asthmaticus, was still only 40 mmHg.

*Dornhorst:* That must have been exceptional; the usual $Pa_{O_2}$ range would be from 55–65 mmHg.

*Flenley:* In three out of eight patients described by these authors the $Pa_{O_2}$ was between 42 and 52 mmHg, six to seven days after an acute attack of asthma. The overall effect of blood-gas tensions and cerebral blood flow is probably what matters in producing these abnormal sensations. In hypoxia, the oxygen tension of cerebral venous blood is higher under conditions of hypercapnia than of hypocapnia. The fractiousness of the asthmatic may have something to do with a poorly oxygenated cerebrum, resulting from the low oxygen and low carbon dioxide tensions.

*Godfrey:* Part of the origin of these sensations may lie in the shape of the chest. The over-inflation and distortion of the chest, and the abnormal use to which its muscles are put, may be an important source of sensation when breathing is driven by abnormal gas tensions.

*Dornhorst:* We have already noted that an external load—elastic or resistive—does not reproduce the mechanical pressure changes across the airways that are caused by intrinsic airways obstruction (or stiff lungs). Although one does more muscular work and the chest and the lungs are more distorted when one breathes through an external load, the airways are not stretched as they are with intrinsic resistance. The sensation of tightness may occur in response to hyperirritability of receptors in the bronchi. Can this sensation be distinguished from the sensations caused either by excessive strain due to stretched airways or by greater breathing work necessitated by an external load? We have described two different subjective effects when airways resistance is increased by the introduction of foreign materials into the bronchi: the inhalation of acetylcholine produces almost no symptoms whereas the inhaling of inert dust gives rise to discomfort (tightness) long before bronchoconstriction can be detected objectively and out of all proportion to its severity (unpublished personal observations). During acute bronchospasm, bronchial receptors (probably the irritant receptors) are undoubtedly being excessively stimulated, but does the resultant sensation differ according to whether these receptors are hypersensitive or normal? All these problems require further discussion.

*Howell:* My comment concerns respiratory sensation in response to increased mechanical loading at the mouth. I was convinced that this sensation really was different from sensations arising in other conditions of respiratory stress because many patients with byssinosis volunteered the information about it spontaneously.

*Dornhorst:* This does not answer my question about possible differences between the sensations associated with excessive stretching of normal airways and with increased excitability of the irritant bronchial receptors.

*Howell:* The patient I described with a high spinal cord transection, when his airways were distorted by adding expiratory loads, referred to his discomfort as a sensation of tightness, as did Dr Guz's patient with a similar transection.

*Dornhorst:* Would the irritant bronchial receptors be normal in these two patients?

*Howell:* Yes; it is unlikely that the bronchi would be hyperreactive unless the patients were bronchitic.

*Guz:* These patients lose sympathetic but retain parasympathetic tone. This autonomic imbalance gives rise to a high airways resistance. Zechman, O'Neill and Shannon (1967) first observed an increased airways resistance in patients with high spinal cord transections.

*Zechman:* The two quadriplegic patients we described (Zechman, O'Neill and Shannon, 1967) had elevated airways resistances even though they had no history of pulmonary disease. We associated this finding with the changes observed in respiratory mechanics: on inspiration the circumference of the upper chest decreases while that of the lower chest increases.

*Dornhorst:* I cannot accept this because adrenergic blockade has little effect on normal subjects, but only on asthmatics. There is no evidence for standing adrenergic inhibition, whether humoral or neural, of the bronchi (Sterling, 1968).

*Fillenz:* Cholinergic and noradrenergic nerve fibres supply the smooth muscle of the airway in the dog (unpublished data), whereas the rat and guinea-pig have only cholinergic innervation of this musculature (White, 1968). And there may be other species differences in airway innervation.

*Dornhorst:* Sterling (1968) measured airways resistance by whole-body plethysmography and found no changes in normal subjects after the injection of intravenous propranolol, whereas asthmatic subjects, even when asymptomatic, showed a substantial increase in airways resistance after propranolol injection. The inference from this study is that adrenergic activity is increasing conductance in asthmatics but not in normal subjects. Sterling also showed that the absence of this response in normal subjects is not due to absent bronchoconstrictor tone, because there is increased conductance when either isoprenaline or atropine aerosol is given to normal subjects. In other words, there is no evidence of adrenergic influence on the bronchi in the normal state. But there is evidence for such adrenergic influence in patients under conditions in which blood catecholamines would be expected to be normal, that is, in the asthmatic patient in remission. Catecholamines have not been measured in asthmatics in remission but nevertheless these data convince me that the bronchi in man do have some adrenergic innervation.

## REFERENCES

FLENLEY, D. C., and MILLAR, J. S. (1967). *Clin. Sci.*, **33**, 319–334.
McFADDEN, E. R., and LYONS, H. A. (1968). *New Engl. J. Med.*, **278**, 1027–1032.
PALMER, K. N. V., and DIAMENT, M. L. (1967). *Lancet*, **2**, 1232–1233.
REES, H. A., BORTHWICK, R. C., MILLAR, J. S., and DONALD, K. W. (1967). *Lancet*, **2**, 1167–1169.
REES, H. A., MILLAR, J. S., and DONALD, K. W. (1967). *Lancet*, **2**, 1164–1166.
REES, H. A., MILLAR, J. S., and DONALD, K. W. (1968). *Q. Jl Med.*, **37**, 541–561.
STERLING, G. (1968). Doctoral thesis, University of Cambridge, Faculty of Medicine.
TAI, E., and READ, J. (1967). *Thorax*, **22**, 543–549.
WHITE, A. M. S. (1968). Doctoral thesis, University of Oxford, Faculty of Physiology.
ZECHMAN, F. W., JR., O'NEILL, R., and SHANNON, R. (1967). *Physiologist, Wash.*, **10**, 356.

# BREATHING FREQUENCY AND TIDAL VOLUME: RELATIONSHIP TO BREATHLESSNESS

J. E. Cotes, G. R. Johnson and Ann McDonald

*Pneumoconiosis Research Unit of the Medical Research Council, Llandough Hospital, Penarth, Glamorganshire*

In this paper we suggest a possible physiological basis for second-wind, examine the mechanism of shallow breathing in patients with proliferative disease of the lung parenchyma and suggest that tachypnoea, whilst not synonymous with breathlessness, may nonetheless give rise to unexpected symptoms.

We are accustomed to think of breathlessness in terms of the relationship of exercise ventilation to maximum breathing capacity (dyspnoeic index) and are aware that a notable increase in frequency of breathing occurs at or near the breaking point of exercise. Analysis of the latter phenomenon has been simplified by the finding of a linear relationship between exercise ventilation and tidal volume ($\dot{V}e/Vt$ relationship: Hey *et al.*, 1966)* up to a limiting volume which in normal subjects is about 50 per cent of vital capacity (Åstrand, 1960). Thus, for exercise which is limited by breathlessness the breaking point is heralded by an increase in frequency at a tidal volume which is already maximal. The maximal frequency in healthy young adults is of the order of 50/min, but it is less in patients in whom the work of ventilating the lung is increased; recent evidence is reviewed by Otis and Guyatt (1968). The relevance for breathlessness of the relationship, during sub-maximal exercise, of respiratory variables to the work of breathing and transpulmonary pressure is reviewed by Otis (1964). Less attention has so far been paid to indices which may be derived from the relationship of ventilation minute volume to tidal volume. These have the advantage of being readily obtained from a simple exercise test and, compared with lung mechanics, may be more appropriate for study of control mechanisms.

* See also p. 41.

*Inflection of Ve/Vt relationship*

During progressive exercise, the transition from an increase in ventilation being determined mainly by tidal volume to this increase being determined mainly by frequency is usually well defined (Fig. 1). Thus, we sought the change-over point in 18 young adult male cyclists of mean age 22 years, on whom we obtained the data for another purpose, and were able to identify this point in 16 of them. For these subjects the critical ventilation

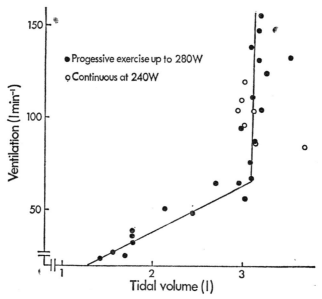

FIG. 1. Relationship of ventilation to tidal volume in a normal subject (R.S.) during exercise on a cycle ergometer. W: watt.

was on average 78 l min⁻¹, which was almost exactly half the average maximal ventilation of 155 l min⁻¹. We might expect some sensation at this point, particularly where the change-over is abrupt, and it may thus be more than coincidence that its location is where some subjects acquire second-wind; this, in our experience at least, is associated with an increase in frequency of breathing. The abruptness of the change-over presumably reflects the strength of the drive to respiration, the sensitivity of the control mechanisms and the extent to which the subject voluntarily anticipates the need for an increase in frequency of breathing; in addition, when the drive to respiration is intense some degree of overshoot of tidal volume may be expected due to temporary overriding of the cut-off mechanism. We examined this possibility in the cyclists, using data obtained during continuous

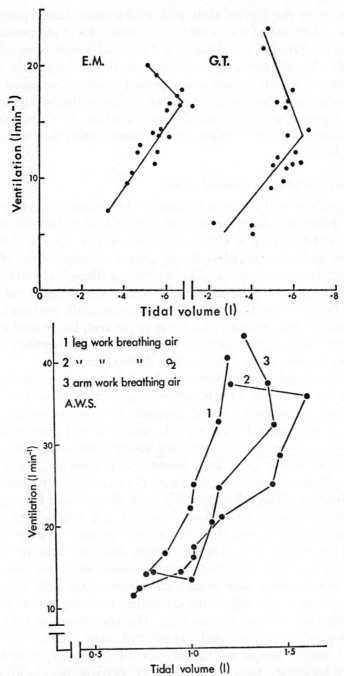

FIG. 2 (a), (b). Relationship of ventilation to tidal volume during exercise to the point of breathlessness in three patients with chronic lung disease.

exercise at 80 per cent of their peak performance during progressive exercise. Eight out of the 18 subjects exhibited the phenomenon. The overshoot was on average maximal in the second minute of exercise and was fully corrected by the tenth minute or by the breaking-point, whichever occurred sooner. Pronounced overshoot was also observed on at least some occasions in three out of 18 patients with lung disease (Fig. 2) and a minor degree of overshoot was observed in others. In all these subjects breathlessness was related to maximal frequency rather than to maximal tidal volume.

*Hindrance to respiration in normal subjects*

The maximal tidal volume is presumably determined by the response to afferent information from the lung and chest wall and we have investigated the $\dot{V}e/Vt$ relationship in circumstances when these may be abnormal. First, we studied on ourselves during progressive exercise the effect of breathing through an orifice of diameter 8 mm and length 25 mm and have reanalysed from this point of view the data of Gee, Vassallo and Gregg (1968). For both series the degree of obstruction was sufficient to reduce the maximum breathing capacity by about 30 per cent, but in neither series was there any change in the relationship of breathing frequency to tidal volume or to the maximal tidal volume during exercise.

We next considered the effect of an elastic hindrance to inspiration. For this purpose we studied, in eight subjects, the effect on the $\dot{V}e/Vt$ relationship of inspiration from a closed container; the effective volume of the container, as calculated from the relationship of oral pressure to tidal volume, was on average 37 l. Breathing from it led to a conscious need for increased inspiratory effort even during rest; in these circumstances the peak oral pressures were in the range 6–17 $cmH_2O$. The inspiratory vital capacities obtained by inspiration from the container following full expiration were on average reduced by 29 per cent. During the study the container was recompressed to atmospheric pressure between breaths. The subjects exercised a total of four or eight times on a cycle ergometer at work rates which were increased over a 15-minute period from zero to 120 watts; measurements were made each minute, either with the subject inspiring from air throughout the experiment or during periods of eight consecutive breaths from the container. The latter procedure reduced the exercise ventilation on average by 13 per cent (range $-29$ to$+8$ per cent) but the minute volume returned to normal during longer periods of hindered breathing. The effect upon the $\dot{V}e/Vt$ relationship varied materially between subjects. In one subject there was no change either initially

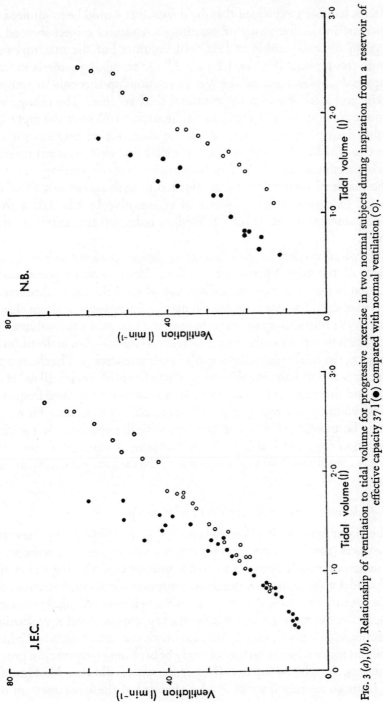

FIG. 3 (a), (b). Relationship of ventilation to tidal volume for progressive exercise in two normal subjects during inspiration from a reservoir of effective capacity 37 l (●) compared with normal ventilation (○).

or after it had been explained that the discomfort would be minimized by an increase in the frequency of breathing. A second subject showed no change in the relationship at low tidal volumes but the maximal tidal volume was reduced (Fig. 3a, J.E.C.). All the remaining subjects showed an upward displacement of the $\dot{V}e/Vt$ relationship throughout rest and exercise and a reduction in the maximal tidal volume. The change was reproducible and did not show any systematic trend over the eight test breaths. However, the magnitude of the effect varied between subjects from one which, whilst significant in the statistical sense, was not material to an approximate doubling of the frequency and corresponding reduction in the maximal tidal volume (Fig. 3b, N.B.). In some but not all of the subjects, extension of the number of consecutive breaths taken from the container had the effect of further reducing the maximal tidal volume.

We shall now consider the effect upon exercise performance in normal subjects of the two types of obstruction. Both cause dyspnoea and a reduction in maximal exercise ability; but whereas the external resistance exerts its effect through a reduction in maximal frequency without change in the $\dot{V}e/Vt$ relationship or, in most case, the maximal tidal volume, the elastic hindrance reduces the maximal tidal volume and also, in the majority of subjects, the tidal volume during sub-maximal exercise. The changes are in the direction of reducing the energy cost of ventilation (cf. Bland et al., 1967), and those that come into effect at or near to the maximal frequency or tidal volume may reasonably be "explained" on this basis. However, it may be questioned whether the mechanical hypothesis is sufficient explanation for a marked increase in breathing frequency at rest; this aspect is considered below after review of the data for patients with lung disease.

*Use of tidal volume to describe the $\dot{V}e/Vt$ relationship*

The linear part of the $\dot{V}e/Vt$ relationship is described by Hey and co-workers (1966) in terms of the parameters $m$ (regression coefficient of ventilation on tidal volume) and $c$ (the intercept of the regression line on the tidal volume axis) of the linear regression equation, but where the data are scanty or exhibit scatter the description is not particularly accurate. In these circumstances the tidal volume at an appropriate level of ventilation, for example 30 l min$^{-1}$, may be obtained with greater certainty. We have found this index of practical use for study of breathing frequency in groups of subjects. Its relationship to $m$ (Hey et al., 1966) is illustrated in Fig. 4 for data from 40 untrained subjects who attended at the laboratory on one occasion for assessment of suspected occupational lung disease. The relationship is described by the equation:

$$m = 58/Vt,30 - 12\cdot5 \quad \text{S.D. } 5\cdot5 \ (r = 0\cdot92),$$

where Vt,30 is tidal volume at a ventilation of 30 l min$^{-1}$, S.D. = standard deviation and $r$ = the correlation coefficient.

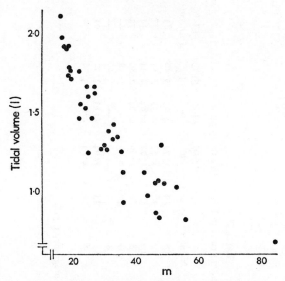

FIG. 4. Relationship of tidal volume at ventilation 30 l min$^{-1}$ (Vt,30) to the regression coefficient of ventilation on tidal volume ($m$). The data were obtained during exercise on men referred for assessment of suspected occupational lung disease.

*Vt,30 in groups of subjects*

In healthy adults we find the tidal volume at a ventilation of 30 l min$^{-1}$ (Vt,30) to be independent of age and not materially different between arm and leg work. Some average values for different groups of subjects are listed in Table I. This indicates what may be expected in different circumstances but any conclusions drawn from the data should be regarded as tentative until a more formal analysis has been carried out. The findings for patients with obstruction to the lung airways are at first sight contradictory; whereas the tidal volume is apparently reduced in the patients with irreversible disease, tidal volume for the asthmatics in remission is the same as for control subjects. The latter observation is supported by Aitken, Zealley and Rosenthal (1970), for similar subjects studied at rest, and our own unpublished data for normal subjects during exercise following inhalation of cotton dust. However, tachypnoea is a feature of status

TABLE I

MEAN DATA FOR TIDAL VOLUME AT VENTILATION 30 l min$^{-1}$ (Vt,30) IN GROUPS OF SUBJECTS

| Subjects | Sex | Number | Age (years) | Height (m) | FEV$_1$ (l) | FVC (l) | FEV% (per cent) | Vt,30 (range) (l) |
|---|---|---|---|---|---|---|---|---|
| Amateur racing cyclists | M | 18 | 22 | 1·74 | 4·63 | 5·56 | 83 | 1·52 (1·19–2·13) |
| Random sample | F | 79 | 48 | 1·59 | 2·43 | 3·14 | 77 | 1·34 (0·80–1·90) |
| Chronic non-specific lung disease | M | 10 | 56 | 1·72 | 0·84 | 2·44 | 34 | 1·22 (0·94–1·60) |
| Pulmonary fibrosis | M | 8 | 60 | 1·66 | 2·04 | 2·89 | 72 | 1·13 (0·95–1·42) |
| Pulmonary fibrosis (West and Alexander, 1959) | M & F | 9 | 47 | — | — | — | — | 0·72* (0·54–1·07) |
| Pregnancy (Guzman, Caplan and Becklake, 1969) | F | 8 | — | — | — | 1·58 | — | 1·20† (0·70–2·27) |
| Asthma in remission | F | 15 | 35 | 1·64 | 2·13 | 3·32 | 61 | 1·33 (0·88–1·80) |
| Obesity | M & F | 8 | 36 | 1·64 | 2·92 | 3·72 | 79 | 1·29 (0·93–1·77) |

* Control subjects 1·56 l.
† At ventilation 25 l min$^{-1}$, mean after pregnancy 1·51 l.

asthmaticus. The difference in response may reflect the degree of airways obstruction at the time of observation. To examine this possibility we have related the maximal tidal volume to the forced expiratory volume in the first second ($FEV_1$) in 15 patients with different types of irreversible lung disease. For these subjects the $FEV_1$ expressed as a percentage of the forced vital capacity varied between 23 and 61 per cent. However, for all but one of the subjects (range of FEV% : 31–61%) the maximal tidal volume was approximately 50 per cent of vital capacity, that is, the same proportion as in the normal subjects, and was independent of the degree of airways obstruction. Only in the patient with the very low FEV% was the maximal tidal volume reduced. Thus, airways obstruction, except when it is very marked, is not apparently a cause of tachypnoea during exercise. Of possibly greater interest in the present context is the low tidal volume of 0·7 l and the increase in frequency observed by West and Alexander (1959) in patients with "pulmonary fibrosis". These patients had an average vital capacity of only 1·5 l, so if we are right that the maximal tidal volume does not exceed half the vital capacity then the observed value is what would be expected on a mechanical basis. Persistent mild tachypnoea is also apparent in patients with radiological and physiological features of interstitial fibrosis seen in our Unit; however, these patients were less disabled than the patients in this study. In both series the disease was of long-standing and, in our series at least, the $\dot{V}e/Vt$ relationship was reproducible.

*Proliferative disease of the lung parenchyma*

In contrast to the stable relationship in patients with pulmonary fibrosis, we have observed considerable fluctuations in frequency with, at times, pronounced tachypnoea out of proportion to the change in vital capacity in patients with clinically mild disease of the lung parenchyma due to farmers' lung (Cotes, 1968) and inhalation of beryllium oxide. The fluctuations in frequency reflect changes in dosage of steroid drugs (Fig. 5) and are thus a feature of the proliferative rather than of the fibrotic stage of this group of diseases. The fluctuations are accompanied by changes in the same direction in vital capacity and transfer factor (Fig. 6), and, in subject E.M.M., in static lung compliance. This patient experienced subjective feelings of personal inadequacy but, despite at times having an increased ventilation during exercise, at no time did he experience breathlessness. Another subject, D.P.T., developed tachypnoea without hyperventilation or breathlessness, but both these features developed subsequently (Fig. 6) and may thus have been causally related.

We have shown above that tachypnoea without increase in exercise ventilation occurs in some healthy subjects during breathing against an elastic load. For resting subjects a similar observation had been made by Pope, Holloway and Campbell (1968) whilst Freedman (1969) has shown that tachypnoea is invariable when the hindrance to respiration is increased. However, in all these situations the work of ventilating the lung was

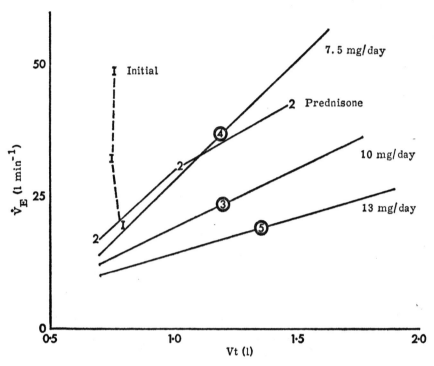

FIG. 5. Relationship of exercise ventilation to tidal volume in E.M.M., a patient with beryllium disease. The measurements were made on first assessment, after the start of steroid therapy and subsequently at approximately yearly intervals.

increased to a material extent. Of greater interest in the present context is the occurrence of tachypnoea in subjects with a relatively normal ventilatory capacity, as occurred with patient E.M.M. in whom the vital capacity never fell below 5 l. In this instance the tachypnoea is likely to be of reflex origin and this may also be true for those of our normal subjects in whom there is a marked increase in breathing frequency at rest. However, the mechanism in the two cases may be different since in the patients there is an increase in transpulmonary pressure which has not been demonstrated for normal subjects breathing from a reservoir.

The hypothesis that the tachypnoea we have observed in patients with beryllium disease is of reflex origin receives indirect support from the studies of Guz and his colleagues on vagal nerve block which are reported here (Guz *et al.*, 1970); the tachypnoea may be presumed to arise within the lung by the disease process activating the sensory component of a reflex arc. The receptors which when stimulated may conceivably lead to this

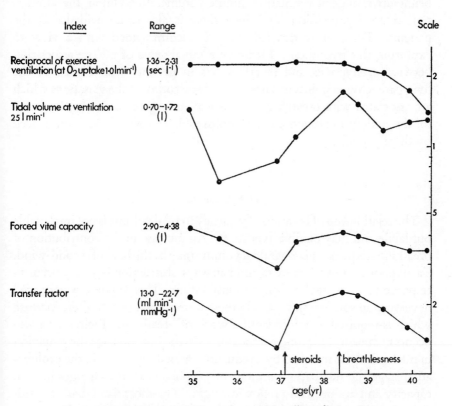

FIG. 6. Lung function in D.P.T., a patient with beryllium disease. Deterioration is represented by downward displacement of the curves. In order that equal proportional changes are represented by equal distances down the figure the data are plotted on a semilog scale.

response include the irritant receptors of Widdicombe and his colleagues (Mills, Sellick and Widdicombe, 1970), the stretch receptors and the deflation or type J receptors of Paintal (Paintal, 1970). The likelihood of the first two of these receptors being responsible is small: stimulation of the irritant receptors might be expected to cause airways obstruction, which is not a feature of these patients; if the stretch receptors were stimulated the lesions would need to involve the bronchial muscle but this usually looks normal (Seal, R. M. E., personal communication). The evidence on the possible role of the deflation receptors is necessarily tentative but rather less negative. In particular, the disease process involves the walls of alveoli and small blood vessels, where the receptors are presumed to be located, and their stimulation is known to cause tachypnoea without there necessarily being any change in ventilation minute volume. In addition, the stimulation causes hypotension for which there is also some evidence in the patients. Thus, more detailed study is recommended with a view to exploring this hypothesis. Meanwhile the absence of a close association between tachypnoea and breathlessness in patients with disease of the lung parenchyma points to a need for close scrutiny of the sensations which are associated with breathing. In this way an organic basis may be found for the anxiety and functional symptoms which are sometimes experienced by these patients.

CONCLUSIONS

The relationship of breathing frequency to tidal volume is not immutable but labile and may exhibit overshoot. An increase in the contribution of breathing frequency *vis-à-vis* tidal volume may be the basis of second-wind. Tachypnoea is not a feature of mild airways obstruction but may occur in response to an elastic hindrance to inspiration. This response is very well developed in some subjects and in these it may be in excess of the increase which is required to minimize the work of breathing. Tachypnoea also occurs in disease of the lung parenchyma. In the fibrotic stage the reduction in tidal volume is matched by a reduction in vital capacity. In the proliferative stage the fluctuations are out of proportion to the changes in vital capacity and are probably reflex in origin. The most likely basis for this reflex is activation by the disease process of the deflation or type J receptors of Paintal. The observation itself is of importance for management of the patients concerned; the underlying mechanism needs to be examined further.

SUMMARY

(1) The relationship of ventilation minute volume to tidal volume ($\dot{V}e/Vt$ relationship) has been used to explore the sensations which arise during strenuous exercise in normal subjects and patients with lung disease.

The effects on the relationship both of internal and external obstruction to the lung airways and of inhaling from a closed space of effective volume 37 l have been examined.

(2) The point of inflexion of the $\dot{V}e/Vt$ relationship is labile, and unduly high tidal volumes may obtain during the first three minutes of near-maximal exercise. Sensations associated with reversion to a smaller tidal volume and higher frequency may be the basis of second-wind.

(3) Moderate obstruction to the lung airways does not affect the $\dot{V}e/Vt$ relationship but in some subjects inhalation against an elastic hindrance causes tachypnoea and reduces the maximal tidal volume.

(4) In patients with proliferative disease of the lung parenchyma the tidal volume standardized to a ventilation of 30 l min$^{-1}$ reflects the degree of involvement of the lung parenchyma. Tachypnoea may be due to the disease process activating the deflation or type J receptors of Paintal. The associated sensations may be of a type associated with anxiety rather than breathlessness.

ACKNOWLEDGEMENTS

We are indebted to Miss J. M. Dabbs, Miss A. M. Hall, Mr C. Morgan and Mr E. Williams for help in these investigations, to colleagues who kindly referred patients for assessment or gave us access to data, and to Dr J. G. Widdicombe for advice on lung reflexes. We also thank Mr R. T. Harris and Mr R. W. Evans for photography, and Miss J. A. Vevers for secretarial assistance.

REFERENCES

AITKEN, R. C. B., Zealley, A. K., and Rosenthal, S. V. (1970). This volume, pp. 253–267.
ÅSTRAND, I. (1960). Acta physiol. scand., 49, 7–92.
BLAND, S., LAZEROU, L., DYCK, G., and CHERNIACK, R. M. (1967). Resp. Physiol., 3, 47–54.
COTES, J. E. (1968). Lung Function: Assessment and Application in Medicine. 2nd edn. Oxford: Blackwell.
FREEDMAN, S. (1969). The Functional Capacity of the Respiratory Muscles in Man. Ph.D. thesis. University of London, Faculty of Medicine.
GEE, J. B. L., VASSALLO, B. C., and GREGG, J. (1968). Am. Rev. resp. Dis., 98, 1003–1012.
GUZ, A., NOBLE, M. I. M., EISELE, J. H., and TRENCHARD, D. (1970). This volume, pp. 315–329.
GUZMAN, C. A., CAPLAN, R., and BECKLAKE, M. R. (1969). Fedn Proc. Fedn Am. Socs exp. Biol., 28, 786.
HEY, E. N., LLOYD, B. B., CUNNINGHAM, D. J. C., JUKES, M. G. M., and BOLTON, D. P. G. (1966). Resp. Physiol., 1, 193–205.
MILLS, J. E., SELLICK, H., and WIDDICOMBE, J. G. (1970). This volume, pp. 77–92.
OTIS, A. B. (1964). In Handbook of Physiology, sect. III, vol. 1, pp. 463–476, ed. Fenn, W.O., and Rahn, H. American Physiological Society. Baltimore: Williams and Wilkins.
OTIS, A. B., and GUYATT, A. R. (1968). Resp. Physiol., 5, 118–129.
PAINTAL, A. S. (1970). This volume, pp. 59–71.
POPE, H., HOLLOWAY, R., and CAMPBELL, E. J. M. (1968). Resp. Physiol., 4, 363–372.
WEST, J. R., and ALEXANDER, J. K. (1959). Am. J. Med., 27, 529–544.

# DISCUSSION

*Dornhorst:* You asked your normal subjects to breathe more quickly when they were exercising with external loads to see if this reduced their discomfort. Did you do the same experiment with subjects exercising with resistive loads?

*Cotes:* No. Our results with elastic loads agreed so closely with the results of Gee, Vassallo and Gregg (1968) that we left it at that.

*Dornhorst:* I have been the subject in this sort of experiment and know how easy it is to adopt a strategy that one knows will lessen total respiratory work. Could you avoid this pitfall?

*Cotes:* All our subjects, apart from myself, were naive, which would at least minimize this risk.

*Howell:* I am interested in the effect of elastic loads on minute volume. You found that elastic hindrance reduced ventilation by about 13 per cent in eight normal subjects. Is that right?

*Cotes:* Yes.

*Howell:* We have studied the effect of an elastic load on the ventilation response to increasing concentrations of carbon dioxide at rest. We observed no difference in ventilatory volume but an increase in ventilatory frequency for a given $Pco_2$ when the load was added (Howell, 1966).

*Cotes:* We have not studied carbon dioxide, but you may have made measurements only after the load had been applied for a long period of time. Our experience suggests that if you had measured the ventilation after a short period you might have detected an initial decrease in minute volume, as we did; the level returns subsequently to normal.

*Howell:* We made our measurements over several minutes with the load added. In our experiment differences in transmural pressures only occurred in the upper airways; there were no transpulmonary changes. So the change in respiratory frequency is probably mediated by a non-pulmonary somatic reflex.

*Cotes:* I agree.

*Cross:* The traditional physiological explanation for second-wind is that this state is reached when oxygen consumption per minute equals oxygen requirement. Do your observations on second-wind support this hypothesis, Dr Cotes?

*Cotes:* We have no observations on oxygen consumption in second-wind, nor have we yet worked out the relationship to the steady level of such variables as ventilation, oxygen uptake or blood lactic acid concentration. But my impression is that a steady level of oxygen uptake occurs later than the events we are describing. If our hypothesis that second-wind reflects the adaptation of ventilation to a constant tidal volume is correct, then its attainment will be critically determined by the level of exercise studied.

*Paintal:* Is second-wind reached sooner when subjects breathe high concentrations of oxygen during exercise?

*Cotes:* We found a striking reduction in ventilation in hyperoxic conditions but the relationship of ventilation to tidal volume was unchanged.

*Cross:* Bannister and Cunningham (1954) showed that athletes can go on running at their maximum rate more or less indefinitely when they are breathing high concentrations of oxygen.

*Widdicombe:* Does a runner whose breathing is synchronized with his leg movements (so that respiratory frequency is constant) get second-wind? His data would give a straight line through the origin on the minute volume/tidal volume graph (the Hey plot, see pp. 41-44). The condition could be reproduced by someone running to a metronome. If second-wind is achieved in those experimental conditions, does this mean that your hypothesis that second-wind depends on the ability to increase respiratory frequency may not be correct?

*Cotes:* I do not know, but I would be very surprised if the subject could exceed his normal maximal tidal volume by this means.

*Widdicombe:* Presumably a subject can achieve second-wind without reaching the upper limit of tidal volume for any particular set of conditions.

*Paintal:* Your observations on second-wind support some of my observations on the J receptors. I suggest that second-wind is achieved when, after a gradual build-up, exertional dyspnoea reaches a plateau or even decreases. Thus, with an appropriate pulmonary capillary pressure during exercise, we could reasonably assume that the J receptors are stimulated; and even though excitation of the nerve endings in the lung is constant or even increased, adaptation at a higher level gives rise to second-wind.

*Cotes:* This is not what I have in mind. I suggest that in normal subjects a conflict arises out of the need both for an increase in ventilation and for stabilization of tidal volume; the outcome determines the time taken to attain maximal tidal volume. The control mechanism may be overridden in some individuals so that supramaximal tidal volumes are achieved, which then revert to the normal maximum for the subject in question. But in patients with, say, proliferative disease of the lung parenchyma, tachypnoea may be mediated reflexly through the J receptors. I am postulating two separate mechanisms which operate in different circumstances for the limitation of tidal volume.

The maximal tidal volume is less than the forced expiratory volume in the first second ($FEV_1$) in most subjects but it may exceed the $FEV_1$ in patients with airways obstruction. The anxious subject may also show a reduction in tidal volume and an increase in respiratory frequency at rest.

*Sears:* Dr Newsom Davis and I have observed a similar differential effect on tidal volume and breathing rate when spontaneous breathing movements resume, under the analogous condition of extreme respiratory drive which exists during breath-holding. For example, whereas the rhythmic swings of pleural pressure reach a peak-to-peak value of 30–50 $cmH_2O$, about 30–40 seconds after the onset of breath-holding at functional residual capacity (FRC), and remain at this plateau level, the breathing rate continues to increase steadily until the break-point.

*Godfrey:* We have studied normal subjects who performed sub-maximal expiratory or inspiratory efforts up to pressures of plus or minus 30 $cmH_2O$ throughout a period of breath-holding at various levels of $P_{CO_2}$. Drs R. H. T. Edwards, D. A. Worrell and I (unpublished observations) plotted breath-holding/carbon dioxide curves* and obtained several points on each curve. We were disappointed to find no difference in breath-holding time at different levels of $P_{A_{CO_2}}$. The breath-holding time was not, therefore, related to the strength of contractions of the respiratory muscles and, at least in this kind of experiment, the pattern of the breath-hold cannot be influenced reflexly.

*von Euler:* We (Euler von, Herrero and Wexler, 1970) studied the relationship between ventilation and tidal volume in the cat with intact and with divided vagi. We found that after vagotomy the inflection point, at about half vital capacity, disappears and tidal volume continues to increase to much higher values than in the intact state. The slope of the curve also became less steep after vagotomy because respiratory frequency can no longer influence ventilation: after vagotomy, respiratory frequency does not increase with increased drive (Scott, 1908). I have two questions about temperature: Hey and co-workers (1966) described the effect of changes in body temperature on the relationship between ventilation and tidal volume. When ventilation is plotted against tidal volume, the slope of the plot increases significantly with small increases in temperature. We have confirmed these findings in the cat at temperature ranges well below the panting threshold (Euler von, Herrero and

---

* See also p. 331.

Wexler, 1970). We also found that maximal tidal volume decreases with temperature. Dr Cotes, did body temperature remain constant throughout your experiments or were these repeated at different temperatures? Did you find that it was easier to pick up second-wind at raised body temperature? Nielson (1938) suggested that "setting" the temperature regulation to a higher temperature in exercise would improve the muscular performance, a hypothesis which later has been amply verified (see, for example, Asmussen and Bøje, 1945).

*Cotes:* That is an attractive idea. These cyclists did have a warm-up. They also performed maximal exercise so their body temperatures would certainly have increased. We did not measure this and we should have done. For the other subjects the period of exercise was brief and the level not very high, so the body temperatures are unlikely to have risen much.

*Prys-Roberts:* Dr Keatinge and I (Keatinge *et al.*, 1969) studied the effect of temperature on respiratory frequency and tidal volume in four normal subjects during free swimming in warm water (24°C) and then in cold water (4°C). Body temperature did not change in the thin subjects, but fell from 37°C to 35°C in a fat subject. They swam for about twelve minutes in warm water, and their efforts were limited by muscle fatigue rather than by breathlessness or inhibition of breathing. Minute volumes reached maximal values of between 25 and 60 litres per minute, and respiratory frequency increased to 21–35 per minute. When the same subjects swam in cold water, exercise could only be maintained for periods between 1·5 and 8 minutes, and was limited by severe breathlessness, with marked increases in minute ventilation, up to 90 litres per minute with respiratory frequencies of up to 60 per minute. These observations suggest that environmental temperature acting through chest wall afferents may be a potent influence on the frequency and volume of ventilation.

*Plum:* Did your subjects shiver?

*Prys-Roberts:* I do not know if they shivered when they were in the water but they did not shiver until about two to three minutes after they came out.

*Godfrey:* Asthmatics undergo marked bronchodilatation during exercise whereas normal subjects do not (Jones, 1966). This may be an important factor in our assessments of respiratory function during exercise. The possibility that bronchodilatation has occurred should not be forgotten during experiments in which the relationships between tidal volume and vital capacity, or other measurements of airways obstruction, are being studied.

*Howell:* Dr Cotes, the chemical situation in your two patients with airways obstruction was quite different from that in any of the groups of normal subjects. I calculate that the $FEV_1$ in the two patients was about 0·8 litres, and such patients would probably be flow-limited at rest (N. Hodges, personal communication). These two patients could only increase their ventilation by increasing lung volume until their flow-volume curve during ventilation reached what was the maximal level for them, or by increasing respiratory frequency. I have seen a patient who actually reached his maximum flow-volume curve at rest and could only increase ventilation by increasing breathing rate. So the two patients in your study could have been in a rather different situation from the normal subjects who were not flow-limited at rest.

*Cotes:* I agree that this should be further investigated.

REFERENCES

ASMUSSEN, E., and BØJE, O. (1945). *Acta physiol. scand.*, **10**, 1–22.
BANNISTER, R. G., and CUNNINGHAM, D. J. C. (1954). *J. Physiol., Lond.*, **125**, 118–137.
EULER, C. VON, HERRERO, F., and WEXLER, I. (1970). *Resp. Physiol.*, in press.
GEE, J. B. L., VASSALLO, B. C., and GREGG, J. (1968). *Am. Rev. resp. Dis.*, **98**, 1003–1012.
HEY, E. N., LLOYD, B. B., CUMMINGHAM, D. J. C., JUKES, M. G. M., and BOLTON, D. P. G. (1966). *Resp. Physiol.*, **1**, 193–205.
HOWELL, J. B. L. (1966). In *Breathlessness*, pp. 55–64, ed. HOWELL, J. B. L., and CAMPBELL, E. J. M. Oxford: Blackwell.
JONES, R. S. (1966). *Br. med. J.*, **2**, 972–975.
KEATINGE, W. R., PRYS-ROBERTS, C., COOPER, K. E., HONOUR, A. J., and HAIGHT, J. (1969). *Br. med. J.*, **1**, 480–483.
NIELSON, M. (1938). *Skand. Arch. Physiol.*, **79**, 193–230.
SCOTT, F. H. (1908). *J. Physiol., Lond.*, **37**, 301–326.

# EXPERIMENTAL RESULTS OF VAGAL BLOCK IN CARDIOPULMONARY DISEASE

A. Guz, M. I. M. Noble, J. H. Eisele, and Diana Trenchard

*Department of Medicine, Charing Cross Hospital Medical School, London*

This review summarizes our experience of vagal block in patients, and then attempts to supplement this information with a few relevant animal studies in which disease has been simulated.

## OBSERVATIONS IN MAN

The study of the role of vagal afferents and reflexes in patients with dyspnoea due to cardiopulmonary disease is in its infancy. The study of the inflation reflex is particularly difficult; general anaesthesia is required and this can seldom be justified in this sort of patient. The deflation reflex can hardly be examined in the way outlined in normal subjects (Guz et al., 1970), but it may be possible to see if this reflex is present using chest wall compression; this has not yet been done. The most direct approach is to examine the effect of bilateral vagal block, to see, first, if there are abnormal influences modulating breathing and, second, if there is any change in the symptoms of patients who are dyspnoeic at rest. Since many patients are only dyspnoeic on exercise, it would be desirable to study the effect of vagal block on exercise; this has proved to be very difficult (Guz et al., 1970). Vagal block cannot sort out abnormalities of reflex mechanisms.

The studies to be summarized have been done over a period of six years; the protocol has differed in every case. Sometimes the vagi have been exposed in the neck under local anaesthesia and blocked by the direct application of 2 per cent lignocaine. This procedure requires a certain fortitude on the part of the patient, but it can be done without pain and has the advantage of being a pure vagal block. More usually the vagi have been blocked at the base of the skull (Guz et al., 1970). Care has had to be taken to control the hypertension consequent upon baroreceptor denervation. Ease of interpretation in the presence of the inevitable associated chemoreceptor block requires that the hypoxia that is commonly present be eliminated.

We have studied six clinical groups. These are (*a*) cardiovascular abnormalities, (*b*) lung infiltrations with inflammatory tissue, fibrous tissue and carcinoma, (*c*) panacinar emphysema without bronchitis, (*d*) asthma, (*e*) chronic bronchitis and emphysema, and (*f*) rigid chest wall. No attempt at selection has been made, but disabling dyspnoea, usually at rest, has been the principal clinical indication for study. All the patients expressed a wish for this study, the common motivating factor being a desire for something to relieve their dyspnoea. One of the subjects, J.P., was not in this category; he is a respiratory physiologist. All patients were given atropine 2 mg intravenously before any study, to block parasympathetic efferents.

### Cardiovascular disease

*M.F., female, aged 38 years,* had gross pulmonary vascular obstruction with most of the cardiac output diverted to the right upper lobe of the lung; the pulmonary artery pressure at rest was 60/30 mmHg and on minimal exercise it rose to 115/50 mmHg. The heart was not large and there was

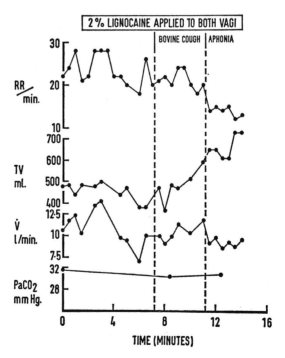

FIG. 1. Effect of cervical vagal block on respiratory rate (RR), tidal volume (TV), minute ventilation (V̇) and $Pa_{CO_2}$. (Patient M.F.)

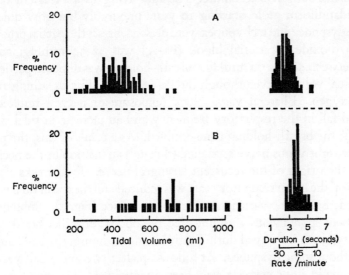

FIG. 2(*a*). Percentage frequency of tidal volumes and durations of 100 consecutive breaths (A) before and (B) during bilateral cervical vagal block. (Patient M.F.)

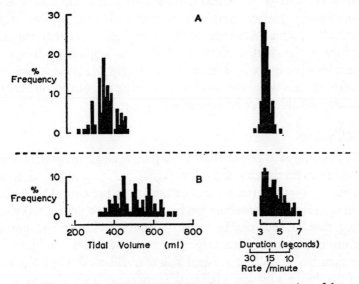

FIG. 2(*b*). As above. (A) before and (B) after permanent section of the right vagus nerve.

no evidence of right heart failure. The underlying disease was a metastasizing hydatidiform mole, starting 10 years previously but now quiescent. Severe dyspnoea and tachypnoea were present at rest; the partial pressure of carbon dioxide in arterial blood ($Pa_{CO_2}$) was 32–34 mmHg, and the $Pa_{O_2}$ between 58 and 70 mmHg. Breath-holding was difficult, particularly at residual volume, even though the $Pa_{O_2}$ was raised by breathing 100 per cent oxygen. Bilateral vagal block (exposure of nerves) resulted in a marked fall in the respiratory frequency and an increase in tidal volume (Fig. 1); the breath-holding time doubled. As a result of this, the patient had her right vagus nerve sectioned (through an incision in the neck) just below the origin of the recurrent laryngeal nerve. Two weeks after the operation the mean respiratory rate was reduced and the mean tidal volume elevated; both their variances were also increased (Fig. 2). Subsequently the patient spontaneously volunteered the observation that her dyspnoea was very much improved during activities in the house; she still could not run without some dyspnoea. At follow-up after two and a half years, the symptomatic improvement had been maintained. The heart had not enlarged and there was no evidence of right heart failure.

The strength of the inflation reflex was assessed during the patient's operation and was found to be on the weak side of our normal range.

H.L., *male, aged 56 years*, had chronic left ventricular failure due to a cardiomyopathy. He was dyspnoeic at rest, with a tachypnoea of 28–32/min and a $Pa_{O_2}$ which remained at 75–80 mmHg. A bilateral vagal block at the base of the skull resulted in a fall in the respiratory frequency to 19/min with a rise in $Pa_{CO_2}$ from 28 to 33 mmHg. He became tachypnoeic again after 20 min when the block was wearing off. No comments by the patient are available since he was heavily sedated.

## Lung infiltrations

A.S., *female, aged 42 years*, had bilateral pulmonary lymphangitis carcinomatosis due to carcinoma of the breast (Fig. 3). Very severe dyspnoea at rest, with tachypnoea (mean rate 41/min) was present. The $Pa_{CO_2}$ was 35 mmHg. Hypoxia was abolished by breathing 100 per cent oxygen and the $Pa_{O_2}$ rose to 180 mmHg from 65 mmHg without changes in the symptoms or pattern of breathing. The patient could not hold her breath longer than ten seconds at residual volume. Bilateral vagal block at the base of the skull resulted in a fall in the respiratory rate to 32/min, and an increase in its variance. The patient commented that she had "ceased to feel her breathing". Breath-holding time at residual volume rose to 26 seconds. The comments made were, "I did not feel the bursting sensation

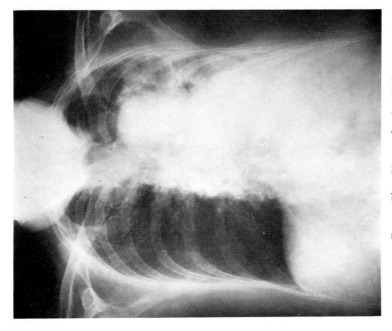

FIG. 4. Chest X-ray of patient D.L.

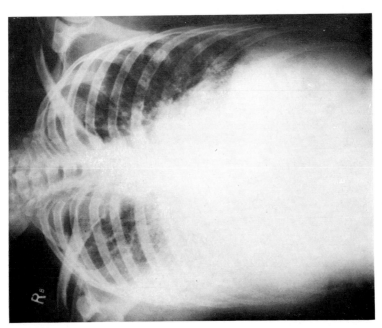

FIG. 3. Chest X-ray of patient A.S.

[To face page 318

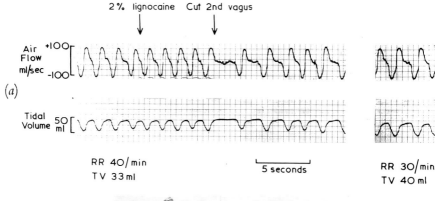

2% lignocaine    Cut 2nd vagus

Air Flow ml/sec  +100 / -100

($a$)

Tidal Volume 50 ml

RR 40/min
TV 33 ml

5 seconds

RR 30/min
TV 40 ml

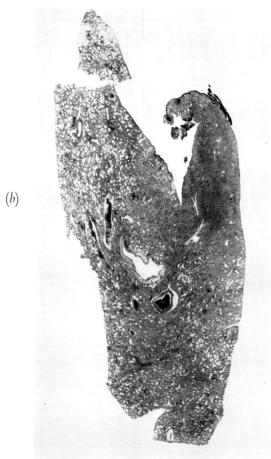

($b$)

FIG. 12 ($a$). Effect on breathing of lignocaine block and section of a cervical "C-fibre vagus" in a rabbit; the other vagus and abdominal vagi had already been cut. RR: respiratory rate; TV: tidal volume. ($b$). Horizontal section of lung on the side of the vagus that had been cut in ($a$); the section shows a collapsed upper lobe (top right) and patchy collapse elsewhere; (magnification: × 2).

in the chest at all during breath-holding—I felt I could go on holding the breath for ever but I was too frightened."

*D.L., female, aged 71 years,* had a carcinoma of the left main bronchus just distal to the origin of the left upper lobe bronchus. The left lower lobe and lingula were collapsed and there was gross shift of the mediastinum to the left (Fig. 4). There was a gross tachypnoea (mean rate 65–70/min) by day and night. The $Pa_{CO_2}$ was 31 mmHg and $Pa_{O_2}$ was 95 mmHg. Vagal block at the base of the skull was performed on one side at a time. Left vagal

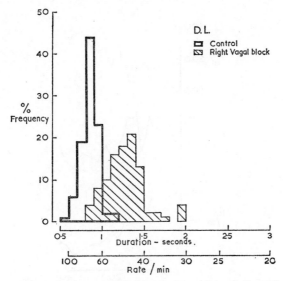

Fig. 5. Effect of right vagal block at the base of the skull on the percentage frequency of durations of 100 consecutive breaths. (Patient D.L.)

block caused no change in the pattern of breathing. Right vagal block (Fig. 5) reduced the frequency of breathing and increased its variance. The patient was unable to comment on any change in her sensations. Right vagal section was performed in the neck below the recurrent laryngeal nerve. The patient was bedridden for the remaining three months of her life, but numerous records of respiratory frequency showed it to be lower, in the range 38–45/min. During the operation the strength of the inflation reflex was assessed and found to be on the weak side of the normal range. It is of interest that at post-mortem carcinomatous tissue was found to be involving numerous pulmonary vagal branches on the right side as well as the left.

*E.K., female, aged 67 years*, had diffuse pulmonary fibrosis of unknown cause; both lungs were equally affected. There was severe dyspnoea on mild exercise and tachypnoea at rest (mean respiratory frequency 35/min). Deep breaths produced a distressing cough. The $Pa_{CO_2}$ was maintained at 30–31 mmHg. The patient could not hold her breath for longer than 11 seconds at functional residual capacity (FRC). Bilateral vagal block (exposure of nerves in neck) was done, the left vagus being anaesthetized before the right. Ventilation changed after the block of the first vagus only (Fig. 6). No change in the sensation of breathing at rest occurred but

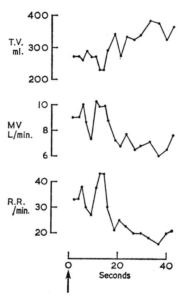

Fig. 6. Changes in tidal volume (TV), minute ventilation (MV) and respiratory rate (RR) immediately following the application of 2 per cent lignocaine (at arrow) to the left cervical vagus. (Patient E.K.)

this patient was not dyspnoeic at rest. Breath-holding time at FRC increased to 26 seconds.

The right vagus nerve was sectioned in the neck below the origin of the recurrent laryngeal nerve. No improvement in the dyspnoea was present during the remaining year of the patient's life; the chronic tachypnoea also remained unchanged. The operation resulted in a striking improvement in the amount of cough.

*S.P., male, aged 24 years*, had extensive infiltration of the lungs due to sarcoidosis. The mean respiratory frequency was 21/min. The $Pa_{CO_2}$ was kept at 29–30 mmHg but the $Pa_{O_2}$ did not fall below 70 mmHg. The patient was not dyspnoeic at rest but was severely so with mild exercise. He could not hold his breath for longer than ten seconds at FRC, but distress was present at three seconds. During bilateral vagal block (exposure of the nerves in the neck) the unpleasant sensation of breath-holding was absent for the same time—ten seconds; the maximal breath-holding time was not ascertained. The mean respiratory rate did not change although its variance increased. The $Pa_{CO_2}$ remained constant. We have reported this case elsewhere (Guz et al., 1966).

H.H., *male, aged 52 years*, had a diffuse pulmonary fibrosis affecting both lungs equally; he was dyspnoeic at rest and tachypnoeic (mean respiratory frequency by day and night was 30/min). $Pa_{CO_2}$ was kept at around 43–45 mmHg and $Pa_{O_2}$ between 60–73 mmHg. Pulmonary function tests suggested a considerable destruction of lung tissue with a normal airway resistance. The FRC was 1900 ml (predicted value, 3750 ml) and the diffusing capacity of carbon monoxide was 25 per cent of the predicted value. Bilateral vagal block at the base of the skull (under hyperoxic conditions) caused a reduction in mean respiratory frequency from 30 to 20/min with an increase in mean tidal volume from 280 to 470 ml. The breath-holding time at FRC increased from a control level of 48 seconds to 80 seconds. The patient's comments were that the tight feeling in the chest, present continuously at rest, was absent with vagal block.

A right cervical vagotomy below the recurrent laryngeal nerve did not cause any objective or subjective changes in breathing. The pulmonary branches of the left vagus were then cut during thoracotomy but the patient never recovered from this operation and died with pulmonary infection.

Post-mortem showed that much of his lungs were replaced by fibrous tissue. Before the first vagal section, while the patient was under anaesthesia, the strength of the inflation reflex was shown to be within the normal range but on the weak side.

*Panacinar emphysema*

R.S., *female, aged 72 years*, had gross panacinar emphysema with no evidence of bronchitis. She was severely dyspnoeic at rest and also tachypnoeic (mean respiratory rate, 60–70/min); she felt unable to take a deep breath. She kept her $Pa_{CO_2}$ at 43–45 mmHg and her $Pa_{O_2}$ in the 75–90 mmHg range. Bilateral vagal block at the base of the skull resulted in a fall in the respiratory frequency to 40/min. The patient realized that she was breathing more slowly but was not certain that this relieved her dyspnoea. The right vagus nerve was sectioned in the neck below the recurrent laryngeal nerve, and when this operation was seen to be ineffective the left vagus nerve was sectioned in the chest above the hilum of the lung and below the left recurrent laryngeal nerve. Recovery from the thoracotomy operation was complete, and for the remaining year of the patient's life all observers agreed that she was breathing more slowly—in the range of 30–40/min. She was still unable to take a deep breath but no longer felt so distressed. Although she was more comfortable at rest her dyspnoea on exertion did

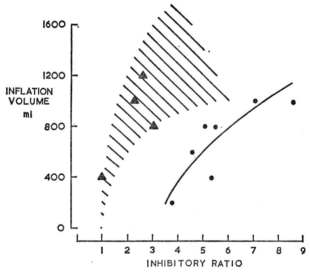

FIG. 7. Hering-Breuer inflation reflex (Guz *et al.*, 1970) before (closed circles, continuous line) and after (closed triangles) right vagal section. Cross-hatched area indicates range for normal subjects with both vagi intact. (Patient R.S.)

not improve. The patient stated that the sensation of "shortness of breath" had not changed in character after bilateral vagotomy.

Before the time of the first vagotomy, while the patient was anaesthetized, the strength of the inflation reflex was assessed. The reflex was stronger than our normal range; this is the only occasion when such an increased sensitivity has been found. The reflex was active within the tidal range (Fig. 7). After the right vagal section the strength of the reflex was reduced but tachypnoea was unchanged.

*Asthma*

J.P., *male, aged 41 years*, is a respiratory physiologist; he has chronic asthma with acute exacerbations. He was studied at a time when he felt well, and was not wheezing, but the total pulmonary resistance was $4 \, cmH_2O/l/s$. Vagal block at the base of the skull resulted in a fall in respiratory frequency and tidal volume with a rise in end-tidal $Pco_2$. Breathing during the block showed a striking increase in the variance of both rate and tidal volume (Fig. 8).

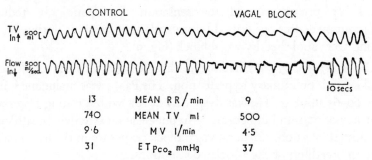

| | | |
|---|---|---|
| 13 | MEAN R R / min | 9 |
| 740 | MEAN T V ml | 500 |
| 9·6 | M V l/min | 4·5 |
| 31 | E T $Pco_2$ mm.Hg | 37 |

FIG. 8. Effect on ventilatory variables and pattern of breathing of bilateral vagal block at the base of the skull in subject J.P. TV: tidal volume; RR: respiratory rate; MV: minute ventilation; ETP$co_2$: end-tidal $Pco_2$.

*Chronic bronchitis and emphysema*

*N.W., male, aged 55 years,* had severe chronic bronchitis and emphysema. His FRC was 7·7 litres (predicted value 4·6 l) and his airways resistance was $5 \cdot 2 \, cmH_2O/l/s$. The resting blood gas tensions were $Pa_{O_2}$ 78–80 mmHg and $Pa_{CO_2}$ 40–45 mmHg. The respiratory frequency at rest ranged between

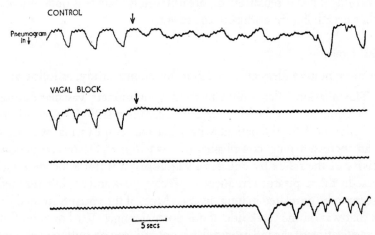

FIG. 9. Breath-holding (starting at arrows) before and during vagal block. The record of pressure in corrugated tubes strapped to the chest and abdomen (pneumogram) shows deflections indicating muscular contractions during control but not during block. (Patient N.W.)

18 and 26/min awake and 18–20/min asleep. He was not dyspnoeic at rest. Bilateral vagal block was done at the base of the skull. There was no change in respiratory rate and tidal volume. The patient thought that his breathing felt the same. A simple leg-raising exercise test was sufficient to cause dyspnoea and vagal block did not alter this in any way.

In spite of this completely negative result, the breath-holding time was remarkably prolonged and the sensation correspondingly reduced. Pneumogram deflections caused by muscular contractions during breath-holding were abolished by vagal block (Fig. 9).

*T.E., male, aged 55 years*, had severe chronic bronchitis and emphysema, together with pulmonary hypertension. His $Pa_{CO_2}$ was maintained in the range 60–65 mmHg. He was dyspnoeic at rest with a resting respiratory frequency of 20/min but became tachypnoeic and extremely breathless on the slightest exertion. Bilateral vagal block (exposure in the neck) had no effect on breathing or the associated sensations.

*Rigid chest wall*

*D.W., female, aged 36 years*, had developed a rigid chest wall as an unusual complication of right middle, and lower lobectomy carried out for bronchiectasis as a child. She was dyspnoeic and grossly tachypnoeic with a respiratory frequency at rest of 30–60/min by day and 24–40/min by night. Lung function tests showed little pulmonary abnormality. The vagi were blocked (exposure in the neck) without any change in the pattern of breathing or the sensation of breathlessness. She was quite unable to hold her breath before or during the block.

*Clinical summary*

Certain tentative ideas emerge from this clinical study, as follows:

(*a*) The inflation reflex is not sensitized by pulmonary vascular disease or by infiltrations within the lungs which make them stiff. The sensitization of the reflex in R.S., the patient with panacinar emphysema, was present with an increased lung compliance of 0·33 l/cmH$_2$O; the reduction in sensitivity of the reflex by unilateral vagotomy was not associated with a decrease in the respiratory frequency. Tachypnoea and the inflation reflex thus seem to be unrelated in lung disease. Most of the patients studied had a reflex that was on the weak side of our normal range. We have also found that sensitization of the inflation reflex is not induced by pulmonary micro-embolism in rabbits. This is in keeping with the experiments of Frankstein (1970) who found that the inflation reflex decreased in cats that were tachypnoeic with an experimental pneumonia. Thus the hypothesis of Christie (1938) has not been substantiated.

(b) Breathing may become slower (and sometimes deeper) in patients with lung infiltrations, pulmonary vascular obstruction and left heart failure when conduction in the vagi is blocked. This is often associated with a decrease or abolition of the sensation of dyspnoea. Unilateral vagal block is unlikely to be effective in bilateral lung disease. The striking result found with unilateral block in M.F. may be due to the fact that it is only on the right side that pulmonary vascular receptors are exposed to the high pulmonary artery pressure.

(c) Patients with chronic bronchitis and emphysema are unlikely to show a change in the ventilatory pattern or symptoms of dyspnoea with vagal block.

(d) The patient with asthma (J.P.) who showed alveolar hyperventilation must have had a "drive to breathe" mediated by the afferent vagi presumably coming from the constricted airways. A similar effect has been observed in two further asthmatic patients studied by one of us (J.E.) elsewhere. Irritant receptors in the lung (Mills, Sellick and Widdicombe, 1970) may be responsible.

(e) Dyspnoea can still be felt when pulmonary vagal innervation is absent.

RELEVANT ANIMAL OBSERVATIONS

It is difficult to incriminate the inflation reflex pathway in the abnormal ventilatory pattern and dyspnoea shown by some of the patients. Studies of stretch receptor discharge in experimental lung pathology (for example, pulmonary vascular congestion) have shown either no increase in discharge (Bülbring and Whitteridge, 1945), or a small increase only (Marshall and Widdicombe, 1958). What sort of reflexes or receptors are involved? Abnormalities in deflation reflex activity have not been studied; irritant receptor activity is a possibility and has been discussed (this volume, p. 77). The pulmonary branches of the vagi contain many non-myelinated C fibres (Evans and Murray, 1954; Hoffman and Schnitzlein, 1961). Their function is largely unknown, although they certainly conduct a discharge originating in the lung and resulting from the intravenous injection of phenyl diguanide (Paintal, 1953; Sergeeva and Frankstein, 1967). The effect of stimulating the C fibres is an increase in inspiratory activity and tachypnoea. Pulmonary oedema and inflammation, produced by the injection of hot water into the lung, causes a C-fibre discharge (Sergeeva and Frankstein, 1965). These workers think that this is responsible for the tachypnoea seen in pulmonary oedema.

We have looked at this problem in a different way. In the anaesthetized rabbit, one cervical vagus nerve has been cut and the other has been differentially blocked using direct current, by the technique outlined previously (Guz *et al.*, 1970). We have now stimulated this cervical vagus nerve, in which only C fibres conduct, below the area of block. A graded tachypnoea merging into an inspiratory apnoea results (Fig. 10), dependent on the frequency of stimulation (range 1–10/s). The effect closely resembles the response to intravenous phenyl diguanide. As yet, we have not been able to do this study by stimulating pulmonary vagal branches alone in the presence of a differential block in the cervical vagus.

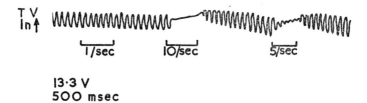

FIG. 10. Integrated pneumotachograph record, in the rabbit, showing the effect of stimulating one vagus nerve in which conduction has been blocked, in fibres other than the C group, by anodal block. Note graded tachypnoea merging into inspiratory apnoea dependent on frequency of stimulation. TV: tidal volume. Stimulation by square wave pulses (500 ms duration; voltage 13·3).

We have also tried to demonstrate a C-fibre influence on the pattern of breathing by cutting through such a differentially blocked nerve. Lignocaine, 2 per cent, has been applied below the area of anodal block and the nerve has then been cut, through the site of application of the local anaesthetic; this procedure avoids stimulation of the nerve by cutting. The other nerve has always been cut previously. Hyperoxia has been maintained to avoid chemoreceptor stimulation. The results in 23 rabbits are summarized in Fig. 11. The series of rabbits included three with chronic pulmonary microembolism (due to starch or 50-μm-diameter plastic spheres). Many, but not all, of the lungs have been submitted to a pathologist who was unaware of the physiological findings. Diffuse patchy collapse was almost invariably reported after the prolonged studies (more than three hours) particularly if the animals' lungs had been previously deflated and inflated; the lungs after short experiments lasting less than one hour were normal.

The results have therefore been divided into two groups—normal and pathological; the animals in whom no histology was available have also been allocated to these two groups depending on the length of the study. The rabbits in the pathological group clearly show much greater falls in

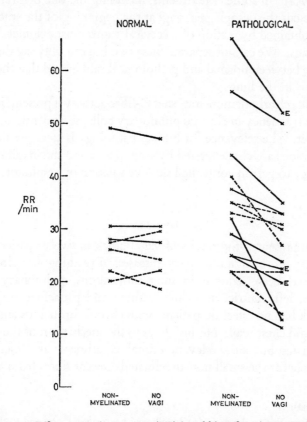

FIG. 11. Effect on respiratory rate (RR) in rabbits of cutting a cervical vagus nerve in which only the non-myelinated fibres are conducting (anodal block); the other vagus had been cut previously. Left: rabbits whose lungs were normal on histology (solid lines) or when the experiment lasted less than an hour (dashed lines); right: rabbits showing patchy collapse on histology (solid lines) or when the experiment lasted more than three hours (dashed lines). E: starch or microsphere embolism.

respiratory frequency when a "C-fibre vagus" is cut than the normal rabbits do. Collapse of the right upper lobe was present in one rabbit with patchy collapse elsewhere, and it was in this animal that we obtained our most striking result on section of a right "C-fibre vagus" (Fig. 12, p. 319). In this particular experiment the tidal volume increased, but this was only true for some of the series. The tidal volume often remained unchanged as the respiratory frequency decreased, and on occasions tidal volume even fell.

We know that most of the C fibres that we cut in the neck originate in the abdomen and that the rest come from the heart and lungs (Evans and Murray, 1954). In some experiments, including the one demonstrated in Fig. 12, we cut the oesophageal vagi at the beginning of the study so that any effect obtained by section of a cervical vagus must originate from the heart or lungs. We cannot separate these two but can only say that there is a difference between normal and pathological rabbits and that the obvious pathology is in the lungs.

The results clearly demonstrate that C-fibre activity is present, increasing respiratory frequency in chronic pulmonary collapse and microembolism in the rabbit. The relevance for human pathology is clear, particularly as these conditions are characterized by tachypnoea and the inability to hold the breath or to permit controlled slow ventilation by respirator.

SUMMARY

We have presented the results of vagal block in twelve patients with a wide variety of cardiopulmonary diseases. Breathing has slowed and dyspnoea has been reduced in lung infiltrations, pulmonary vascular obstruction, left ventricular failure, asthma and panacinar emphysema. Vagal block had no effect on patients with chronic bronchitis and emphysema, or rigid chest wall. No insight as to the mechanism of the effect has been elucidated but some relevant animal experiments are described that suggest a role for the small non-myelinated afferent fibres from the lungs.

ACKNOWLEDGEMENTS

Our thanks are due to the patients who allowed us to study them, and to the referring doctors, Dr P. Hugh-Jones, Professor W. I. Cranston, Sir John Richardson, Dr J. Goodwin, Dr V. Rosenor, and Professor J. G. Scadding.

REFERENCES

BÜLBRING, E., and WHITTERIDGE, D. (1945). *J. Physiol., Lond.*, **103**, 477–487.
CHRISTIE, R. V. (1938). *Q. Jl Med.*, **7**, 421–454.
EVANS, D. H. L., and MURRAY, J. G. (1954). *J. Anat.*, **88**, 320–337.
FRANKSTEIN, S. I. (1970.) This volume, pp. 53–58.
GUZ, A., NOBLE, M. I. M., EISELE, J. H., and TRENCHARD, D. (1970). This volume, pp. 17–40.
GUZ, A., NOBLE, M. I. M., WIDDICOMBE, J. G., TRENCHARD, D., MUSHIN, W., and MAKEY, A. R. (1966). *Clin. Sci.*, **30**, 161–170.
HOFFMAN, H. H., and SCHNITZLEIN, H. N. (1961). *Anat. Rec.*, **139**, 429–435.

MARSHALL, R., and WIDDICOMBE, J. G. (1958). *Q. Jl exp. Physiol.*, **43**, 320–329.
MILLS, J. E., SELLICK, H., and WIDDICOMBE, J. G. (1970). This volume, pp. 77–92.
PAINTAL, A. S. (1953). *J. Physiol., Lond.*, **121**, 182–190.
SERGEEVA, Z. N., and FRANKSTEIN, S. I. (1965). *Bull. exp. Biol. Med. USSR*, **60**, 1241–1243.
SERGEEVA, Z. N., and FRANKSTEIN, S. I. (1967). *Sechenov. physiol. J. USSR*, **8**, 964–968.

# DISCUSSION

*Dejours:* Have you ever blocked the vagi by injecting the local anaesthetic through the skin?

*Guz:* We have never succeeded in doing this.

*Paintal:* Dr S. K. Jain (personal communication) has now used a simple technique of this sort, similar to one used for cerebral angiography, in about ten cases. The needle is inserted between the sternomastoid and the trachea until pulsation of the carotid artery can be felt, and local anaesthetic is injected close to the artery at this point. The technique is easy and induces complete vagal block.

*Guz:* This would be an extremely useful technique as it avoids blocking the glossopharyngeal nerve. One problem about any technique in which local anaesthetic is injected into the neck is that the anaesthetic may spread to the recurrent laryngeal nerve and produce aphonia, which thus loses its value as the cardinal sign of complete vagal block.

*Merton:* Holton and Wood (1965) showed that when both carotid bodies were excised in patients with asthma there were some remarkable effects on respiration. In your patients with nerve block at the base of the skull, what part of the results was due to blocking the ninth cranial nerve?

*Guz:* We think that ninth nerve block did not affect our results because all the experiments were done under hyperoxic conditions to avoid stimulating the arterial chemoreceptors. This is important in normal subjects, and even more so in hypoxic patients. In my view, the data on carotid body resection are not convincing.

*Dornhorst:* But they do suggest that patients without the ninth nerve lose their sensitivity to hypoxia. And a patient after excision of the carotid body is a very convenient pharmacological preparation (Skinner and Whelan, 1962).

*Prys-Roberts:* During 1963 and 1964 I blocked the vagi at the base of the skull in three patients with asthma (unpublished material). I blocked the nerve, consecutively, on alternate sides, because of the danger of hypertension after bilateral block. An interesting result of these procedures was that in all three subjects the right vagal block decreased tachypnoea and produced tremendous relief of dyspnoea, whereas the left block did not. No significant changes in blood gases or in the $FEV_1/FVC$ ratio occurred in spite of the subjective improvement.

*Guz:* These interesting findings are supported by Culver and Rahn (1952), who also suggested that the right vagus is more important than the left. Did you use atropine preoperatively? It is important to block the efferent vagal pathways with atropine, especially in asthmatics.

*Prys-Roberts:* I did use atropine.

*Dornhorst:* What effect does vagal block have on the blood pressure in your subjects, Dr Guz?

*Guz:* Increases in arterial pressure to levels of 220/140 mmHg were recorded in one subject (J.W.) after blocking the ninth and tenth cranial nerves at the base of the skull (Guz *et al.*, 1966), but it is obviously immoral to increase the blood pressure to such high levels. It can be kept low with hexamethonium, which does not interfere with the symptoms we want to study, although using a drug has the disadvantage that it makes the interpretation of results more difficult.

*Noble:* In our more recent studies the blood pressure has generally been much lower, even without hexamethonium.

*Karczewski:* We have recently studied this strange suggestion (Culver and Rahn, 1952) that the effects of the right and left vagus on breathing may be different. Our results are inconsistent but the influence of the right vagus on the respiratory responses to inflation and to histamine injection does seem to be more important than that of the left.

*Widdicombe:* Species differences may be important in this context. In the rabbit the right side of the lung is much larger than the left because of the presence of a subcardiac pulmonary lobe.

*Paintal:* This is also true in the cat.

*Plum:* Some of the interest of your paper, Dr Guz, lies in what you did not claim. Why does respiratory frequency remain high during vagal block in patients with infiltrative lung disease if the frequency is reflexly generated from the lung?

*Guz:* Fink (1961) showed that if you have become accustomed to breathing fast you tend to go on doing it even when the original cause has been removed. This rather feeble explanation is all I can offer.

*Plum:* Is this habituation?

*Guz:* Perhaps. After prolonged exposure to high altitudes, respiratory frequency continues for some weeks at inappropriately high levels.

*Godfrey:* We need a reliable preliminary screening technique for the selection of dyspnoeic patients who will respond symptomatically to vagotomy. A plot of breath-holding time against $P_{CO_2}$ might be useful in this connexion.* With Drs R. H. T. Edwards, G. Copeland and P. Gross (personal observations) I have investigated a series of patients with chronic bronchitis and emphysema, normal subjects and athletes, studying mainly their ventilatory responses to hypoxia and carbon dioxide, but including breath-holding/carbon dioxide curves in some of them. The most useful data for our present purposes came from this relationship in four normal subjects and 15 patients with chest disease, matched for age with the four controls. Nine out of the 15 patients had a flat breath-holding/carbon dioxide curve. There are two possible explanations for this flattening: either the non-chemical drive to breathing is increased or the chemical drive is decreased. Three of the nine patients were also "truly" insensitive to carbon dioxide so this left only six patients with flat breath-holding/carbon dioxide curves and good evidence of increased non-chemical drive to breathing. The mean slope of the curve was 1·9–2 s/mmHg in the normal subjects and 0·4 s/mmHg in the patients. If we had taken these patients at random for vagotomy we might have only achieved benefit in six out of the 15, or 40 per cent.

Another useful guide for the selection of suitable patients for vagotomy might be the increase in pulmonary artery pressure with exercise. The best response to vagotomy in your series, Dr Guz, was in the woman with pulmonary hypertension (M.F., p. 316). Would an abnormal increase in pulmonary artery pressure on exertion pick out the patients who would benefit from vagotomy?

*Guz:* Possibly. In a physiological analysis of a dyspnoeic patient, pulmonary artery pressure is often the one thing that is not measured.

*Dornhorst:* Pulmonary artery pressure correlates extremely badly with dyspnoea. High pulmonary artery pressures can occur without dyspnoea and *vice versa.*

*Paintal:* The relevant measurement is the increase in pulmonary artery pressure on exertion, not the resting value.

*Cotes:* The pulmonary artery pressure in our patient E.M.M. (p. 305) was well within the normal range, both at rest and on exercise.

*Fillenz:* Isn't the important measurement the pulmonary capillary pressure? Is this related to pulmonary artery pressure in any simple way?

*Dornhorst:* A high capillary pressure entails a high arterial pressure but the converse is not true.

*Paintal:* Pulmonary artery pressure rises before pulmonary capillary pressure in dyspnoeic patients.

* See also p. 312.

*Dornhorst:* Studies on wedge or left atrial pressure in pulmonary artery disease are rather few, but the available evidence suggests that pulmonary capillary pressure is raised in patients with cardiac but not pulmonary dyspnoea, whereas pulmonary artery pressure may be raised in the latter, probably because of an increased precapillary resistance.

*Paintal:* The patchiness of pulmonary arteriolar constriction may be the most significant factor in the production of pulmonary oedema at high altitudes. Subjects with uniform constriction of the pulmonary arterioles are probably lucky. Subjects in whom some capillaries feel the entire impact are the individuals who develop pulmonary oedema.

*Dornhorst:* This is true, but oedema is not a normal response at high altitude.

*Paintal:* When one lives at sea level one thinks that anyone who lives at a high altitude is abnormal. If physiologists lived at high altitudes we would have a different "normal" physiology.

*Merrill:* The technical difficulties with experiments using an intact nerve on one side and an anodal block on the other are formidable. Even with a checking electroneurogram on the side of the blocked intact nerve it is difficult to be sure that the nerve is not being stimulated as it re-enters the medulla.

*Guz:* I agree that technical difficulties are considerable.

*Dejours:* Dr Guz, would you comment on the experiment in which you cut the vagus above the nodose ganglion?

*Guz:* We wanted to compare electroneurograms from an intact vagus and from a vagus containing sensory fibres only, and then study this pure "sensory" preparation with antidromic techniques. As all sensory fibres except those from the skin have cell bodies in the nodose ganglion of the vagus nerve, section proximal to this ganglion leaves a perfect sensory nerve but one that is entirely without central connexions. Thus, provided the nerve does not degenerate, discharges up the vagus from the lung can be recorded but there will be no central, efferent or reflex effects. We did this supranodose section in ten rabbits. In eight animals the nerve degenerated but in two it was still functioning one year after section. Stimulation of the abnormal nerve did not elicit any responses, whereas stimulation of the uncut vagus induced the typical respiratory responses. But the electroneurograms of the normal and abnormal nerves were almost identical; A, B and C fibres were present in both tracings. We were not able to use antidromic techniques in these preparations but the lungs from the two rabbits were finally sent to Dr Fillenz for histological examination (this volume, p. 104).

*Dornhorst:* Did you interfere with the blood supply to the nerve?

*Guz:* Yes, for a length of about two millimetres between the ganglion and the base of the skull.

*Paintal:* The cat would be a useful experimental animal for this sort of study. We have complete evidence about the types of fibres in the vagus for the cat (Paintal, 1963) but not yet for the rabbit.

*Karczewski:* Frankstein and co-workers (1962; see also Frankstein and Sergeeva, 1966) showed that in experimental pneumonia, lung oedema and focal overdistension of the lung, the neural information from this organ is mediated mainly by C fibres.

*Cross:* Were the rabbits with pulmonary collapse tachypnoeic due to their pulmonary pathology before you cut the vagal C fibres? In other words, did the actual process of collapsing the lung produce tachypnoea?

*Guz:* Yes.

*Cohen:* Was there a change in respiratory frequency in normal subjects after vagal block?

*Guz:* Respiratory frequency was unchanged in the only three normal subjects whose vagi we have blocked.

*Dornhorst:* The vagus seems to play no part in the integration of the pattern of breathing at rest. To recapitulate, the evidence is that afferent traffic passes continuously up the vagus but is ignored centrally, and that there is a functional backlash* which is central rather than peripheral. We have assumed that, under conditions of altered mechanics in the chest, the effect from the stretch receptors becomes more important because the stimulus is greater than the normal stimulus at normal tidal volumes, and the afferent volley is therefore greater. But, surprisingly, Dr Guz has demonstrated an increased sensitivity of the threshold for the stretch reflex in only one patient; threshold (at rest) in the four patients in whom it was tested was within the normal range. Of course this does not mean that thresholds in these patients are normal through the whole range; these studies are not yet complete enough to determine this. Patients might even habituate to the new abnormal situation so that their afferent vagal traffic becomes greater than normal.

*Campbell:* Dr Guz's observations suggest that tachypnoea in patients with respiratory disease is not due to increased sensitivity of the inflation reflex.

*Sears:* The inflation reflex in the normal subject has a threshold of about 800 ml, thus vagotomy has no effect on quiet breathing. On the other hand, we know that the reflex is present in the asthmatic. Dr Guz, were there any features in the mode of breathing in your asthmatic subject,

* See also p. 51.

J.P., that might reconcile these facts? For example, if J.P. habitually breathed at a higher lung volume, the volume threshold would be reached during his quiet breathing, as you have demonstrated.

*Guz:* I cannot answer this question because we did not consider it ethical to anaesthetize this subject to study his inflation reflex, so we could not compare him with the other subjects who were all anaesthetized. Dr Petit, do you breathe at a higher lung volume than normal when your pulmonary resistance is 4 cmH$_2$O/s?

*Petit:* Yes, I do.

*Dornhorst:* Is it appropriate to use volume threshold at all when one is dealing with increased airways resistance? The stimulus to the stretch receptors is trans-airway pressure, which is only indirectly linked with volume, and the pattern of stimulation will be different in patients with increased airways resistance. A pneumographic trace of oesophageal pressure in the normal subject follows this pressure closely, with only a slight deviation due to airways resistance. An asthmatic, free from bronchospasm, will have a pneumographic record fairly similar to the normal but his oesophageal pressure trace will show an abnormal pattern; it reaches its peak earlier and passes off more quickly. The asthmatic may be producing a pressure gradient to stimulate the stretch receptors in his airways and this gradient will be greater than normal at a much lower inflation volume. But if he takes a slow breath the curve will be similar to the normal curve because, except in status asthmaticus, compliance at slow inspirations is similar in asthmatics and normal subjects.

*Widdicombe:* This is just what Davis, Fowler and Lambert (1956) recorded for pulmonary stretch receptors.

*Howell:* Dr Guz, your patient with panacinar emphysema had an exaggerated inflation reflex, which was reduced to normal by vagal blockade. Is that right?

*Guz:* This was with a right-sided vagal block alone.

*Howell:* I see. You expressed this return to normality in terms of a volume applied to the lung. I doubt if this is valid in a patient such as this with an extensively destroyed lung, because inflated volume may only reach the better-ventilated parts of the lung. These regions will therefore be more distended than they would have been if the rest of the lung had been normal. If you could express the volume increment in terms of the functioning lung volume, it might be normal. Is that fair comment?

*Guz:* The two curves (this volume, p. 322, Fig. 7) were recorded within five minutes of each other and separated by right vagal section.

Air must have reached the same part of the lungs on both occasions. The only difference in the circumstances was the presence of right vagal block when the "normal" curve was recorded.

*Dornhorst:* It depends on what was a normal level for the inflation reflex in this particular patient. Vagal section may have reduced a supranormal response to an apparently normal, but in fact subnormal, level for this patient.

*Cohen:* But the actual stage of inspiration at which you introduce the added volume is bound to vary.

*Guz:* Yes, it does.

*Cohen:* One reliable way of measuring the Hering-Breuer reflex in man would be to occlude the airway at the time of minimum lung volume, that is, during the expiratory pause. Individual tests would be more replicable with this method since it is relatively easy to apply the occlusion at the proper time. The Hering-Breuer reflex response would be shown in two ways—by lengthening of the inspiratory phase and by increased discharge of inspiratory muscles, which could be evaluated by an integrated electromyogram. The strength of the Hering-Breuer reflex is a function of the time in the cycle when inflation is applied, and therefore to obtain accurate results it is necessary to control the timing of the test inflation.

*Guz:* We always try to inflate the lungs at the beginning of a normal inspiration. Reproducibility of response for similar inflation volumes is good, but we have not yet subjected these data to statistical analysis.

*Noble:* In the patient with panacinar emphysema the curve for the inflation reflex moved (when one vagus was blocked) into the range that would be normal for normal subjects with both vagi intact. But I agree with your criticism, Dr Howell. We have plotted inflation volume against the inhibitory ratio, but I am not convinced that inflation volume is the best index of the stimulus to the stretch receptors. The inhibitory ratio is the ratio of the duration of apnoea to the duration of the previous cycle, and the latter can vary enormously, depending on respiratory frequency. A short period of apnoea following tachypnoea will give an unrealistically high inhibitory ratio.

*Guz:* All these comments raise the difficult problem of how to assess the strength of the inflation reflex. What are your views about this, Dr Widdicombe?

*Widdicombe:* There is no perfect method. If the main motor action is inhibition of inspiratory muscle contraction, then this can be expressed as the relative length of inhibition of breathing. This ignores other motor effects such as bronchodilatation, expiratory muscle contraction and cardio-vascular responses. The size of the stimulus must also be determined. Transpulmonary pressure is probably the best measure because it mini-mizes variations due to body size and species differences; it also takes account of the fact that pulmonary stretch receptors have a more con-sistent relationship to the size of pressure stimulation than to the volume stimuli. But, in physiological terms, volume changes are a more im-portant result of inspiration than pressure changes are.

## REFERENCES

CULVER, G. A., and RAHN, H. (1952). *Am. J. Physiol.*, **168**, 686–693.

DAVIS, H. L., FOWLER, W. S., and LAMBERT, E. H. (1956). *Am. J. Physiol.*, **187**, 558–566.

FINK, B. R. (1961). *J. appl. Physiol.*, **16**, 15–20.

FRANKSTEIN, S. I., GAIDINA, G. A., GORYUNOVA, T. I., SERGEEVA, Z. N., and SMOLIN, L. W. (1962). *Trudy Inst. norm. patol. Fiziol.*, **6**, 102–104 (in Russian).

FRANKSTEIN, S. I., and SERGEEVA, Z. N. (1966). *Nature, Lond.*, **210**, 1054–1055.

GUZ, A., NOBLE, M. I. M., WIDDICOMBE, J. G., TRENCHARD, D., MUSHIN, W. W., and MAKEY, A. R. (1966). *Clin. Sci.*, **30**, 161–170.

HOLTON, P., and WOOD, J. B. (1965). *J. Physiol., Lond.*, **181**, 365–378.

PAINTAL, A. S. (1963). *Ergebn. Physiol.*, **52**, 74–156.

SKINNER, S. L., and WHELAN, R. F. (1962). *J. Physiol., Paris*, **162**, 35–43.

# GROUP DISCUSSION

*Merrill:* Our general understanding of the Hering–Breuer reflexes is still very poor and even at the descriptive level our knowledge of them is inadequate. The reflexes classically described by Hering and Breuer probably consist of composites that can be separated into a number of simple reflexes, all of which may be mediated by slowly adapting pulmonary afferents. The role of the inflation reflexes in normal breathing is not clear, even in animals like the rabbit which have strong reflexes. The central mechanisms and pathways for these reflexes are not at all understood and our knowledge does not even extend as far as the first synapse. We know little about the anatomy of the nucleus of the tractus solitarius and no reliable recordings from secondary and tertiary cells in these central pathways have been published. The pathways from the nucleus of the tractus solitarius to the "respiratory centres" and respiratory motor neurones are totally obscure.

*Guz:* What is known about the anatomy of vagal afferents when they reach the medulla?

*Karczewski:* Rhoton, O'Leary and Ferguson (1966), in a publication dealing with vagal, trigeminal, glossopharyngeal and other afferents, described vagal afferents after they enter the medulla. These workers showed that some of these fibres bend down again and reach as low as the third cervical (C3) segment of the spinal cord.

*Fillenz:* I have traced the degenerating nerve fibres (with the Nauta technique) following supranodose section of the vagus in the cat (unpublished observations). I too found that degenerating fibres pass down to the second cervical segment of the spinal cord. I found bilateral projections to the spinal nucleus of the fifth nerve, which means that afferents from one vagus reach both sides of the medulla.

*Guz:* What function does this serve?

*Fillenz:* I do not know. These projections to the fifth nerve nucleus did not occur in all the animals I examined. Their occurrence seemed to depend on whether the section was above both the nodose and the jugular ganglia.

*Cohen:* Little is known about the synaptic pathways of vagal afferent fibres. In my own studies on neurones' responses during the Hering–Breuer reflex I used a descriptive approach. It would be difficult to trace the pathways beyond the first few synapses, at least if one used only classical methods, because there is probably a good deal of convergence and divergence through both parallel and serial pathways.

To return to the problem of measuring the Hering–Breuer reflex in conscious man, I suggest that the method of occlusion at the extreme points of the cycle (minimum and maximum lung volume) might give the clearest results. Since naive subjects might be upset by airway occlusion, the most suitable subject is the conscious respiratory physiologist.

*Campbell:* Obstruction of breathing at the end of the inspiratory phase has no effect on the duration of the next expiratory phase as judged by spirometry (Campbell *et al.*, 1961).

*von Euler:* There is a period of low responsiveness to inflation at the onset of the inspiratory phase. Fig. 1 illustrates the type of results obtained by Dr F. Clark and myself (unpublished data). A respirator, actuated by the cat's own phrenic activity, delivered rapid pulses of inflation triggered to appear at variable times after the start of inspiratory phrenic activity. In this way a responsiveness curve was obtained by plotting the volume increments needed to terminate inspiration (ordinate) against the time elapsed after the start of inspiration, that is, inspiratory duration (abscissa). The same curve was obtained when, in a rebreathing run, progressively increasing tidal volumes were plotted against the corresponding inspiratory durations of the individual breaths. This responsiveness curve of the Hering–Breuer reflex thus appears to determine the volume–frequency relationships both at rest and at increasing ventilatory drive. With increasing drive the rate of active inflation increases, so that the volume threshold for the Hering–Breuer (inspiration cut-off) reflex is reached progressively earlier but, depending on the shape of the threshold curve, it also takes a progressively larger tidal volume to reach this volume threshold. This explains the fact that tidal volume increases in response to increased ventilatory drive in spite of the Hering–Breuer reflex checking inspiration according to volume.

In the vagotomized cat, inspiratory duration is uninfluenced by volume effects and respiratory frequency is constant, independent of changes in ventilatory drive (Scott, 1908; Cohen, 1964). The rate of increase of inspiratory activity (or the rate of active inspiratory inflation) is directly dependent on the prevailing drive for ventilation but is not dependent on whether the vagus nerves are intact or blocked (Head, 1889; Hammouda and Wilson, 1932; Larrabee and Knowlton, 1946; Euler von, Herrero and Wexler, 1970). The tidal volume–inspiratory duration relationship therefore plots out as an almost vertical line, the time value of which is dependent on how the pneumotaxic mechanism happens to be "set" (this may depend on various other factors). If the pneumotaxic mechanism is set to give a relatively high respiratory frequency (that is, a short inspiratory duration), then tidal volume at conditions of low drive and thus with low rates of lung expansion will not

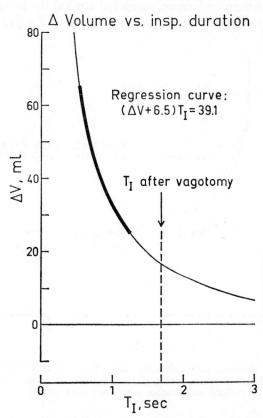

FIG. 1 (*von Euler*). Minimum volume of short pulses of inflation (V) needed to cut off inspiratory activity at different times after the beginning of inspiration ($T_1$). (When V is plotted against the reciprocal of $T_1$ the observed points fit a straight line.) The heavy line indicates the range over which the experimental data were observed. The same curve obtained when, in a rebreathing run, tidal volumes were plotted against inspiratory duration (Clark, F., and Euler, C. von, unpublished).

have time to reach the volume threshold but will be cut off earlier by the pneumotaxic mechanism.

*Merrill:* I can support these conclusions and give some relevant details from my own work. I gave ramp-shaped inflations asynchronously with the naturally occurring central rhythmic activity, which was recorded from the lateral inspiratory cells and the phrenic nerves. Barbiturate anaesthesia was used because it greatly diminishes carbon dioxide sensitivity while apparently leaving the responsiveness to mechanical inputs unaltered. The experimental animal was the cat.

Fig. 2 shows the curve obtained from one such experiment. The ordinate is chest circumference, measured around the caudal ribs with a mercury length-gauge. Two rough indications of inflation amplitude

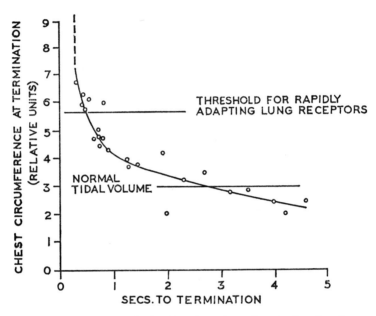

FIG. 2 (*Merrill*). Graph showing chest circumference plotted against time from the onset of phrenic activity to its termination by ramp inflation in the anaesthetized cat (see test).

are shown: the "threshold" for the brief inspiration contraction characteristic of rapidly adapting receptor activation and the tidal volume immediately preceeding paralysis. The abscissa is time from the onset of phrenic activity to its termination by the ramp inflation, whose amplitude at termination is plotted. The initial 0·25 seconds or so of inspiration cannot be terminated by inflation. The threshold, large even at a half-second, then gradually falls to levels of tidal volume at inspiratory durations near those recorded before paralysis. The threshold curve extends beyond this point to inflations below tidal volumes. In the paralysed animals, the addition of slight negative pressures at the trachea during inspiration results in a reduction in the volume of the naturally occurring inspiration and a longer inspiration, as shown in Fig. 2.

These observations suggest that the respiratory system seeks a certain, predetermined tidal volume, which, once reached, abruptly terminates the inspiration. The shape of the inspiration in the barbiturate-anaesthetized cat appears to be fixed, although it varies greatly with factors such as carbon dioxide levels, temperature and so on.

*Campbell:* Bishop (1967) disentangled some of these responses from the classical Hering–Breuer reflex in the cat. She showed that some of the afferent impulses were not vagal.

*Sears:* My view in 1964 (Sears, 1964), and now, is that one is dealing with a summation of two inputs at the motoneurone level. The work of Euler von and Fritts (1963), comparing vagotomy with posterior rhizotomy, also supports this view. Breuer, in his original description, emphasized that the inflation reflex is inspiratory-inhibitory/expiratory-activating. Thus one consequence of the Hering–Breuer reflex is a facilitatory or excitatory (these amount to the same thing) input to expiratory motoneurones during the prolonged expiratory pause. The gamma loop at a segmental level provides another excitatory input to these neurones. Thus the recruitment of expiratory motoneurones during the expiratory pause can be abolished in two ways, either by abolishing the Hering–Breuer reflex by vagotomy, thus losing the excitatory input along direct central pathways, or by opening the gamma loop by posterior rhizotomy. This will also reduce the ability of the central input to recruit into activity expiratory motoneurones whose excitability has been diminished by the loss of excitation from the primary afferent fibres of the muscle spindle. The two inputs are mutually dependent with regard to their effects on motoneurone discharge.

*Flenley:* We have studied the effects of changes in lung volume on the ventilatory response to carbon dioxide in conscious human subjects (Flenley, Pengelly and Milic-Emili, 1970). A constant positive pressure at the mouth was added to both inspiration and expiration (Fig. 3). A typical record obtained when a positive pressure of 15 cmH$_2$O was suddenly applied is shown in Fig. 3. There is an immediate increase in lung volume but the tidal volume is considerably diminished over the next four breaths. A pressure-volume diagram depicting the results is shown in Fig. 4, the solid line joining the end-expiratory points during application of positive pressure coinciding with the "relaxation" pressure-volume relationship for the whole thorax, thereby confirming Heaf and Prime's (1956) method of determining total respiratory compliance.

Fig. 4 also shows that the mean tidal volume of these first four breaths progressively falls as the inflation pressure increases; the lines at different levels of end-tidal $Pco_2$ ($PA_{CO_2}$ in Fig. 4, which was measured immediately before the inflation) during the breathing of carbon dioxide forming a family of lines which converge as inflation pressure increases. Three possible explanations for this fall in tidal volume are offered. First, the length-tension relationship of the inspiratory muscles will lead to a decline in force of contraction resulting from a constant stimulus as the resting

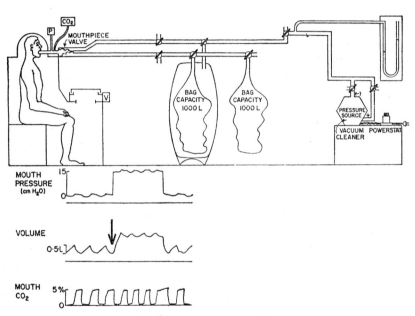

FIG. 3 (*Flenley*). The method used to study the effects of positive pressure on the ventilatory response to carbon dioxide. A typical record of mouth pressure, lung volume (from the body plethysmograph) and mouth carbon dioxide (by infrared analyser) is shown below. At the arrow, mouth pressure was suddenly increased to +15 cmH$_2$O for four breaths.

length increases with inflation; second, Marshall (1962) originally showed that when the diaphragm flattens as lung volume increases so the pressure generated for a given degree of shortening falls; and finally, tidal volume decreases as the thorax becomes less compliant at high lung volumes.

We also studied (unpublished) the effects of maintaining the positive pressure for ten minutes. After some delay, the initial decline in tidal volume was replaced by hyperpnoea along with a fall in the apparent functional residual capacity, so that the apparent "relaxation" pressure-volume line moved towards the volume axis at positive pressures, as originally observed by Fenn (1951). At the same time the electromyogram of the expiratory muscles showed an increase in tone at the end of expiration. Both hyperpnoea and the increase in expiratory tone did not develop until five to eight minutes after application of the positive pressure.

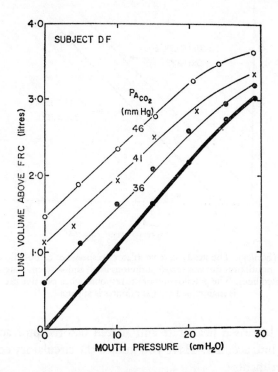

FIG. 4 (*Flenley*). Pressure-volume diagram during acute exposures to positive mouth pressures over four breaths. The heavy line joins points at the end of expiration, and the lighter lines are drawn through end-inspiratory points at the three levels of $P_{ACO_2}$ shown, as numbers, on the graph. These three values of $P_{ACO_2}$ were those obtained immediately before the positive pressure was applied. The vertical distance between the heavy end-expiratory line and any end-inspiratory line represents the tidal volume for those conditions of pressure and $P_{ACO_2}$.

When we express the results as a steady-state ventilatory response to carbon dioxide we see that positive pressure potentiates the ventilatory response to carbon dioxide (Fig. 5). This effect persists even when the stimulus is expressed as arterial carbon dioxide tension, thus it cannot arise from changes in alveolar dead space on inflation (Flenley and King, unpublished results). We cannot as yet explain this potentiation.

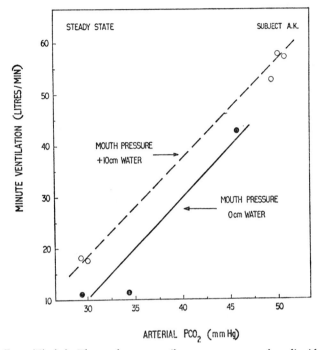

FIG. 5 (*Flenley*). The steady state ventilatory response to carbon dioxide, when mouth pressure was zero (continuous line), and + 10 cm water (interrupted line). The potentiation of the response when positive pressure is maintained for ten minutes is apparent.

*Dornhorst:* Increased heart rate and altered baroreceptor activity must also be taken into account. Have you studied the circulatory consequences of your experiments?

*Flenley:* No, but I agree that these are important. A rise of intra-oral pressure of 30 $cmH_2O$ could cause a fall of 30 per cent in cardiac output (Ernsting, 1965). There was no counter-pressure to prevent these falls in cardiac output in our experiments. If the hyperpnoea I have described is a reflex phenomenon, how does one explain the delay of five to eight minutes before it becomes established?

*Cohen:* Could there have been some chemical influence as well as the reflex factor?

*Flenley:* If there is, we did not find it in arterial blood; the $Pa_{CO_2}$ did not change during these eight minutes when carbon dioxide was being inhaled.

*Paintal:* What was the $Pa_{O_2}$ in these experiments?

*Flenley:* About 150 mmHg.

*Cross:* It is remarkable that the $Pa_{O_2}$ was maintained at such a high level for eight minutes.

*Flenley:* All these experiments were done with the subject breathing 30 per cent oxygen to avoid stimulation of the chemoreceptors; inspired oxygen tension was about 210 mmHg.

*Cross:* But you said that the total volume of inspired gas was only 200 ml.

*Flenley:* That was in the first four breaths following pressure. Hyperpnoea developed gradually after five to eight minutes when the pressure was continued. End-tidal $Pco_2$ fell initially by about 2–4 mmHg but returned to the original level within five minutes. This fall is partly the result of a pressure artefact on the infrared analyser. $Pa_{CO_2}$ does not fall, as hyperpnoea develops when the subject is breathing carbon dioxide, but a slight fall in $Pa_{CO_2}$ occurs as hyperpnoea develops when the subject is breathing 30 per cent oxygen without carbon dioxide.

*Howell:* These results are reminiscent of the effects that Campbell and I observed (unpublished observations) using threshold expiratory loads in conscious subjects. When the threshold expiratory load was first applied there was an immediate elevation of the end-expiratory level, but this was followed by a gradual return, over the next few minutes, towards the original end-expiratory level, although the time course was variable. In the anaesthetized subject we never observed this fall in the end-expiratory level. (For details of method used, see Campbell, Howell and Peckett, 1957.)

*Flenley:* The absence of a fall in the end-expiratory level must be peculiar to the anaesthetized subject. I have not seen the progressive increase in tidal volume following the initial fall over the first five breaths following an elastic load that you described (Campbell, Dinnick and Howell, 1961). In any studies on conscious man in which a respiratory physiologist is the subject, it is difficult to know when we are consciously producing the results we want. This was certainly a problem for me during the first four breaths in the experiments I have described. But when I breathe 5 per cent carbon dioxide at a positive pressure of 20 cm-$H_2O$ for ten minutes, I doubt that I have any volitional control over what I am doing. The subjective unpleasantness appears to preclude any manipulation of psychological influences.

*Howell:* Does the development of subsequent hyperpnoea depend on the extent of the inflation induced by the pressure applied?

*Flenley:* This is certainly true for the pressures we used—between 10 and 20 $cmH_2O$ for ten minutes. The time before hyperpnoea developed was shorter at the higher pressures.

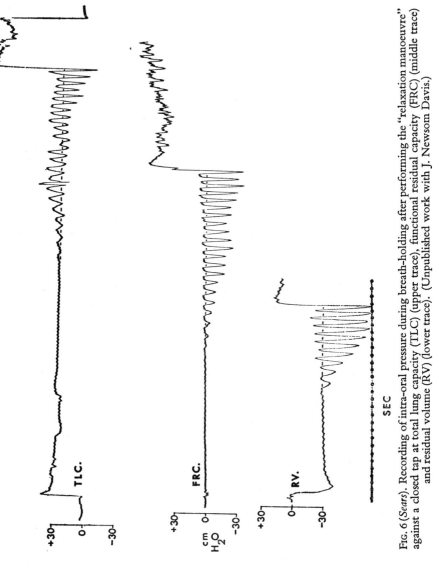

Fig. 6 (*Sears*). Recording of intra-oral pressure during breath-holding after performing the "relaxation manoeuvre" against a closed tap at total lung capacity (TLC) (upper trace), functional residual capacity (FRC) (middle trace) and residual volume (RV) (lower trace). (Unpublished work with J. Newsom Davis.)

*Sears:* Dr Newsom Davis and I have also studied the effects of positive and negative pressures on the spontaneous breathing that occurs during breath-holding. But instead of applying negative or positive pressures from an external source we commenced breath-holding after carrying out the "relaxation manoeuvre". In these circumstances an interesting response can be demonstrated (Fig. 6). This figure shows the subject carrying out the relaxation manoeuvre at total lung capacity (TLC), functional residual capacity (FRC) and residual volume (RV), followed by breath-holding at those volumes. As spontaneous breathing resumes, with breath-holding at FRC and RV the periodic swings of pressure are negative with respect to atmospheric pressure, indicating the rhythmic excitation of inspiratory motoneurones. But at TLC both the first and subsequent breaths actually increase the positive pressure, that is, they add to the existing relaxation pressure, indicating that at this volume (or pressure) expiratory motoneurones are not only the first to be activated, but that the entire balance of rhythmic respiratory motoneurone activation is shifted to the expiratory side. We believe that this result in man reflects Breuer's original finding that the inflation reflex is inspiratory-inhibitory, *expiratory-activating*. It is also in accord with the work of Bishop (1963) on the effect of pressure breathing.

*Dornhorst:* Can the afferent impulses arise in receptors in the chest?

*Sears:* Certainly. All I would add is that at the expiratory motoneurone level there is a summation of inputs of central and segmental origin.

*Dejours:* We have all been surprised by the species differences in the Hering–Breuer reflex between man and other animals. Have these reflexes been studied in any species intermediate between the rabbit, say, and man—non-human primates, for example?

*Widdicombe:* I studied the Hering–Breuer reflex in aesthetized animals including the rhesus monkey, and the cat, dog, rat, mouse, guinea-pig and rabbit (Widdicombe, 1961). I measured two responses, the ventilatory response to vagotomy and the duration after lung inflation of the apnoeic pause. I found that the strength of the Hering–Breuer reflex in the monkey is intermediate between its strength in man and in the other mammals tested.

*von Euler:* The "hot cat" may be a useful intermediate model between man and other mammals. In a cat whose body temperature is raised, respiratory frequency is increased via the pneumotaxic centre. Thus inspiratory duration is shorter than at normal body temperatures and determines respiratory frequency, at least at low ventilatory drive when the rate of lung expansion in inspiration is relatively slow. Similarly,

12*

in human beings with low ventilatory drive, the volume threshold of the Hering–Breuer reflex is not reached and the pattern of breathing is determined by the pneumotaxic mechanism, which alters respiratory rate. In conditions of augmented ventilation, the increased rate of lung expansion permits tidal volume to reach the volume threshold for the Hering–Breuer reflex in a shorter time than when the pneumotaxic mechanism is in control. In conditions of increased ventilatory drive, the Hering–Breuer reflex determines respiratory frequency in man as in animals, and permits increases in both frequency and tidal volume.

*Dornhorst:* What is the normal panting temperature of the cat?

*von Euler:* This depends on the anaesthetic used; an anaesthetized cat starts to pant at 39–40°C; with urethane the panting threshold is 38°C or lower, and with pentobarbitone the cat usually does not pant at all. Below the panting threshold, respiratory frequency in the cat increases with temperature in a similar way as occurs in man (Hey *et al.*, 1966).

*Widdicombe:* Does hypothermia, in man or the cat, increase the strength of the inflation reflex?

*von Euler:* We have studied the effects of temperatures below 35°C. In relatively cold cats, respiratory frequency is reduced and inspiratory duration increased, with the consequence that at the end of inspiration the responsiveness of the inflation reflex has increased according to the plot shown in Fig. 1 (p. 339).

*Karczewski:* If the Hering–Breuer reflex is similar in man and in the hot cat, is this because the pneumotaxic mechanism is well developed in man? And, if so, would inhibition of this mechanism induce in man an inflation response more like this response in other mammals?

*von Euler:* Yes, that is our working hypothesis. I must emphasize that what matters is the *relative* dominance of the pneumotaxic mechanisms over the vagal ones in eupnoeic man.

*Cohen:* It seems reasonable to deduce from the evidence that the higher a species is in the phylogenetic scale, the more its breathing is controlled by higher neural systems (upper pons, midbrain, forebrain) and, therefore, the weaker is its Hering–Breuer reflex.

*Plum:* Our finding (Plum and Alvord, 1964) that pontine damage without vagotomy in man almost totally disrupts respiratory rhythm is good evidence in favour of strong intrinsic pontine control of this rhythm.

*Cross:* A syndrome similar to the Ondine's Curse syndrome (Severinghaus and Mitchell, 1962) occurs in some premature babies. These babies are, in effect, decerebrate and they may "forget" to breathe but be stimulated to start again by any sort of reflex (such as kicking the incubator). A typical story is that a premature baby is found asphyxiated and collapsed, and is resuscitated. The baby will continue to breathe for as long as a nurse stands by and agitates the incubator but as soon as the baby is left unstimulated it stops breathing, becomes asphyxiated again and eventually dies. Professor Plum, can the patients you described with brainstem damage, who breathe to order but not spontaneously, be stimulated to breathe by any other reflex mechanism?

*Plum:* My clinical impression is that they can. I have studied, at post mortem, the brains of two premature neonatal infants who had needed reflex stimulation to maintain the act of breathing. Although these babies had striking suprapontine cerebral abnormalities, the lower brainstem appeared grossly and microscopically normal. Has any other work been published in this subject?

*Cross:* Yes. Cross and Oppé (1952) have shown that periodic breathing can be induced in 85 per cent of all premature babies by giving them 15 per cent oxygen to inhale. Periodic breathing can be abolished in any baby, premature or full-term, by giving it 60 per cent oxygen or high concentrations of carbon dioxide.

*Dejours:* We have not yet adequately discussed the functions of the pulmonary stretch receptors. The classical theory (Adrian, 1933) describes a general relationship between afferent activity and lung volume. Dr von Euler, could you expand your comments on the hypothesis that discharge frequency of the lung receptors is related to the square root of the lung volume?

*von Euler:* Dr F. Clark and I (unpublished results) have recently re-investigated this relationship. We found that, at low and moderate lung volumes, the data usually give a straight line relationship between vagal discharge rate and the square root of volume increase from FRC (or [see Fig 7] between the square of the vagal response and volume), At higher volumes, the discharge rate increases more steeply with volume increments according to a linear relationship. Adrian (1933) used very large inflations, up to 300 ml in a cat, and showed more or less linear overall relationships. Within the physiological ranges, however, his data are in agreement with a square root relationship.

*Petit:* The rate of variation in lung volume as well as its square root are important.

*von Euler:* We obtained a square root relationship when we plotted discharge frequency against the corresponding volume in single breaths, and also when rapid inflations of different amplitudes were applied to the

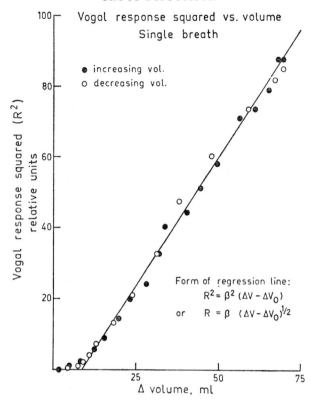

FIG. 7 (*von Euler*). Cat under light pentobarbitone anaesthesia. Afferent discharge from a thin filament of left vagus nerve, and tidal volume (TV) simultaneously recorded during hypercapnia (rebreathing oxygen-rich gas). Simultaneously occurring values of vagal discharge (R) and volume above FRC (V) taken. Vagal response squared plotted against V for a single large breath, both during volume increment (filled circles) and during volume decrement (expiration) (open circles) (Clark, F., and Euler, C. von, unpublished).

trachea and peak discharge frequency plotted against the imposed volume.

*Widdicombe:* I agree in general with your findings, Dr von Euler. I have found a near linear relationship between the square root of lung volume and the frequency of discharge from single pulmonary stretch receptors over most of the range (Widdicombe, 1954). But for all vagal fibres together there are complications at both ends of the graphical relationship. At the lower end of the curves recruitment must be reckoned with; at the upper end (recording from a multifibre vagal preparation) impulses from high threshold, irritant receptors as well as from stretch receptors are registered. This may mask flattening of the curve.

*von Euler:* If the stretch receptors sense an increase in the circumference of the air passages, one would expect a square root function, because circumference is linearly related to the square root of volume. But if, at high volumes, it is mainly length of the bronchi that is increased, then a direct relationship between impulses and volume would be expected (see also p. 107).

*Widdicombe:* Dr Cotes (this volume) has presented good evidence that in his patients the main pathological change (and presumably the site of afferent discharge in the lung) was in the alveoli and so must have involved J receptors. But when the juxtacapillary nerve endings are stimulated, such respiratory changes as an increase in respiratory frequency will initiate secondary afferent activity from the lungs because irritant receptors (which are rapidly adapting and therefore sensitive to rate of change as well as magnitude of change) will also be stimulated. Thus both irritant and J receptors will be excited and act on the respiratory muscle control system of the subjects. The primary reflex response may originate in the J receptors but other receptors must play a role, and possibly a major one, in what is going on. By what criteria do you recognize the J reflex in man, Professor Paintal?

*Paintal:* J receptors are stimulated by any increase in pulmonary capillary pressure, which is therefore the ideal index of activity of the J receptors. But if pulmonary capillary pressure cannot be measured, a tendon reflex such as the knee jerk can conveniently be used to detect activity of these receptors, by means of the J reflex.

*Dornhorst:* Professor Campbell, would you now draw some general conclusions about the lessons we should have learned in the past three days?

*Campbell:* I would like to offer some generalizations for discussion or contradiction. I present these from my standpoint as a respiratory physiologist and clinician without much neuroanatomical or neurophysiological background. Three general points seem to have emerged: about sensation, about the vagus and about afferent information from the chest. First, we have mobilized a number of observations suggesting that sensation can be elicited from the lung or airways, presumably through impulses travelling up the vagus. Examples of this sensation (often referred to as "tightness") occurred in Dr Howell's patients with byssinosis, who feel tightness in the chest in the morning but are otherwise normal; in the man described by Dr Newsom Davis with a high transection of the spinal cord who, when his lungs were emptied from within the airways, felt tightness in his chest; and in Dr Petit himself, who described one component of the sensation during his asthma as a feeling of tightness which is relieved by vagal block. I am not so certain about the tearing sensation Dr Prys-Roberts reported in subjects after prolonged breathing of high concentrations of oxygen. But, with this exception, I suggest that this particular sensation—tightness—could arise in the large bronchial tubes or the trachea. Second, some afferent information, travelling in the vagus, does not seem to me to be directly sensory. This includes information that subserves the Hering-Breuer reflex and that is responsible for the frequency component of the ventilatory response to carbon dioxide and perhaps also the drive (but not the sensation) that limits breath-holding.

Finally I would like to suggest that some sensations exist which are not vagally mediated: first, the awareness of movement of the lung, because, as Dr. Newsom Davis observed, a patient with a cervical cord transection was unaware of such movement within any reasonable range; second, the awareness of excessive ventilation; and third, the awareness of mechanical hindrance to breathing, whether this awareness lies in the ability to detect external loads or in the sensation at the limit of breath-holding.

*Noble:* Our patient with a high cervical cord transection knew exactly where his chest was. Although there is a discrepancy between the findings in this man and in Dr Newsom Davis' rather similar patient, it seems that awareness of the position of the chest could be mediated, at least partly, through the vagi.

*Campbell:* So, we end this symposium in a nice position; much better informed about the origins and effects of information from the lungs travelling in the vagi, but uncertain whether or not any of this information is directly perceived as sensation. Fortunately this uncertainty can probably be resolved by simple clinical observations.

## REFERENCES

ADRIAN, E. D. (1933). *J. Physiol., Lond.,* 79, 332–358.
BISHOP, B. (1963). *J. appl. Physiol.,* 18, 37–42.
BISHOP, B. (1967). *J. appl. Physiol.,* 22, 959–965.
CAMPBELL, E. J. M., DICKINSON, C. J., DINNICK, O. P., and HOWELL, J. B. L. (1961). *Clin. Sci.,* 21, 309–320.
CAMPBELL, E. J. M., DINNICK, O. P., and HOWELL, J. B. L. (1961). *J. Physiol., Lond.,* 156, 260–273.
CAMPBELL, E. J. M., HOWELL, J. B. L., and PECKETT, B. W. (1957). *J. appl. Physiol.,* 135, 40P.
COHEN, M. I. (1964). *Am. J. Physiol.,* 206, 845–854.
CROSS, K. W., and OPPÉ, T. E. (1952). *J. Physiol., Lond.,* 117, 38–55.

ERNSTING, J. (1965). In *Textbook of Aviation Physiology*, pp. 343–373, ed. Gillies J. A. Oxford: Pergamon.

EULER, C., VON, and FRITTS, H. W. (1963). *Acta physiol. scand.*, **57**, 284–300.

EULER, C. VON, HERRERO, F., and WEXLER, I. (1970). *Resp. Physiol.*, in press.

FENN, W. O. (1951). *Am. J. Med.*, **10**, 77–90.

FLENLEY, D. C., PENGELLY, L. D., and MILIC-EMILI, J. (1970). *Clin. Sci.*, **38**, 12P (Communication to Medical Research Society, London, December, 1969.)

HAMMOUDA, M., and WILSON, W. H. (1932). *J. Physiol., Lond.*, **74**, 81–114.

HEAD, H. (1889). *J. Physiol., Lond.*, **10**, 1–71.

HEAF, P. J. D., and PRIME, F. J. (1956). *Clin. Sci.*, **15**, 319–327.

HEY, E. N., LLOYD, B. B., CUNNINGHAM, D. J. C., JUKES, M. G. M., and BOLTON, D. P. G. (1966). *Resp. Physiol.*, **1**, 193–205.

LARRABEE, M. G., and KNOWLTON, G. C. (1946). *Am. J. Physiol.*, **147**, 90–99.

MARSHALL, R. (1962). *J. appl. Physiol.*, **17**, 917–921.

PLUM, F., and ALVORD, E. C., JR. (1964). *Archs Neurol., Chicago*, **10**, 101–112.

RHOTON, A. L., O'LEARY, J., and FERGUSON, J. P. (1966). *Archs Neurol., Chicago*, **14**, 530–540.

SCOTT, F. H. (1908). *J. Physiol., Lond.*, **37**, 301–326.

SEARS, T. A. (1964). *J. Physiol., Lond.*, **174**, 295–315.

SEVERINGHAUS, J. W., and MITCHELL, R. A. (1962). *Clin. Res.*, **10**, 122.

WIDDICOMBE, J. G. (1954). *J. Physiol., Lond.*, **123**, 71–104.

WIDDICOMBE, J. G. (1961). *Clin. Sci.*, **21**, 163–170.

# CHAIRMAN'S CLOSING REMARKS

## A. C. DORNHORST

THE only way in which I can attempt any sort of summary of these proceedings is by trying to present the lessons that I personally have learned during the past three days.

Hering and Breuer originated the idea that the sensory or afferent side of the reflex pathways to and from the lung was important in respiration. Although the particular reflex that they demonstrated is associated with one particular type of receptor they would surely not object to having their idea generalized to include reflexes from the other receptors in the thorax. We have heard good evidence of the existence of these other receptors, which have different fibre sizes, are located in different situations and respond at different speeds to different stimuli. The differential effects of afferent impulses from these different receptors are still poorly understood. Vagal block experiments have shown that under normal resting conditions none of the afferents is important. However, the classical stretch receptors may be important in exercise, and all the receptors are important in a great variety of pathological circumstances. I had always thought that the classical stretch receptor reflex would be shown to be the most dominant in pathological states but I have now had my opinion about this changed. Although it would be rash entirely to sweep aside the importance of the classical Hering–Breuer reflex (for the reason indicated by Dr Widdicombe—interaction of impulses from different receptors) it does now seem likely that the epithelial irritant receptors of Widdicombe and the type J receptors of Paintal play the dominant roles in the production of pathological breathing patterns. When we group all this material together we can at least say that good evidence now exists for the importance of various afferent impulses in the production of abnormal patterns of breathing in man.

We next spent some time (outside Hering and Breuer's original interest) considering the subjective aspects of these afferent pathways and their role in respiratory sensation in normal subjects and in patients. And here there are still many unanswered questions. A good deal of sensation from respiratory events is undoubtedly mediated through the vagus. This includes much of the abnormal sensations in pulmonary disease, although it is not always clear which afferents are concerned or whether different afferents give rise to different and distinguishable sensations. Whether the interruption of vagal afferents will be therapeutic in any type of pulmonary disease is still an open question. Differential blocks by pharmacological means may become possible and this would certainly open up fresh therapeutic possibilities.

We next discussed a related but quite different problem: the role of the phrenic nerve in respiratory sensation. I have been particularly struck by the apparent contrast between afferents travelling in the phrenic nerve and in nerves from the chest wall. The dissociation between these two pathways came as a complete surprise; I did not know that the chest wall played so little and the phrenic nerve so large a role in unpleasant respiratory sensation. Another surprising finding that has emerged from studies of patients who had a therapeutic vagotomy for dyspnoea, and in some of the patients with damage to the cervical cord, is that the sensations in respiratory disease are derived from a complex of abnormal inputs from many sources. The unpleasant sensations experienced by these patients cannot therefore be eliminated by interrupting just one pathway.

Finally, I hope that our discussions have added some facts to two poorly understood aspects of respiratory disease: the control of respiratory drive, and respiratory sensation. Clinicians and the more basic scientists such as the neurophysiologists may have benefited from the exchanges of information in the past three days. It only remains for me to express the appreciation of us all to the Ciba Foundation and its staff for arranging this symposium, and for the excellent way they have looked after us.

# THE TWO ORIGINAL PAPERS BY HERING AND BREUER SUBMITTED BY HERING TO THE K.K. AKADEMIE DER WISSENSCHAFTEN ZU WIEN IN 1868

Translated by

ELISABETH ULLMANN

*Department of Physiology, Medical College of St. Bartholomew's Hospital, London*

## PREFACE

In the hundred years since Hering and Breuer wrote on self-regulation of breathing, changes have taken place which create difficulties for the translator. The meaning of many German words and German usage have altered. Physiological concepts which had only just emerged, or were non-existent in the mid-nineteenth century have developed and become commonplace in current thinking. Medical and physiological terminology still fluid, protean and vague in 1868, has now crystallized and has become rigid as well as clearer.

It was my intention to make a readable English version in the modern idiom, but to remain as far as possible faithful to the original text and not to lose altogether its historical flavour. This frequently required compromise; I have not been consistent in the treatment of all difficult passages.

Without much compunction I have chopped up many of Breuer's long, convoluted sentences into several shorter ones, often changing the sequence of statements contained in his complex clauses and sub-clauses, where this helped to clarify the sense. Other sentences I left unaltered, either because I could do no better or because they are characteristic of the author's style of thought. An example is the immensely long "peroration" (p. 32) in which Breuer proudly sums up and gives a name to the new discovery.

It is evident from their papers that Hering and Breuer had clearly developed the concept of 'feedback'. But they lacked the word, and to use the term in a modern translation would be a crude anachronism. 'Selbst-steuerung' sounds better in German than 'self-steering' does in English. But steering—with its implication of a goal, two-way deviation and two-way adjustment—was the word Hering and Breuer chose from several others (for example *Kontrolle*, *Regulierung*) they might have selected; and no English substitute seemed entirely satisfactory. The temptation to use the concise contemporary lingo was less easy to resist in other instances: for example, 'respiratory centre'. It is today impossible to guess what precisely Hering and Breuer understood by 'the central organ of respiration', or the term respiratory centre itself.

In his next paper: *On the Influence of Respiration on the Circulation* (Hering, 1869) Hering writes: "We propose to distinguish four main kinds of arterial blood and, for the sake of brevity, to call these by special names:

"(1) Apnoeic arterial blood, which is so absolutely arterial that the need to breathe and hence spontaneous breathing movements cease.

(2) Eupnoeic arterial blood, as found in the arteries of a quite normally breathing animal.

(3) Dyspnoeic arterial blood which approximates more or less to the venous blood of the normally breathing animal, and which causes an increased urge to breathe, together with augmented frequency or depth of the spontaneous respiratory movements.

(4) The blood of suffocation, as found in the vessels of an animal that has just choked to death."

Although Hering and Breuer describe as dyspnoea, or dyspnoeic, sometimes a pattern of breathing and sometimes a state of the blood, and never use the terms in the currently accepted sense, I have retained these words in the translation wherever they appear in the original, because no misunderstanding is likely to arise. Here the change in nomenclature between their day and the present is in itself some measure of progress in this field. By contrast, where technical terms employed by the authors have come to be used in a sense so different that the original meaning can no longer be understood, I have followed contemporary usage and have added a note giving the literal translation.

Breuer's references to the literature are fragmentary and sometimes inaccurate. This was not the custom of the period, nor of Breuer himself in later days. It may have been the result of his heavy burden of clinical duties at the time of writing. Not all authors and statements which he quotes could be traced.

An asterisk in the text indicates an original foot-note, which is printed at the bottom of the page. Numbers in the text refer to other notes which are collected together at the end of the translations.

Finally, I would like to thank Dr. J. G. Widdicombe for reading the first version of the translation, and for suggesting many improvements.

ELISABETH ULLMANN

## REFERENCE

HERING, E. (1869). *Sber. Akad. Wiss. Wien*, **60**, 838.

K.K. Akademie der Wissenschaften zu Wien
Sitzungsberichte der Mathematisch-Naturwissenschaftlichen Classe
Vol. LVII, Part II, 1868, pp. 672–677.

p. 669:
XII. Meeting, April 30th, 1868

Dr. Ew. HERING, k.k. Prof. at the Josephs-Akademie, submits a treatise entitled:

### "Self-Steering of Respiration through the *Nervus vagus*"

Communication concerning an investigation carried out by

### DR. JOSEPH BREUER

at the Physiological Institute of the k.k. Josephs-Akademie

By EWALD HERING
*Professor of Physiology*

THE numerous contradictions contained in published reports on the relationship between the vagus nerve and respiration made a re-examination of this subject desirable. Research until now has essentially been restricted to the application of two methods: trans-section of the nerves, and stimulation of the central nerve stump. The inherent inadequacy of the latter method explains why the results obtained with it have been inconsistent. Most studies of reflex effects suffer from the same uncertainty as regards outcome. But this is certainly not only due to the fact that the prevailing state of the central organ[1] has some influence on the result of artificial stimulation of the severed nerve; it must also be due to our inability to make the artificial stimulus sufficiently equivalent in intensity and quality to the natural mode of excitation of the peripheral endings of the fibres involved. In the investigation of reflex effects, whenever it is feasible to excite a nerve from the periphery by, as it were, natural means this should be tried before any attempt is made to stimulate artificially the central stump of the severed nerve.

Dr. Breuer at the Physiological Institute of the Josephs-Akademie undertook to investigate the relationship between the N. *vagus* and respiration from this point of view. The results obtained up to date during this investigation are of sufficient interest to justify brief communication of the main findings to the k.k. Akademie of Science.

It has long been known to the physician, but has hitherto remained entirely unexplained, that the manifestations of dyspnoea are very diverse, depending on whether it is produced by reduction of the respiratory surface area, as e.g. in pneumonia, or by some mechanical hindrance, like stenosis of the larynx. Exactly analogous differences can be observed in animals, depending on whether they are made dyspnoeic in one way or the other. For instance, an animal placed in an oxygen-poor atmosphere breathes faster and more deeply so that greater ventilation of the lung will more or less compensate for the deficient oxygen supply. By contrast, an animal whose trachea has been artificially narrowed breathes less frequently but more energetically, and by doing so it improves its impaired ventilation while inflow and outflow of air are obstructed. Since it is usually considered that in both instances the cause of the dyspnoea lies in the defective gas exchange, it remains to be elucidated how the same cause can have such different effects.

If a cannula is tied air-tight into the trachea of a conscious or unconscious animal, and the cannula is occluded at the moment when the thorax is in its expiratory position, the very next inspiration will already be found to be markedly prolonged and also, as is easy to show, more forceful. How then does it come about that the inspiratory muscles immediately prolong and intensify their contraction, as if the animal sensed some resistance to inspiration and tried to overcome it? By contrast, if instead of occluding the tracheal cannula one suddenly puts it in communication with a large reservoir of oxygen-free air, no immediate prolongation and intensification of the next inspiratory movement occurs, despite the fact that in this case as in the former uptake of oxygen becomes impossible. Conversely, if one occludes the tracheal cannula at the moment when the thorax is in its deepest inspiratory position, the duration of the subsequent expiratory phase is immediately increased, and a longer, and occasionally much longer, pause takes place before the next inspiration, irrespective of whether the lung was filled with atmospheric or with oxygen-free air during the preceding inspiration.

The explanation of these striking phenomena has now been found to be this: *the central nervous organ for breathing movements is in a condition of continuous dependence on the prevailing state of lung distension, through the agency of vagal fibres which terminate in the lung. In other words, the prevailing degree of distension of the lung contributes a modifying influence on the movements of breathing.*

*I. The lung, when it becomes more expanded by inspiration, or by inflation, exerts an inhibitory effect on inspiration and promotes expiration, and this effect is the greater the stronger the expansion. Every inspiration, therefore, in that it distends the lung brings about its own end[2] by means of this distension, and thus initiates expiration.*

Once an inspiration has started, the faster it reaches its goal, namely expansion of the lung, the faster its further progress will be inhibited. If the attainment of this goal is rendered difficult the inhibition will come into play more slowly, and inspiration will develop more fully. Therefore, every mechanical resistance to inspiration, whether it hinders the inflow of air, or hampers expansion of the thorax in some other way (pressure on abdomen or chest, paralysis of individual respiratory muscles, etc.), will at once elicit a longer and more forceful inspiratory movement. When inspiratory expansion of the lung is rendered impossible by thoracotomy, inhibition through distension of the lung is also no longer possible; the inspiratory movement therefore develops maximally and, so to speak, completely exhausts itself. With an intact thorax the same thing happens if both vagi are divided, because the vagi are the pathway along which the inhibition that starts in the expanded lung is conveyed to the central organ.

If inspiration is allowed to proceed freely while at the same time expiration is made more difficult, either by constriction of the tracheal cannula, or by means of a suitable double valve, then the expiratory phases get longer immediately, because the return of the lung to a smaller size is delayed and the duration of the inhibitory state thereby prolonged. If the tracheal cannula is closed completely while the lungs are expanded in inspiration the lungs cannot collapse, and inhibition therefore becomes continuous. Consequently, the next inspiration is delayed for a remarkably long time, in dogs occasionally for more than one minute, even if the animal has filled its lung with oxygen-free air during the preceding inspiration. Analogous events are seen whether one inflates the lungs with oxygen-containing or with oxygen-free air before closing the tracheal cannula; however, the inhibition lasts longer if oxygen-rich air is used. During the inhibition a dyspnoeic state of the blood develops, and consequently powerful inspiratory movements occur eventually; however, if one keeps the tracheal cannula closed they will initially still be separated by abnormally long expiratory pauses.

Any inspiratory movement that is already under way can instantly be cut short by inflating the lungs, irrespective of whether the thorax is closed or open. For instance, in a rabbit made dyspnoeic by opening the chest, as soon as the lungs are inflated the energetically descending diaphragm relaxes instantly; the nares—widely dilated during inspiration—are narrowed at once, and the ribs fall back. The same effect can be achieved by introducing a cannula, air-tight, into one or both halves of the thorax and then re-expanding the collapsed lung by sucking air out of one or both halves of the chest. During artificial ventilation of the lungs with the aid of a tracheal cannula and bellows one can therefore render the rhythm of an animal's active respiratory movements wholly dependent on the rhythm of inflation. This fact is already known, but has so far not been adequately explained. With every inflation an expiratory phase is initiated, with every collapse of the lung the animal makes an active inspiratory movement, so that active inspirations alternate with passive inflations of the lung.

Abolition of an inspiration in progress, initiation or prolongation of the expiratory phase, enhancement of active expiration, and retardation of the return of active inspiration: these are the reflex effects of natural or artificial expansion of the lung which are mediated by the vagi. We can group all these effects together as *expiratory*. All of them disappear at once as soon as both vagi are severed.

*II. Reduction of the size of the lung affects the movements of respiration in the opposite sense.* Every diminution of the volume of the lung instantly evokes a powerful inspiration, irrespective of whether the volume change is brought about by sucking air out of the trachea when the thorax is intact, or by the spontaneous collapse of the lung when the chest is opened. Sudden collapse of the lung through pneumothorax causes a tremendous inspiratory tetanus. In the rabbit this lasts eight to ten seconds, and it is only interrupted in its later course by small oscillations of the diaphragm about its inspiratory position; until gradually, with mounting dyspnoea, greater expiratory relaxations of the diaphragm make their appearance. By reducing the size of the lungs (suction or pneumothorax) any active expiration can instantly be cut short. By introducing air-tight cannulae into the thoracic wall and alternately sucking air from the pleural cavity and then allowing it to re-enter it becomes possible to govern absolutely the respiratory movements of the animal, just as by inflation of the lung via the trachea. Even when the lung is totally collapsed, with its size determined exclusively by the equilibrium of its elastic forces, it is still possible to call forth an inspiratory movement by sucking air from the trachea.

All these phenomena disappear likewise after the vagi are divided in the neck.

We are still engaged trying to establish as accurately as possible the relation between this inspiratory stimulus which acts so forcefully when lung volume is artificially reduced, and the inhibition that is caused by expansion of the lung. Therefore we cannot as yet deal here with the theory behind the facts described.

All the reflex phenomena mentioned manifest themselves in varying degree, depending on whether the blood is dyspnoeic, apnoeic, or of normal composition. By administering some deleterious gas mixture we are thus able to induce dyspnoea and finally asphyxia; and by artificial ventilation by means of rhythmical inflations, or with a steady air stream, we can suppress breathing more and more to the point of apnoea; on the other hand, we are also able—by finely graded application of the mechanical procedures described above—quite arbitrarily either to elicit or to abolish, to shorten or to prolong, both inspiration and expiration. It is therefore evident that it is entirely in the hand of the experimenter to vary the mode of respiratory movements in numerous ways. This facilitates the collection of further evidence in support of the thesis set out above.

---

As regards artificial stimulation of the central stump of the divided vagus nerve, it can now be appreciated why it has led different investigators to such different results. Just as the pulmonary endings of the vagus sometimes elicit inspiratory and sometimes expiratory effects, so also does the electrically excited central stump of the vagus, depending on the manner of stimulation as well as on other circumstances. If one vagus nerve is preserved the effect of stimulating the divided other nerve is further complicated in that the intact vagus may at the same time transmit excitation originating from inspiratory or expiratory reflex stimuli in the lung, and these could either impede or enhance the effects of the artificial stimulation. In his excellent work on the relation between the vagus and respiratory movements Rosenthal[3] voiced the suspicion that all expiratory effects of electrical stimulation of the vagus are solely the consequence of unipolar stimulation of the superior laryngeal nerve. This our experiments have shown to be incorrect. Although the latter nerve has an expiratory action, as Rosenthal's important discovery demonstrated, this has nothing to do with the expiratory effects of the fibres of the vagus which end in the lung. The second important result of Rosenthal's researches—that the brain centre for breathing movements does not respond to artificial stimulation of the vagus during apnoea—was confirmed. Further, it became apparent that making the lung larger or smaller artificially by blowing or sucking may also become ineffective during apnoea.

*Notes:*

1. Hering's generation was still using the word 'Organ' in its classical sense of 'tool' or 'instrument'. With reference to brain and medulla 'Central Organ' very gradually assumed the meaning of 'centre' in current usage. Breuer, in the subsequent paper, uses the term 'respiratory centre' frequently, but not consistently.
2. In common parlance Hering's expressive phrase: "... *sich selbst ein Ende bereiten*" means: to commit suicide.
3. ROSENTHAL, I. (1862). *Die Athembewegungen und ihre Beziehungen zum Nervus Vagus*. Berlin: August Hirschwald.

K.K. Akademie der Wissenschaften zu Wien
Sitzungsberichte der Mathematisch-Naturwissenschaftlichen Classe
Vol. LVIII, Part II, 1868, pp. 909–937.

## Self-Steering of Respiration through the *Nervus Vagus*

By Dr. J. Breuer
*Clinical Assistant.*

With 3 Plates

From the Physiological Laboratory of the k.k. Josephs-Akademie
Submitted by E. Hering at the Meeting of November 5th, 1868.

A preliminary communication concerning the present work has already been presented at the meeting of April 30th. Personal matters have delayed the full account until now.

I. Rosenthal in his researches on "The Movements of Breathing and their Relationships to the Vagus"[1] arrived at the following result:

"The movements of breathing are stimulated by excitation of the respiratory central organ by the blood. The transmission of this excitation to the nerves and muscles involved encounters a resistance, by means of which the continuous excitation is transformed into rhythmical activity. This resistance is augmented through the influence of the *N. laryngeus*; it is diminished through the influence of the *N. vagus.*" Thus, a continuous stimulus conducted centripetally in the vagus increases the number of breaths by reducing this resistance. Rosenthal denies the presence of fibres which inhibit inspiration or elicit expiration in the vagus below the superior laryngeal nerve. He regards phenomena pointing to their existence as due to current spread[2] or to unipolar effects on the superior laryngeal nerve.

The first question requiring an answer thus appeared to be: what is the nature of this stimulus which is conducted in the vagus towards the medulla ? However, we could not hope to solve this question by the methods employed hitherto, that is, by artificial stimulation of severed nerves. The very variable and contradictory results obtained in a series of experiments carried out with this method confirmed us in our conviction that a different approach had to be found. We saw that even when there could be no question of current leaks or unipolar effects the response to stimulation of the vagus was frequently expiration; and that those instances (admitted by Rosenthal himself) when even weak vagal stimulation produced expiratory and not inspiratory effects were by no means rare exceptions. Burckhardt[3] has likewise found the effect of vagal stimulation to be variable and inconstant, and has demonstrated fibres inhibitory to inspiration in the inferior laryngeal nerve (Pflueger's Archiv, vol. 1, 1st issue). We turned to the pulmonary fibres of the vagus, and instead of applying an artificial stimulus along the course of the nerve we attempted to study the effect of natural stimuli acting on the nerve endings of the receptor apparatus.

*The most important result which emerged is that the change in volume, the expansion and diminution of the size of the lung per se, influences respiration through the pulmonary nerves running in the N. vagus.*

Leaving until the end the discussion of the theoretical consequences, and of the not unimportant clinical implications, we now shall first turn to a presentation of our experiments, and to the proof of the conclusions to be drawn from them. The experiments were performed on dogs, cats and rabbits. The animals were nearly always anaesthetized by intravenous injection of opium. We had to regard the resulting change of respiration as an unavoidable evil, since the respiratory rhythm of an unanaesthetized animal becomes even more grossly and variably altered by the operation itself.

In the majority of cases the breathing rhythm of dogs and cats under opium narcosis is on the whole regular, although their breathing is not entirely normal, since the rate is nearly always slow, and the animals breathe out actively, and with considerable force. If a more pronounced change in respiration occurs, if breathing is irregular or very rapid and panting—in the manner of thirsting dogs—then the animals are more or less useless for the experiments to be described. In such instances the action of the respiratory centre is so profoundly altered that normal reflex effects on it can also no longer be observed.

I

*Expansion of the lung reflexly inhibits inspiration and promotes expiration, the more strongly the greater the expansion. This effect depends on the integrity of the N. vagus; the fibres affecting the Medulla oblongata in this manner run along its path.*

If by vigorous artificial ventilation an animal is rendered so apnoeic that when insufflations are stopped, and its thorax has sunk back into the expiratory position, the animal for a time lies still without taking a breath, then the first respiratory movement to follow will be an inspiration of greater or lesser depth. But if after ventilation is discontinued the lung, instead of being left in the expiratory position, is again expanded by renewed inflation with air, and is maintained in the expanded state by closure of the communication with the atmosphere, then the first respiratory movement that ensues is not an inspiration but an expiration of long duration.

Curve I shall serve as evidence for this. It was obtained by the procedure described below which was followed also in a large number of other experiments. A forked cannula is inserted air-tight into the trachea of the animal. From its branches start two tubes, the shorter one leading to the atmosphere. The animal breathes through this tube which is also used to carry out artificial ventilation by means of a side opening. The other tube leads to the manometer of a kymograph, in the present case to a Fick spring manometer[4].

As long as the animal draws air in and pushes it out again through the open breathing tube the manometer is affected only by a fraction of the pressure fluctuations actually taking place in the lung with every respiratory movement. This fraction (the lateral pressure inside the breathing tube) varies in magnitude with the resistance to air flow through the tube, and with the rapidity of the pressure fluctuations. One can increase or decrease this lateral pressure at will by narrowing the breathing tube at some point to a greater or lesser degree by means of a clamp. The lateral pressure will be greatest, i.e. it will attain the full size of the pressure variations in the lung itself, when the breathing tube is closed off completely, and equalization of the pressure in the tube with the atmosphere is thereby prevented.

Curve I comes from a medium-sized dog taking regularly 10 breaths. per minute under opium narcosis. Expiration was always very active; the end of inspiration was followed after a very short pause by a powerful contraction of the abdominal muscles. The ratio between duration of inspiration and duration of expiration was 2:3 or 2:4.

At the start of the experiment the tube leading to the manometer was closed and artificial ventilation via the breathing tube begun. When the animal appeared to have become apnoeic air was once more blown in, and the inlet tube was clamped immediately so that the thorax remained fixed in its inspiratory position. The connexion to the manometer was now restored and the excess pressure prevailing in the lung at once lifted the writing point of the manometer above the baseline. For about 1 minute no respiratory movement was discernible, the writing point tracing a line parallel to the abscissa. Thereafter one saw how the exposed abdominal muscles slowly began to contract, and at the same time the pointer started to rise slowly, and rising continuously it registered a powerful expiratory effort $(\alpha-\beta)$, terminating with the first inspiration.

We possess several more respiratory tracings illustrating the same course of events, obtained by repeating this experiment on other dogs, and on rabbits. It must be mentioned that in this experiment the distension of the lung must be large enough to result in a considerable excess pressure in the thorax. Besides, the pressure in the thorax must not be allowed to drop very much during the period of apnoea. Since it is sometimes difficult to have everything completely air-tight a fall in pressure frequently occurs and jeopardizes the success of the experiment.

If we now attempt to characterize precisely the peculiar features of the respiratory phenomena seen in this experiment we first have to note that, in the present case, a growing stimulus to breathing, instead of eliciting an inspiration, calls forth as the first respiratory movement an expiration that greatly exceeds a normal expiration both in duration and intensity. Evidently, by maintaining the lung and thorax in their inspiratory position an inspiration that would normally have taken place was abolished; and instead, an active expiration was, at the very least, tremendously augmented and prolonged,—if not actually produced in circumstances in which it would otherwise not have occurred. The proof that this is achieved solely through the expansion of the lung will be deferred until later. However, we must at this point deal at once with the objection that smaller inspiratory movements could not have become manifest in the tracings because of the considerable distension of the thorax and the low position of the diaphragm caused by the inflation. Against this the following has to be noted: the manometer records excess air pressure in the thorax, this being due to the elastic forces of the lung, thorax and abdomen. Any inspiratory muscular contraction, even if it were to alter the position of the thoracic wall only negligibly, would have to overcome some part of the elastic forces that press on the air within the lung; and thereby it would inevitably reduce the pressure excess in the lung. Indeed, when inspiration does at last supervene the pressure drops to atmospheric and the pointer to the base-line.

Besides, the instrument used to register these curves is so sensitive that the oscillations in air pressure which are caused by heart movements are recorded as fine wavy lines in some of the tracings. It would therefore certainly record even the smallest respiratory movement. The fluctuations in the rising portion $\alpha\beta$ of Curve I correspond precisely with the momentary relaxation of one or other of the tetanically contracted abdominal muscles. A mercury manometer does not register these at all; they are only made apparent by the exceedingly sensitive Fick manometer.

A similar long-lasting inhibition of inspiration and production or enhancement of active expiration can be obtained with the same experimental arrangement with a non-apnoeic, spontaneously breathing animal if the air inlet is occluded at the height of inspiration, so that expulsion of air from the lung is prevented and the thorax is arrested in the inspiratory position. If this is done at the height of a perfectly normal inspiration during quiet, shallow breathing the effect is not a very large one (Curve II), and expiration (a–b) is in this case prolonged to only double its normal duration. However, the result is startling if one first makes the animal dyspnoeic by obstructing the tube and preventing air intake during a few preceding breaths, and then allows the animal to make one deep inspiration freely, at the end of which one fixes the thorax in the inspiratory position by again clamping the tube. The pointer of the manometer—having at first risen in consequence of the incipient expiratory movement—starts to drop slightly, but then remains stable for a long time at this level; it then slowly and jerkily ascends to a considerable height until finally the first inspiratory movement drags it back to, or below, the baseline. If one continues to keep the airway closed extremely strenuous and long-lasting expiratory efforts manifest themselves during the next breaths, despite the intense dyspnoea. The great restlessness of the animal eventually forces the experimenter to release the airway. In this manner we have obtained intervals between successive inspirations and expirations lasting 70–75 seconds.

The course of respiration in such an experiment is shown in Curve III. This comes from the same dog as the apnoea Curve I, and was also recorded with the Fick spring manometer. The first four inspirations A–B, each lasting 7 or 6 seconds, progressively increase in depth because the airway is closed, and no gas exchange can therefore take place. At B the tube is opened, and the animal now draws one very deep inspiration. Just before the end of this inspiration the tube is closed again. (This is shown on the tracing by the small downward deflection before C. The trace which ran along the baseline while the inlet tube was fully open suddenly yields to the negative pressure in the chest at the moment when the airway is occluded.) There is now a pause of 75 seconds before the next inspiration. Despite growing dyspnoea the durations of the next breaths are 14, 10 and 9 seconds, and the tracing shows progressively increasing expiratory efforts, with brief inspiratory and very protracted expiratory phases. During the prolonged expiration CD the abdominal muscles were taut from the start and remained like this, but became even more tensely contracted towards the end.

This pattern of respiratory muscle activity is not entirely constant. In other similarly conducted experiments the abdominal muscles relaxed after a few seconds and the pressure in the trachea dropped accordingly, only to

PLATE I

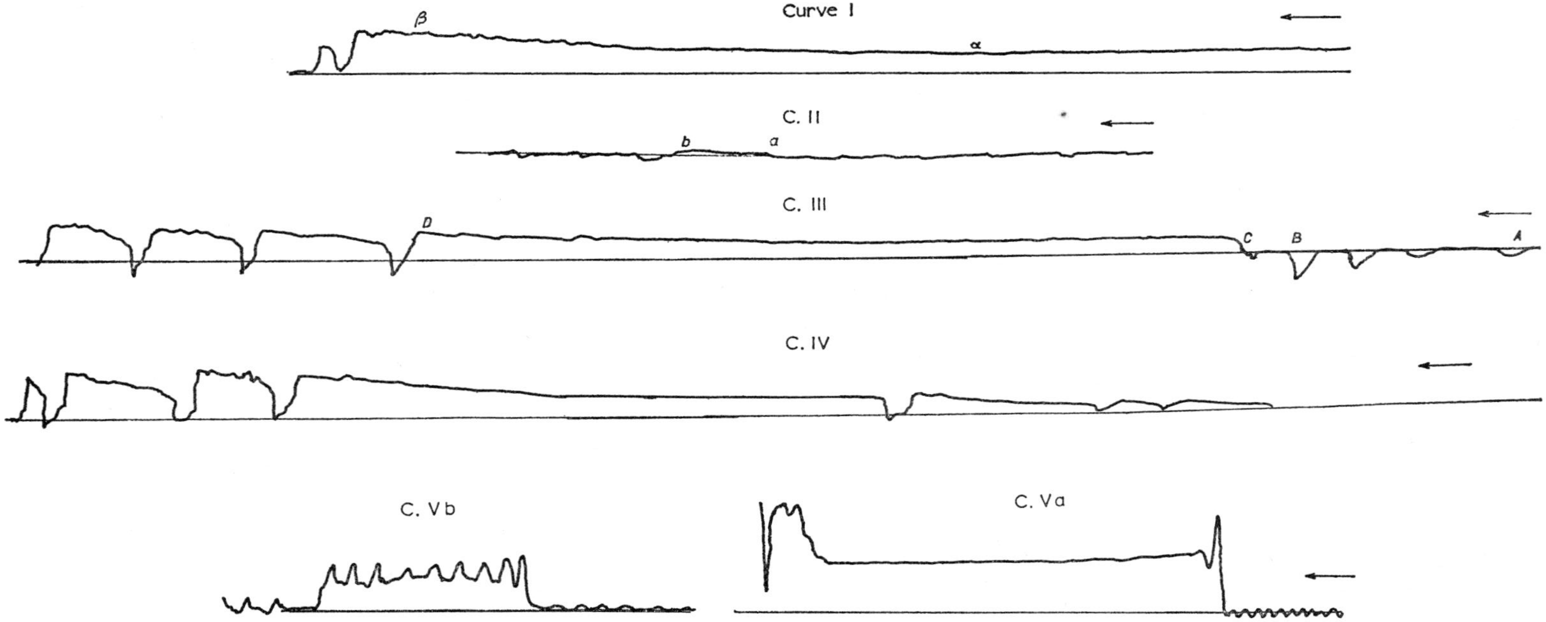

Curve I

C. II

C. III

C. IV

C. Va

C. Vb

PLATE II

C. VI A

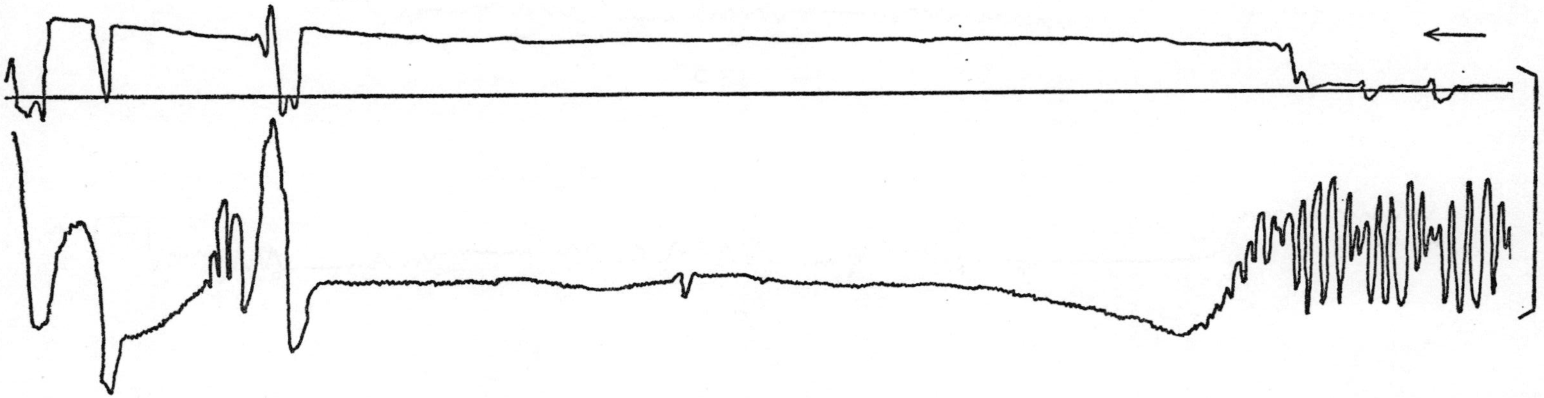

C. VI B

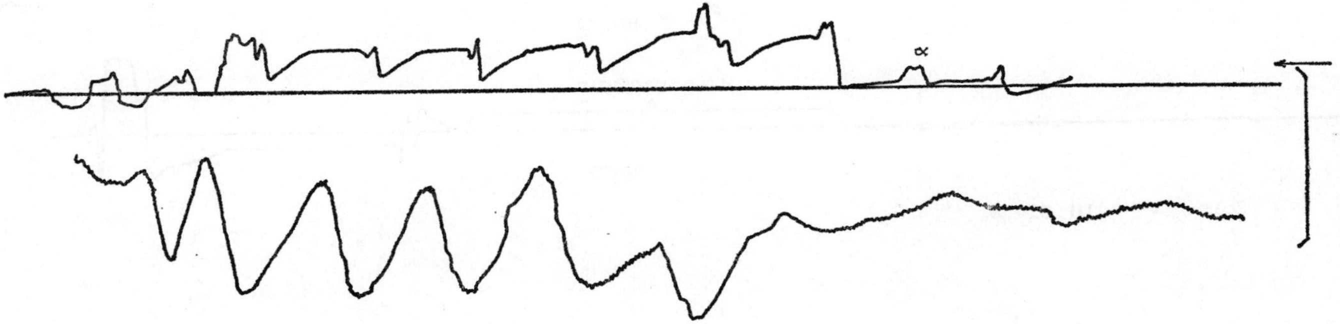

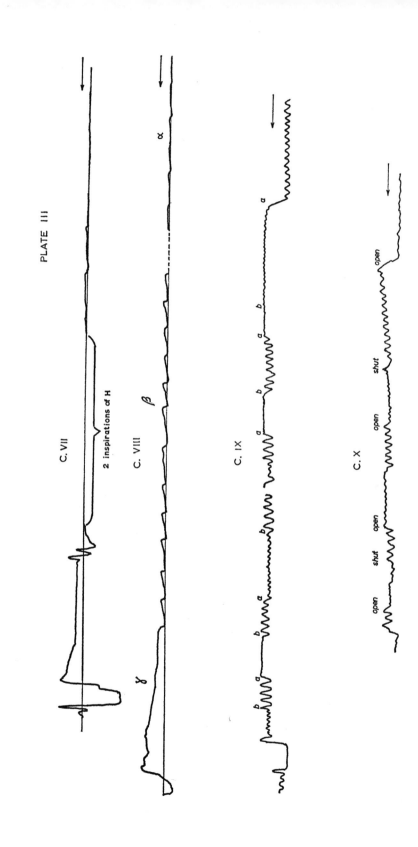

PLATE III

C. VII

2 inspirations of H

C. VIII

C. IX

C. X

become elevated again later by recurrence of the tonic contraction of the expiratory musculature. As previously in the apnoea studies the active movement in these latter cases took place wholly outside the normal respiratory rhythm and was not merely an extension of expiration during undisturbed regular breathing.

An interesting variation of the experiment just described can be obtained if the breathing tube is fitted with a valve which permits inspiration but prevents expiration. A common mercury valve of the kind used in syphons was employed for this purpose; a side branch connected the manometer to the breathing tube and thus to the trachea. Air is sucked into the thorax with every inspiration and since it cannot escape again the lung and thorax become more and more distended. Corresponding with the increasing distension the expirations shown on the tracings become longer and longer and are performed with increasing effort until finally an expiratory thrust bursts the valve, spatters the mercury, and brings the experiment to an end. (Curve IV, from the same dog.)

The same experiment performed on a rabbit provided the following data: with the tracheal cannula open the animal breathed 11 times in half a minute when there was no valve; when the valve was in position 25 seconds elapsed between the first and second inspiration, and another 28 seconds before the third. During the second minute single breaths took place after intervals of 15, 8, 7 and finally 5 seconds. When the experiment was repeated the intervals between breaths lasted 8, 28, 4, 5, 3, 5 and 5 seconds, whereas after removal of the valve 17 respirations occurred in the space of 15 seconds.

If expiration is not completely blocked but only made more difficult it is correspondingly prolonged, and the rhythm becomes predominantly expiratory. We shall see later that an analogous mechanism holds for inspiration also, and that it has an important corollary in pathology.

Instead of letting the lung be expanded by the animal's own breathing one can also blow up the lung through the tracheal cannula and can in this way achieve an even longer duration of expiration, in accordance with the considerably greater distension of the lung. (In this experiment a record obtained from the same dog as Curves I, III, and IV showed a pause of 100 seconds between inspirations.) In this case it makes no difference whether the lung is blown up during inspiration, reinforcing the expansion, or whether it is done immediately after the end of expiration. In the latter case, however, the result is more striking, because the rhythm leads one to expect an inspiratory movement which is in fact suppressed, and an expiration is evoked out of step and against the natural sequence, just as in the apnoea Curve I. The respiratory tracing in Curve VI A was obtained in this manner (mercury manometer); the trace below shows the simultaneous fluctuations of blood pressure.

If one reopens the airway before the start of the first subsequent inspiration, that is during the continuously increasing expiration, so as to bring about collapse of the thorax, an inspiration will follow at once. If the return to the expiratory position is induced earlier—some time before the end of the pause which precedes inspiration—the subsequent course of the breathing pattern may take one of two forms. Sometimes, especially if the air was let out very early and gradually, the animal remained quiescent for a few seconds before the next inspiration. But on most occasions inspiration followed instantly upon return to the expiratory position.

The effect of maintained distension of the lung and thorax is the same if hydrogen [H] instead of atmospheric air is inspired, or blown into the trachea, even if the animal, having previously inhaled a few breaths of H, has—so to speak—washed out its lungs with H. In this case the duration of the inhibition of inspiration is shorter, but the shape of the curve is exactly the same as for inflation with atmospheric air (see Curve VII, Plate III).

The same is true if the animal has been rebreathing air in a closed space for some time. When carrying out this experiment an air-tight connexion is made between the breathing tube and a limply inflated, moist bladder[5]. The animal rebreathes from the bladder air with progressively diminishing oxygen content, becomes dyspnoeic, and at this stage is then prevented from expiring by sudden clamping of the airway at the end of an inspiration. This was the manner in which Curve VIII was obtained. The resistance of the bladder to distension by the expired air was greater than its resistance to collapse when air was sucked out of it. This is why inspiration does not cause the trace to fall below the level of the baseline until the breaths are dyspnoeic at stage $\beta$, whereas expirations are already clearly marked during the first minute, stage $\alpha$. Segment $\gamma$ of the curve, which corresponds to the arrest of the lung in distension, is exactly analogous to the tracings obtained previously in similar circumstances.

The experiments mentioned so far were performed with the thorax intact. Those now to be discussed were done with the thorax open and yielded the same result. In these experiments rabbits and cats were used. In the cats the diaphragm, and in the rabbits the movements of the nostrils, were closely watched. Regarding rabbits, it should be noted that, as is well known, it is difficult to get them fully anaesthetized. It happened occasionally that, quite contrary to expectation, an animal responded to distension of the lung by air inflation with an inspiration instead of an expiration. However, this anomaly always vanished after two or three repetitions and the usual reactions then appeared. In these instances we always noticed that the animal would also respond with a brief inspiration to every other kind of surprising shock, for instance to a tap on the animal board and the like, and that this was merely a psychic reflex. Obviously, in such animals only reactions that are entirely consistent merit consideration. As regards observation of nostril movement in rabbits, it may well be that this method is not sensitive enough for the precise observation of even the minutest inspiratory responses which is necessary for experiments employing electrical stimulation of the vagus; but for the coarse differences produced by our experiments the method is sufficiently accurate. As far as we could see, the movements of the nares are exactly parallel to the movements of the diaphragm and other respiratory muscles. We were unable to establish any special dependence of nostril movement on the vagus, a possibility Rosenthal had suspected; and even if it really did exist this would not diminish the significance of our findings. Observation of the nostrils was not only convenient, but the only way of getting any information at all in animals with intact thorax whose diaphragm was passively displaced by insufflation of the lungs, thereby obscuring any assessment of active diaphragm movement.

If the thorax is opened in a rabbit and artificial respiration then started the animal continues to breathe at its own rhythm, irrespective of the rhythm of inflations, provided lung ventilation is carried out at high frequency so that the lung is not exposed to considerable fluctuations in volume. But as soon as the lung oscillates within wider limits, especially if the amplitude is similar to the volume of a normal expansion, the animal's respiration becomes entirely dependent on the inflations, so that "it responds to every inflation with an expiration and to every collapse of the lung with an inspiration" (Traube)[6]. This can easily be confirmed by watching either the nostrils or the diaphragm of the rabbit. The former are narrowed more or less forcefully during inflation, depending on the degree of dyspnoea, and they dilate during the intervals between inflations. The diaphragm ascends during inflation and descends in the pauses. It is somewhat deceptive that during inflation the expanding lower lobes of the lung impart a slight downward movement to the diaphragm and that during diminution of lung volume the liver, falling backwards, gives it a small upward push. But with careful attention these passive movements are easily distinguishable from those which are due to the contraction and relaxation of the muscle itself. If the lung is maintained in the inflated state no inspiratory movement of any kind takes place for a long time, just as in animals with intact thorax, while nose and abdominal muscles indicate expiration. If artificial ventilation is discontinued for a time and dyspnoea develops, an incipient deep inspiratory movement of the diaphragm will be cut short at once if the lung is inflated, and the diaphragm instantly falls back into its relaxed position.

The following experiment is very neat and instructive, although it permits only observations on the nares. A hole is pierced into the intercostal space on the right or on both sides, and into the opening a double cannula is introduced of the type devised by Ludwig for measurement of lateral blood pressure. These cannulae consist of two pieces of metal tubing of about 2 mm diameter, one being made to slide within the other by means of a small screw. Each tube carries at one end a small elliptical disc mounted at right angles to the axis of the tube. By manipulation of the screw the relative positions of the inner and outer tube can be altered, and the two discs brought close to each other and pressed together. A length of elastic tubing is fixed to the outer, free end of the inner tube through which air can enter into the pleural cavity and be sucked out again.

If such a cannula is placed into the intercostal opening in such a manner that the edges of the wound come to lie between the two plates and the plates are brought together by means of the screw they will form an airtight seal closing the intercostal space. If one then connects the two cannulae through a Y-piece the two pleural cavities are put into communication, and both lungs can be collapsed simultaneously by allowing air to enter both halves of the thorax. By sucking air out again the lungs can subsequently be restored almost to their normal volume.

Every such extraction of air from the pleural sacs, that is, every expansion of the collapsed lung will instantly terminate any inspiration in progress. This is evident from the fact that the nares instantaneously assume their expiratory position. However, it is only very rarely possible to produce in this manner a more prolonged pause between inspirations, such as is achieved by blowing up the lung beyond its normal volume.

Having established the fact that in the experiments described there is a connexion between expansion of the lung and inhibition of inspiration and stimulation of expiration, it now remains to prove the claim that this is directly attributable to lung expansion and not to some other factors which are brought into operation at the same time. Two such factors might be the greater or lesser oxygen content of the blood, and the alterations in blood pressure. However, both these factors can easily be excluded, and they would in any case deserve consideration only with respect to the intervals between inspirations, but certainly not as regards the initiation of active expiration against and outside the prevailing respiratory rhythm.

The most obvious suggestion is that the inspiratory pause is a form of apnoea due to a greater uptake of oxygen by the blood in the distended lung which contains a larger amount of air and hence also of oxygen, and where the pressure is positive even when there is no active expiratory effort. Einbrodt explained these phenomena, as far as they were known to him, in this way (*Sitzungsberichte der k.k. Akademie d. Wissenschaften, mathem.-naturw. Classe*, vol. 40, p. 361). However, this suggestion is untenable in view of the experiments in which the animal was made to breathe pure hydrogen, and also in view of the experiments in which the air retained in the lung was so poor in oxygen that the animal was already intensely dyspnoeic from the start. Furthermore, we exposed the saphenous artery and vein in the rabbit and convinced ourselves that at the moment of the first inspiration after a very large inflation of the lung both these dilated and well-filled vessels were of exactly the same colour; that is, the artery contained blood that was venous.

Another factor involved might be the change in blood pressure brought about by the pressure change within the thorax. Curve VI A on Plate II displays the air pressure in the trachea and the simultaneous carotid blood pressure, recorded synchronously with two manometers both before and during air insufflation. (The behaviour of the blood pressure is in complete agreement with the findings of Einbrodt; by contrast, the change of pulse frequency differs from his account, and I intend to return to a fuller discussion of this later.)[7] As the curve demonstrates, the blood pressure momentarily rises with the onset of a pressure excess inside the thorax, but then declines, because the inflow of blood into the chest is hampered and the pulmonary capillaries are compressed. After some time blood pressure rises again somewhat. *A priori* there is no ground for considering a decline in arterial and a rise in venous pressure as a factor likely to reduce the need to breathe. But this ought to be the case if the above mentioned altered blood pressure relationships are to be responsible for inducing pauses between inspirations. A complete refutation of this entire suggestion is provided by the experiments with open thorax. In these, pressure changes inside the thorax which largely account for the fall in blood pressure just do not take place. Similarly, in the experiments in which the collapsed lung was re-expanded by aspiration of air from the pleural cavity exactly opposite pressure changes occur in the thorax.

If then the expansion of the thorax and lung does not affect the medulla either through a change in gas content, or pressure, or quantity of the blood, the only possible assumption remaining would seem to be *that the alteration in the action of the respiratory centre is directly mediated by nerves;*

*that is, that the observed phenomena are reflex effects of a peripherally acting stimulus.*

The next question now to be answered concerns the site of this peripheral stimulus.

In one series of our experiments lung and thorax were both expanded, or kept distended, simultaneously. But those other experiments with open thorax, in which inflation could not have influenced the chest wall, prove that the effective stimulus is exerted directly on the lung (and its pleura), at least in greater part. Admittedly it is possible, though not proven, that a similar effect may arise to a lesser extent from the thoracic wall. But our findings permit us to regard as conclusively established that expansion of the lung itself reflexly inhibits inspiration and promotes expiration. That the effective agent in this reflex is expansion and stretching of the lung, and not compression of the tissue of the lung by increased intrapulmonary air pressure, was made apparent by the experiments in which the collapsed lung was brought back to its normal volume by suction on the intrapleural cannula. During this latter experiment the pressure inside the lung was not higher than atmospheric; and the inhibition of inspiration which was produced can therefore certainly not have depended on an elevation of pressure.

Conversely, the following experiment served us likewise as proof for this argument. After air-tight insertion of a thoracic cannula[8] the lung was first brought back to its normal volume by sucking air out of the pleural sacs. Next, the tracheal cannula was occluded and air under considerable pressure was pushed back again into the pleural sacs via the thoracic cannulae. In these circumstances the conditions were all exactly the same as during artificial inflation of the lung: the same excess pressure within the thorax, the same blood pressure relationships, the same expansion of the thorax, the same compression of the lung parenchyma by the excess pressure. Only expansion of the lung itself was missing, and not the slightest inhibition of inspiration developed. The animal's nostrils continued to move in their normal rhythm. Hence the agent affecting the respiratory centre is without any doubt just expansion of the lung itself. However, I am not yet in a position to discriminate in this respect between lung parenchyma and *pleura pulmonalis*.

Section of the vagi teaches us which nervous pathway is involved in conveying this stimulus from the lung to the medulla. If only one of these nerves is cut the phenomena described are not altered in any way. But as soon as the second vagus is also divided it becomes impossible to exert any influence whatever on the respiratory rhythm by expanding the lung.

Lung inflation now no longer inhibits inspiration, and respiration continues in the same unaltered rhythm, irrespective of whether the lung is collapsed or grossly distended. Inspiration and expiration now interfere with the inflations of artificial ventilation, whereas previously (as Traube had already shown) they became synchronized with the artificial rhythm. Thus it is evident that the connexion between action of the respiratory centre and change of lung volume is completely abolished.

Curve V B, Plate I, illustrates how respiration continued throughout the period of lung inflation in the same dog from whom Curve V A was obtained before section of the vagi. Curve VI B shows the simultaneous fluctuations of air pressure and blood pressure in trachea and carotid during inflation following section of both vagi. This curve came from the dog who provided Curve VI A before the section. Respiration and the resulting fluctuations of blood pressure proceed undisturbed, in contrast to the long inhibition of inspiration and the steady low blood pressure evident in Curve VI A.

Among the numerous respiratory records of this type which we have obtained there are a few which demonstrate some prolongation of expiration even after division of both vagi. But the usual conspicuous rise of air pressure which is due to the active expiration that precedes the first inspiratory effort was not found in any of these records; and only in one single instance was expiration twice as long as the intervals separating inspirations during free breathing. I do not believe that these infrequent, but definite, occurrences weaken in any way our previous conclusions, and I shall at once attempt to explain them. It should be noted that the observations mentioned above concern exclusively experiments in which the thorax was left intact. By contrast, if the chest was opened we never found respiration to be influenced in any way by the state of expansion of the lung, once the vagi were divided. In those experiments in which the thorax was left unopened the chest wall was always distended as well and, as already pointed out, it is possible that a stimulus, analogous to the one transmitted in the vagi, arises from the chest wall and reaches the medulla. I consider it as very probable that the observed prolongation of expiration after vagal section is attributable to such a stimulus. Anyway, in the great majority of experiments this phenomenon was absent altogether. It probably depends on the depth of narcosis whether a stimulus originating in the chest wall—which in any case is much feebler than the stimulus coming from the lung—will produce an effect or not.

Perhaps the ineffectiveness of lung inflation after section of the vagi might be open to a different interpretation. One could assume that the peripheral

13*

stimulus evoked by lung expansion acts on the medulla as before, and that it is not transmitted by the vagi; but that after section of the vagi the respiratory centre becomes too insensitive to other stimuli, and is insufficiently labile to be capable of inducing marked changes in respiratory rhythm. We cannot at present disprove this view. On the other hand, we can see no ground for regarding it as likely. Furthermore, the following experiment speaks against these assumptions. In one dog both vagi were divided and the central stump of one of them was then stimulated with a current of suitable strength. When the rate of breathing had attained approximately the same frequency as the previous normal respiration the lung was inflated as in earlier experiments. Yet no influence of lung volume on respiration was discernible, although here the respiratory centre appeared to have been restored as far as possible to the *status quo ante*.

In this context the following experiment is also of great interest. If one vagus only is divided in a dog and its central end then stimulated using a current strength which evokes forceful inspiration, such stimulation becomes ineffective if the lung is simultaneously inflated, as long as there is no pronounced dyspnoea. Only when dyspnoea has considerably increased will stimulation of the vagus again elicit inspiration. As shown previously, no true apnoea exists in this situation. Consequently, failure of vagal stimulation cannot be interpreted as an absence of responsiveness of the respiratory centre to inspiratory vagal excitation (as in Rosenthal's beautiful apnoea experiments). Instead, it must be assumed that the inhibition induced or enhanced by expansion of the lung is too intense to be overcome by vagal stimulation which otherwise leads to inspiration.

One further remark may here be permitted, concerning the peculiar behaviour of some dogs whose breathing during anaesthesia was quite abnormal. Not uncommonly one finds animals whose respiration after an injection of opium becomes so rapid and shallow that it is almost impossible to count the frequency. Their breathing pattern strongly resembles the panting of thirsty dogs, as already mentioned. We saw one such animal in whom these small inspirations were superimposed on large slowly executed respiratory movements in such a manner that the slowly descending diaphragm performed a series of regular small contractions in rapid succession during its descent. In such animals the effect of lung inflation is variable. Sometimes it produces no result at all, the animal panting as before with its thorax distended. Sometimes inflation of the lung will inhibit these peculiar inspirations, and they will recommence immediately when inflation ceases. At other times the dogs will breathe quietly and regularly for a while after the end of inflation but will gradually get back into the panting rhythm, and in yet other instances a single inflation of short duration is enough to quieten the animals. They may remain for a few seconds without taking a breath and then start to breathe regularly, but eventually the frequency will increase again until panting is re-established as before. All such observations merely seem to us to indicate quite abnormal conditions, attributable to the powerful influence of opium narcosis, and no relevant conclusions can be drawn from them. But because of their peculiarity they seemed worth mentioning.

## II

We now turn to the effects of reducing the size of the lung, and shall begin by summarizing the results of our investigation: *Reduction in lung volume arrests instantly any expiratory movement that may be in progress at the time, and at once elicits an inspiration.*

When the thorax of a rabbit is opened and consequently its lung suddenly collapses, an intense inspiratory tetanus appears immediately in nostrils, diaphragm and thorax, and in the rabbit this persists for up to 8 or 10 seconds. Subsequently small short-lived relaxations can be seen in the diaphragm while it stands in its lowest inspiratory position. It is shifted upward only very slightly by these relaxations ("it oscillates about its inspiratory position").[9] Only with growing dyspnoea do these expiratory relaxations begin to lengthen, and the upward movements which they cause likewise start to increase in amplitude, until at last the excursions of the diaphragm attain the magnitude usually found during dyspnoea.

If by closing the trachea the lung is kept expanded (but not beyond its normal size) and dyspnoea is allowed to progress until strong, active expiratory movements are generated, these will be instantly abolished as soon as the lung is made to collapse rapidly; a process which, if need be, can be accelerated by sucking air out of the trachea.

If air-tight cannulae are inserted into the thoracic wall in the manner already described the nares of the rabbit will dilate as soon as air is allowed to enter the pleural cavity and the lung is thereby made to collapse; the nares narrow again the moment the air is sucked out. In this manner one can completely control the animal's respiration, just as by inflation with bellows; with every diminution in lung volume the rabbit breathes in, with every enlargement it breathes out.

Since the closed thorax of the rabbit is flexible it is sufficient merely to suck air out of the trachea to make the chest wall fall in, and this instantly brings about dilation of the nostrils. An uninitiated spectator, unfamiliar with the nature of the experiment, would assume, from observing the animal's nose while air is alternately sucked out and blown into the trachea, that the nostrils are blown open by a current of air and then snap shut again like a valve. Naturally, only if the animal does not react with an inspiration to touch or any other kind of accidental mechanical disturbance can one regard the inspiratory movements of the nostrils as specific reflex effects of reduction in lung size.

Sucking air out of the trachea or sudden collapse of the lung through pneumothorax will elicit inspiration also during apnoea, provided the apnoea is not too intense. We are justified in saying this by the following fact: when artificial respiration has been initiated and nares movements have become adapted, so that narrowing occurs with every inflation and dilation with every pause, it is found that these movements become in time progressively weaker and weaker until they finally cease altogether. The time when this occurs varies with different animals. Frequently one finds rabbits whose nostrils cease to move already after the first inflation; but if artificial respiration is then stopped the animal immediately continues to breathe, and can thus not have been fully apnoeic. By contrast, there are many animals whose nares continue to move throughout long periods of ventilation, but are found to be apnoeic when the bellows are stopped. In these latter instances sucking out or blowing in air will still produce the appropriate movement of the nose, but the animal will not continue to breathe rhythmically on its own. Eventually, if one continues further to ventilate the animal artificially a point is reached when the reaction to alteration of lung size is also abolished, and the animal is then in a state of absolute apnoea. The same sort of behaviour which we have here observed during the onset of apnoea is also seen during recovery from apnoea. One can frequently observe a stage when one or the other or both reflex movements return while the animal is still apnoeic when it is not stimulated. These reflexes thus become manifest only if some stimulus to breathing is present in the respiratory centre itself (as Rosenthal[10] discovered and proved for reflexes resulting from artificial stimulation of the vagus). Therefore, even if the animal does not breathe spontaneously it is not in a condition of complete apnoea if reflexes can be evoked, but merely in a state of latent, low, central respiratory excitability. It is thus legitimate to speak of absolute and relative apnoea. We were unable to detect a consistent pattern that held for all rabbits with respect to the selective occurrence of one or other reflex during profound apnoea. Sometimes only the inspiration when lung volume was reduced, sometimes only the expiration when it was enlarged occurred, but no reason for this was apparent.

As previously remarked, the mere return of a greatly inflated lung to its normal volume does not regularly evoke inspiration (at least not in our narcotized animals) as long as the animal is not severely dyspnoeic. We could therefore not ascribe to an inspiratory stimulus consisting of reduction of an inflated lung to its normal volume the same efficacy as to one due to further diminution of lung size downward from the expiratory position. The explanation of yet another phenomenon that is worth mentioning appears to require an assumption of this kind. The respiratory rhythm of an animal adapts to regular inflations not only if the imposed rhythm is slower, but also if it is considerably faster. The former case is readily comprehensible, since any inspiration out of step with the artificial rhythm will be suppressed by the passive lung distension caused by the insufflation. But when the imposed rhythm is speeded up more inspirations take place than before, and they occur in the intervals between inflations. It thus seems that some other respiratory stimulus must be active in this. It might be argued that the return of an expanded lung to its normal volume can provide only a weak stimulus which by itself is inadequate to induce inspiration; but that its periodic repetition nevertheless influences the respiratory centre sufficiently to achieve adaptation to an artificial rhythm. However, such an assumption does not appear to be absolutely necessary, since periodic inhibition of inspiration alone might explain the phenomenon. For with every inflation which interrupts an incipient inspiration some part of the existing inspiratory drive[11] is prevented from being discharged. Consequently the stimulus will now rise more rapidly to reach the intensity required for discharge, because the quantum of excitation which newly arises in every interval of time will add on to the one remaining from the previous, interrupted respiration, instead of building up from zero as after an inspiration that has run its full course.

A lower limit of lung size from which further diminution would be ineffective does not really exist. Even if the lung is completely collapsed and at the point of equilibrium between the elastic forces, suction of air from the trachea still elicits inspiration.

*All these manifestations disappear with section of the vagi.* It is impossible afterwards to evoke an inspiration outside the normal respiratory rhythm in the manner described, or to cut short an expiration.

In the interest of a continuous presentation we have so far omitted to mention to what extent the facts described are already known, and who has previously reported them. This shall now be done. As mentioned above, synchrony[12] between respiration and ventilation, and the disappearance of this synchrony after trans-section of the vagi was observed by L. Traube.

Our investigations agree with the findings of Budge (*Virchow's Archiv*, vol. 16, p. 433)[13] only as far as one result is concerned, and even there only apparently. We differ from him completely as regards the causes and interpretation of the observed facts. Budge concludes, on the basis of phenomena seen when the vagus is stimulated or divided, that the vagus conveys centripetal impulses to an expiratory vagal centre which stands in antagonistic relationship to an inspiratory centre. Budge considers $CO_2$ to be the peripheral stimulus to the lung. A part of the observations described here were reported by Einbrodt in his paper "On the Influence of the Movements of Breathing on Heart Beat and Blood Pressure".[14] Einbrodt exposed the lung to positive and negative pressure ($+D$ and $-D$)[15] within wide limits (10–125 mm Hg), and registered respiratory movements by means of a simple lever. (The present investigation was in part still carried out with the apparatus used by Einbrodt.) He reports: with $+D$ of about 10 mm Hg breathing movements are not significantly impaired; at 10–20 mm Hg they become laboured, and the rhythm alters. Inspiration takes place rapidly and is extraordinarily brief. Expiration, by contrast, becomes extremely laboured and occupies a much longer time; as a rule, expiration is followed by a long pause. At 20–35 mm Hg respiratory movements cease altogether for long periods of time, frequently for several minutes, and only take place after long intervals; a prolonged pause follows every more or less deep inspiration. Einbrodt tried the effect of elevating the pressure in the lung also on himself. He experienced a distressing sensation of extreme oppression[16] which compelled violent attempts to expire. (This, indeed, is the simplest experiment, and was the starting point for the present investigation. If one inspires fairly deeply, and then holds one's breath by closing the glottis, or mouth and nose, a series of expiratory efforts will ensure, until after some considerable period—that is, if one can bear the distress of dyspnoea for so long—an inspiratory movement will eventually be performed.) That the long pauses between breaths are neither wholly nor in major part due to large amounts of oxygen diffusing into the blood when the pressure in the lung is raised has already been fully discussed. Besides, Einbrodt thought that these phenomena could be explained by the fact that a raised air pressure would make inspiration easier and expiration more difficult. So that ventilation could proceed at all brief inspirations would therefore have to alternate with laboured and long-lasting expirations. Such behaviour would obviously be highly purposeful; but that in itself does not clarify how it comes about that the respiratory centre acts in such a purposeful manner, but does no longer do so after the vagi are cut. This Einbrodt did not consider any further, having made only incidental observations on these relationships. The facts he observed correspond entirely with our own findings during lung expansion, especially if it is remembered that in Einbrodt's experiments a whole large chamber full of compressed air was connected to the trachea, and that the air in the lung could come into thorough diffusion equilibrium with this air during the pauses between breaths. Consequently the dyspnoea did not grow nearly as rapidly as in our experiments, and the long pauses between successive inspirations could therefore manifest themselves undiminished for a much longer time. With regard to negative pressure, Einbrodt states that the animal always continues to breathe, but that inspiration now becomes very laboured; and this too has now been elucidated.

---

We have seen that increases in the volume of the lung cause expiratory, and decreases cause inspiratory impulses to be sent to the respiratory centre via the vagi. To forestall any possible misunderstanding, it should here be mentioned at once that we do not consider these to be the only stimuli which are transmitted to the respiratory centre along the vagi, as is to be amplified later. The question now arises whether both stimuli, the expiratory was well as the inspiratory, are transmitted in the same or in different fibres. The nerves from the skin which are thought to mediate the sensation of heat as well as of cold would offer an analogy in favour of the former assumption. This matter can not be decided at the present, any more than the question whether there exists a medium, neutral lung volume which evokes neither inspiration nor expiration. One might argue, against the existence of a neutral volume, that expansion of the collapsed lung produces an expiratory effect, even if the inflation has not restored the lung to the volume it would occupy in the closed chest at maximum expiration. However, by analogy with the sensation of temperature, the effect of contrast comes to mind here. That it is not merely fluctuations in lung volume which are instrumental in causing excitation is demonstrated by the fact that the inflated lung stimulates expiration for a minute or more, during which time the volume of the lung does not change at all.

Finally, it is conceivable that one of the two stimuli, e.g. the inspiratory, is continuously active, and not in any way dependent on the state of inflation of the lung tissue, but is determined instead by some other factors, such as the chemical state of the lung, or the $O_2$ or $CO_2$ content of the alveolar air or blood. Expiratory activity, on the other hand, might be dependent on expansion of the lung, and if this were reduced the effectiveness of the inspiratory drive would be augmented owing to the opposite effect. In the present state of this investigation I dare not proffer a definite suggestion as to which of these hypotheses is the correct one. I hope to come closer to a conclusion by further experimentation.[17]

It was stated above that we do not regard stimuli conditioned by the state of the lung to be the only inspiratory stimuli transmitted in the vagi. We convinced ourselves of the existence of a continuously active inspiratory excitation in the following manner. Supposing we succeeded by one means or another in maintaining an animal in a state of steady respiratory chemistry, without at the same time having the volume of the lung affected by breathing movements. In that situation the usual stimuli which arise through volume changes would not be acting on the medulla. If in these circumstances section of the vagi still reduced the rate of breathing, this would indicate that before vagal section some other stimulus must have been transmitted in the vagi, accelerating respiration. The experiment which was based on these reflections was performed as follows. As in Hook's experiment, air from a gasometer was driven under constant pressure through the trachea and lung of a rabbit with open thorax after its lungs had been perforated in many places. This resulted in a fairly regular respiration, and the lungs remained, by and large, in a state of constant distension. It is true that individual parts of the lung were in constant motion, as if bubbling, owing to gas issuing from the small perforations. But since very small and rapid movements, even of the entire lung, hardly influence the rhythm of breathing at all (very fast artificial ventilation), we felt justified in regarding this bubbling as irrelevant. The rate of breathing, observed at the nostrils was 20 per minute in this experiment. After section of the vagi respiratory frequency dropped from 20 to 12, which appeared to confirm our assumption.

---

Keeping in view the picture thus assembled and turning back to the controversial reports regarding the effects of stimulation of the divided vagus, the contradictions in the published accounts now appear readily explicable, even without Rosenthal's suggestion that only excitation of the superior laryngeal nerve through current spread or unipolar effects evokes expiration. For, as we have seen, antagonistic stimuli are transmitted also by the pulmonary fibres of the vagus. Presumably, both effects can also be produced if the fibres are stimulated electrically along their course, and unascertainable circumstances—current strength, the anatomical arrangement of nerve fibre bundles, etc.—will determine which of the two kinds of influence operating on the medulla will outweigh the other. Rosenthal denies absolutely the possibility that this might be so only in his summary [18], but not in his discussion of the facts. He concedes that Traube's suggestion may be correct, namely that electrical stimulation of the vagus might occasionally be inhibitory and bring about expiration as the result of pain: but he doubts that the vagus trunk exhibits pain sensitivity. All these circumstances are completely irrelevant in relation to our findings, and these are therefore not as directly contradictory to Rosenthal's observations as might appear at first sight.

Yet another source of inconsistency in the results of electrical stimulation of the vagus has now become evident to us. As long as only one nerve is divided impulses tending to inhibit inspiration will still reach the medulla via the other one with every expansion of the lung in inspiration; and this must complicate appreciably, and in varying degree, the effect of the stimulation of the severed nerve.

### III

In what follows we shall not be concerned with new facts but shall only attempt to see which phenomena and relationships that are already well known may be viewed in a new light, or receive an explanation hitherto lacking, through our discoveries. We can thus test, so to say, whether the facts of daily experience tally with the conclusions deduced from our experimental results.

If expansion of the lung really initiates a commensurate, greater or lesser degree of inspiratory inhibition this should also be the case in every ordinary, normal inspiration. Every inspiration should by its own effect (lung expansion) prepare its own inhibition which will terminate it before the time for which inspiration would continue in the absence of such reflexly generated opposition. In this mechanism a part of the available inspiratory nervous energy is, so to speak, prevented from exciting [19] the inspiratory musculature, and has, as it were, to be kept in reserve. Let us examine whether this is really so. The experiments in which one divided vagus is stimulated while the other remains intact prove that for every inspiration a greater quantity of nervous excitation [20] of the muscles could be used than is actually used.

When a current strength is chosen which evokes inspiration, and the central stump of the vagus is stimulated at the peak of an inspiration, there follows a further forceful inspiration. If then, according to Rosenthal, stimulation of the vagus merely serves to discharge available respiratory energy, a considerable amount of this energy must still be present, unused, at the end of inspiration. This by itself, however, would not prove anything in regard to our problem. For it has to be shown that as soon as expansion of the lung during inspiration is prevented, by whatever means, inspiration will *ipso facto* continue beyond its usual measure without the influence of any other factor. This requirement can be fulfilled either by abolishing the inflow of air into the lung during inspiration by closing the trachea; or by resisting chest expansion from the outside (pressure); or by a pneumothorax that will render enlargement of the thorax ineffective for lung expansion; or by making inspiration harder through paralysis of important muscles. In all these circumstances the duration of the succeeding inspiration may easily double in length, as is well established; and it is surely only an accidental slip if Rosenthal mentions diminished entry of air into the lung as causing increased respiratory frequency (*loc. cit.*, p. 2).[21] Budge, coming close to the correct explanation, describes what occurs in these words: "As soon as the quantity of air that penetrates into the lungs becomes in some way diminished, and pressure inside the alveoli is reduced and hence also their distension, breathing movements instantly get slower." One cannot regard the rising venosity of the blood as the cause of the behaviour we are discussing; for the very first inspiration following closure of the trachea is already prolonged, whereas inspiration of irrespirable gas, e.g. hydrogen, will affect respiration only with the rise of dyspnoea after several breaths, and even then inspiration becomes more forceful, but not appreciably prolonged. The most instructive experiment in this context is the following, involving pneumothorax: in a rabbit with two openings in the intercostal space the air-tight thoracic cannulae already described are inserted; the lung is collapsed, and the animal now exhibits dyspnoeic respiration with long, deep breaths. If the cannulae are now occluded, but without sucking air from the thorax, so that the chest movements are again transmitted to the lung and are once more able to distend them a little, breathing immediately becomes more frequent. And when the cannulae are then opened again, so that air from the outside gains access to the pleural cavities, the rhythm instantly reverts to its former rate.

Examples are shown in Plate III. In Curve IX the contractions of the diaphragm were recorded by means of a needle stuck into the diaphragm; in Curve X by means of a small, water-filled bag slipped between diaphragm and liver and connected to a Marey cardiograph. The latter method of recording is usually unreliable, because expiration also increases the pressure in the bag; but here, where only the frequency of respiration was of importance, it was adequate for the purpose. At *a* the communication between the pleural sac and the atmosphere was opened, at *b* it was closed. With the communication shut the excursions become smaller, firstly because they are more frequent, and secondly because the diaphragm in its descent has to overcome the resistance against expansion offered by the lung in these conditions. The differences in the level of the record depend on whether the communication was clamped in the inspiratory or expiratory position.*

As regards expiration, the fundamental experiment of this investigation has taught us that whenever emptying of the lung and the diminution of its volume are hampered expiration will be of very long duration and will be accompanied by a marked increase in effort. If one opposes the flow of air arbitrarily in either phase of respiration without, however, preventing it completely one can change the time relationships of the phases as well as the amount of work expended on each of them as one pleases. Now this reflex mechanism by means of which the movements of respiration terminate themselves as soon as their effect has reached a sufficient magnitude; by means of which part of the available respiratory excitation is held in reserve, so that the necessary height for discharge may then be attained sooner than would otherwise be the case (and it is this which determines why in normal breathing no real pause occurs and inspiration recommences as soon as the lung has regained its initial small size); this mechanism, then, which in this way combats a variety of obstacles to breathing with a variety of purposeful modifications of breathing, this mechanism can be designated as "self-steering of respiration through the vagus nerve".

Clinical medicine applies the term dyspnoeic breathing to two entirely different forms of increased respiratory activity, in as much as this name is used both for slow and deep, as well as for rapid and shallow breathing. Relatively little attention is paid to the profound difference between these. After the foregoing far-ranging discussion it should now suffice merely to call to mind those pathological phenomena which are explained by the self-steering of breathing.

Stenoses of the larynx and trachea either cause definite slowing of respiration, or at least prevent the development of high respiratory frequencies,

---

* In both experiments the animals were incompletely anaesthetized, only one pleural cavity had been opened, and the lung had not been re-expanded to its normal volume even after suction had been applied to the thoracic cannula. For this reason the inspiratory tetanus accompanying entry of air is not seen distinctly. Incidentally, I find the phenomenon described above in the text mentioned in a paper by Schuh (1843, collected papers, p. 34). Schuh[22] remarks: If in a rabbit the pleura has been perforated and the breathing has become slow it is sufficient simply to close the opening with a finger to produce doubling of the rate of breathing, provided it is done after expiration. If the hole is closed at the height of inspiration the dyspnoea increases further, and even fewer breaths are taken. The latter observation is incorrect, as our curves demonstrate; but without recording apparatus it is easy to overlook the small but frequent oscillations of the diaphragm.

such as would otherwise correspond with the existing degree of dyspnoea. Biermer[23] confirms that this slowing of respiration occurs with stenosis of the large airways, and refers to analogous findings in the rabbit with experimental narrowing of the trachea. He adds that in contrast to the predominantly expiratory, asthmatic type of breathing inspiration is prolonged and enhanced. This becomes more comprehensible if we remember that during an attack of asthma the diaphragm is always found to remain in a fixed low position, and that consequently the lung is always expanded. Wintrich[24] believed that this could only be explained as a tonic spasm of the diaphragm, while Biermer regards it as a necessary consequence of the bronchial spasm. However this may be, we know that with expansion of the lung beyond its normal volume it is expiration that is predominantly prolonged and enhanced.

Concerning acute stenosis in croup Gerhard[25] states: in the second stage of laryngeal croup respiration, though somewhat more rapid in absolute numbers, rarely exceeds 1/4 of the pulse frequency; it is only slightly faster than the normal rate for the age group, and is only negligibly accelerated compared with rates found in pneumonia, pleuritis etc. On the influence of stenosis in croup we have the figures given by Bretonneau[26] concerning frequency of breathing before and after tracheotomy.

Child aged 8, Resp. 20; after tracheotomy 32.

Man aged 16, Resp. 12; after tracheotomy 22.

The peculiar modification of respiratory rhythm which some paediatricians actually designate as "croup breathing" now also becomes explicable; there apparently occurs a pause between inspiration and expiration, whereas inspiration immediately follows expiration. As in croup inspiration is usually much harder to carry out than expiration (F. Niemeyer[27] equates this situation with the breathing of young animals whose recurrent laryngeal nerve has been severed, and relates it to paralysis of the glottis), it is not really suprising that the inspiratory muscles continue for a while in a state of contraction even though they can not expand the thorax any further, and that this creates the impression of a pause at the end of inspiration.

On breathing in diaphragmatic paralysis we possess Purkinye's experimental data (in Heinke: de Functione Diaphragmatis. Berol. 1845). According to these the number of inspirations fell from 100 to 50 after trans-section of the phrenics, whereas Gerhard reports that section of one phrenic nerve resulted in a drop of 20 breaths per minute, albeit from a prior frequency of 140.

The same factors may be contributory also in many other modifications of respiratory pattern (pneumothorax, pleuritis), but this is probably not the place for detailed consideration of such complicated conditions, and I therefore confine myself to the mention of the cases already discussed which in their simplicity can be likened to variants of an experiment.

J. Rosenthal has attempted to explain (Reich. u. DuBois Arch. 1864, p. 468)[28] the differences in respiratory frequency depending on the different causes of dyspnoea by the suggestion that expansion of the lung and the stretching of vagal endings associated with it may lead to stimulation of the vagus causing inspiration. "Every cause of dyspnoea in augmenting respiratory movements inevitably induces increased stimulation of the vagi and thus leads to accelerated breathing. By contrast, a mechanical resistance to the entry of air into the lung, by increasing the duration of inspiration, necessarily results in less violent pulling of vagal nerve endings and hence to weaker stimulation; it will thus reduce the frequency of breathing."[29] This hypothesis rests on the observation that "in asphyxial animals an inflation is often followed immediately by a single, deep inspiration."

All experiments reported in the present paper show that expansion of the lung results not in inspiratory but in expiratory stimulation. The observation made on the asphyxial animal can definitely not be transferred to the non-asphyxial. With the collapse of the fundamental assumption the explanation erected upon it likewise falls to the ground.

*Notes:*

1. ROSENTHAL, I. (1862). In *Die Athembewegungen und ihre Beziehungen zum Nervus Vagus*, p. 256. Berlin: August Hirschwald. In quoting this passage Breuer reverses the order in which Rosenthal refers to the respective actions of the *N. laryngeus* and *N. vagus*.

2. Literally: current loops. Unintentional stimulation of distant nerves through current spread from stimulating electrodes applied elsewhere was a hazard well appreciated by most experimenters of the period. Rosenthal (1862, *loc. cit.*, pp. 64–66) describes among his precautions how he connects a frog nerve-muscle preparation in parallel or in series with the superior laryngeal nerve as indicator of stray currents when he stimulates the central stump of the divided vagus at a lower site.

3. BURKART, R. (*not* Burckhardt) (1868). *Ueber den Einfluss des N. Vagus auf die Athembewegungen, Pflügers Arch. ges. Physiol.*, **I**, 107–120. *Nervus laryngeus inferior* ... recurrent laryngeal nerve. The final paragraph of this paper reads: "When the central stump of the vagus which contains

the expiratory fibres of the *N. laryngeus inferior* is stimulated it depends on various factors whether the nerves with inspiratory or the nerves with expiratory activity will tip the balance."

4. FICK, A. (1864). *Ein neuer Blutwellenzeichner, Arch. Anat. Physiol.*, 583–589.

5. Pigs' bladders were frequently used for similar purposes before the advent of rubber balloons.

6. This sentence appears almost word for word already in Hering's first communication (1868, *Sber. Akad. Wiss. Wien*, **57**, p. 675; p. 7 of translation), but without mention of Traube. It was not possible to trace the original source. Traube's publications on this topic are scattered in numerous German local medical journals. Rosenthal (1862, *loc. cit.*, pp. 23, 24) quotes Traube's relevant statements from a book by Pflueger (1857, *Ueber das Hemmungsnervensystem fuer die peristaltischen Bewegungen der Gedaerme*, p. 10. Berlin); Pflueger in turn quoted from an unpublished treatise of Traube's.

7. Breuer did not discuss this matter any further, either in this paper or elsewhere. Hering, however, later devoted a whole publication to this problem (1871. *Ueber den Einfluss der Athmung auf den Kreislauf. 2. Mittheilung: Ueber eine reflektorische Beziehung zwischen Lunge und Herz, Sber Akad. Wiss. Wien*, part 2, **64**, 333–353). He found that moderate inflation of the lung increased heart rate. This did not happen after section of both vagi, even if he first restored the original heart rate by stimulation of the peripheral ends of both vagi.

8. Probably a slip of the pen, as two thoracic cannulae are mentioned in the next sentence.

9. This is a quotation from the first paper—Hering's preliminary communication (1868, *loc. cit.*, p. 676; p. 7 of translation).

10. Rosenthal (1962, *loc. cit.*, p. 241).

11. Literally: part of the existing innervation. Breuer uses the terms: 'innervation', 'innervieren' not, as in modern English and German, in an anatomical sense, but in a functional sense, meaning the degree or amount of excitation transmitted by a nerve to muscle, or the transmitting of such excitation.

12. Literally: isochronism.

13. BUDGE, J. (1858). *Ueber den Einfluss der Reizung des N. vagus auf das Athemholen, Virchows Arch. path. Anat. Physiol.*, **16**, 433–463.

14. EINBRODT. (?1859). *Ueber den Einfluss der Athembewegungen auf Herz-schlag und Blutdruck, Sber. Akad. Wiss. Wien*, part 2, **40**, 361. (Original issue not available.)

15. D for *Druck*—i.e. pressure.
16. There is no exact English equivalent for the German *Beklemmung*. Literally the word means 'the sensation of being squeezed in a vice', but it is virtually never used in the literal sense. Depending on the context, it may be translated as oppression, anguish, depression or suffocation.
17. No evidence has come to light suggesting that Breuer actually carried out further experiments on this problem.
18. ROSENTHAL (1862, *loc. cit.*, p. 256).
19. Literally: innervating. (See note 11.)
20. Literally: quantity of innervation. (See note 11.)
21. Rosenthal here defines "dyspnoeic breathing" as combined increase of rate *and* depth of breathing, and says that this occurs in many different conditions, all of which have in common "a deficiency of oxygen in the blood." He then lists, among several causes of reduction of the oxygen content of the blood "... impaired access of air to the lungs." Breuer appears a little biased in calling this "an accidental slip".
22. F. Schuh (1804–1865), an Austrian surgeon and pioneer of animal experimentation in the investigation of clinical problems. He was Billroth's predecessor as Professor of Surgery at the University of Vienna. Source of quotation not traced.
23. Author and source of quotation not traced.
24. Author and source of quotation not traced.
25. Author and source of quotation not traced.
26. BRETONNEAU, P. (1826). *Des Inflammations spéciales du Tissu Muqueux, et en particulier de la Diphtérite*. Paris.
27. Author and source of quotation not traced.
28. ROSENTHAL, I. (1864). *Studien ueber Athembewegungen, Arch. Anat. Physiol.*, 456–477.
29. Here again Breuer is not entirely fair to Rosenthal. The first passage he cites is a misquotation, in that he changes Rosenthal's "... it will reduce respiratory movement" to "it will reduce the frequency of breathing" which, in the context, considerably alters the meaning. Rosenthal does not refer to rate or frequency of breathing anywhere in this section (pp. 468, 469). It seems likely that what Rosenthal observed (as Breuer himself appears to have done on badly anaesthetized rabbits, see p. 917 of original paper, p. 17 of translation) was "Head's paradoxical reflex". The relevant passages from Rosenthal, in translation, read as follows:
"In an animal rendered asphyxial with H [hydrogen] one frequently

sees that insufflation with air from bellows is immediately followed by one deep inspiration. If one blows in air repeatedly there occurs at first a brief stage of dyspnoea, followed by normal breathing. The first, single inspiration which follows immediately after inflation is absent if both vagi are sectioned."

"... The experiment does therefore not always succeed." [because, in Rosenthal's view, the "single inspiration" depends on the state of excitability of the medulla oblongata under conditions of severe oxygen deficiency, i.e. on the degree of asphyxia]. "But what makes this experiment of special interest is that it provides the proof that the vagal endings in the lung can be excited by the inflow of air, be it that this stimulation results from the mechanical distension of the lung, be it that it is due to chemical processes in the blood.

This entitles us to the conclusion that the continuous excitation which the vagi experience throughout life, and which has such a powerful influence on the movements of breathing, arises from the act of breathing itself. However, it is much more probable that the mechanical distortion which results from breathing movements is the cause of the stimulation of the vagi, rather than some chemical influence of the blood."

# INDEX OF AUTHORS*

*Author and Subject Indexes compiled by Mr. William Hill.

# INDEX OF SUBJECTS

Speech, abnormalities, 180
Spinal cord transection, 176, 177, 235, 243
 breath-holding in, 239
 effect on detection of respiratory loading, 237
 effect on respiratory sensations, 237, 238,
  249, 250–251, 271, 278, 290, 294

Tachypnoea, 31, 305, 306, 307
 abolished by lignocaine, 113
 associated with J reflex, 74
 histamine and, 111
 sense of breathlessness and, 293
Tidal volume,
 in asthmatics, 261, 263–264, 272
 relation to breathlessness, 297–314
 relation to inspiration, 338–341
 relation to ventilation, 303–305
  ventilation, effect of temperature, 313
  effect of vagotomy, 312–313
  in breath-holding, 312
  on exercise, 297, 298–300, 302–303,
   310
Tracheobronchial irritation,
 sensation of, 243–244, 251, 278

Upper airways, sensation of respiratory
 load and, 236

Vagal afferent discharge,
 effect of lung inflation on, 24
 effect on respiratory centres, 184, 189
 electrophysiological studies, 24–31
Vagal block, 234
 breath-holding in, 225–226, 240, 248
 effects,
  of histamine before and after, 111–113
  of response to carbon dioxide, 241, 282
  on blood pressure, 330
  on breathing during hypercapnia, 41–
   52
  on deflation reflex, 38
  on detection of respiratory loading,
   236
  on inflation reflex, 20–21, 38
  on J receptors, 98
  on pattern of respiration, 55
  on respiratory sensation, 237, 240, 241,
   246, 290
 in cardiopulmonary disease, 315–336
 in pulmonary vascular obstruction, 316–
  318

Vagal block—*continued*
 response to, species differences, 44
 technique, 234, 246, 329
Vagal discharge, lung volume and, 193
Vagal drive, 284, 285
Vagal efferents, in medulla, 337
Vagal efferent discharge, augmenting
 response to carbon dioxide, 24
Vagal reflexes, in asthma, 115
Vagotomy, above nodose ganglion, 332
 effects,
  on electrical activity of respiratory
   muscles, 185, 186, 189, 192
  on inflation reflex, 378–381
  on lung infiltrations, 318–321, 330
  on lung inflation, 17–31
  on lung volume, 334–335
  on relation of tidal volume and
   ventilation, 312–313
  on respiration, 325, 359, 363, 378, 383
 in asthma, 322, 323
 in bronchitis, 323
 in emphysema, 321–322, 323
 with intact C fibres, 326–327
Vagus,
 action potential frequency of, effect of
  inflation, 184–185, 189
 C fibres, 326, 333
 effect on breathing during hypercapnia,
  41–52
 myelinated fibres, role of, 48
 non-myelinated fibres, 75
 role in breathing pattern, 333
 role in respiration, Hering-Breuer's
  observations, 359, 365, 375, 385
 stimulation, response to, 35, 46–47
  Hering and Breuer's observations,
   363, 385, 386
Ventilation,
 chemical stimuli, 179
 during exercise, 176, 300
 relation to tidal volume, 297, 298–300,
  302–303, 310
 minute volume and, 41, 42, 43, 49
 pattern, affecting irritant receptors, 81
 relation to tidal volume, 303–305
  effect of temperature, 313
  effect of vagotomy, 312–313
  in breath-holding, 312
Voluntary movement, 213
 initiation of, 207, 208

Weber's law, 268

*Printed by Spottiswoode, Ballantyne & Co. Ltd., London and Colchester*